MEMOIRS OF A MINOR PROPHET

70 Years of Organic Chemistry

Sir Robert Robinson

MEMOIRS OF A MINOR PROPHET

70 Years of Organic Chemistry

Volume 1

Elsevier

Amsterdam — Oxford — New York
1976

ELSEVIER SCIENTIFIC PUBLISHING COMPANY
335 Jan van Galenstraat
P.O. Box 211, Amsterdam, The Netherlands

Distributors for the United States and Canada:

ELSEVIER/NORTH-HOLLAND INC.
52, Vanderbilt Avenue
New York, N.Y. 10017

ISBN: 0-444-41459-2

Printed in The Netherlands

Contents of Volume 1

Volume II is concerned with the period at Oxford University 1930–1955 as Waynflete Professor of Chemistry, as well as other activities during that period and after retirement.

Sir Robert Robinson, O.M.

Jacket design
Philip van Meeuwen

Preface

After my synthesis of tropinone Holger Erdtman told his Professor, Hans von Euler, that he wished to join me in order to undertake some collaborative research. Von Euler said "But isn't he one of the minor prophets?" Erdtman nevertheless said that he wished to persevere with his intention and came to my laboratory and became one of my best friends. I accept von Euler's characterisation and hope I can justify it to some extent in the narrative which follows.

These Memoirs spanning more than 70 years of the life of a scientist have, for convenience, been compiled in two volumes, covering the period before and after 1932, when I was appointed to a Chair at Oxford University. They are largely autobiographical, but the opportunity has been taken to describe certain major developments by others with whom I had some close connection.

In making the first draft my wife Stearn has given me much-needed help and advice. Miss Rachel Eastwood has helped me both in the detail of the composition and the finding of source material.

Writing mainly from memory, at a time when I had been overtaken by blindness, references in my first draft did not reach the standard appropriate for original scientific communications. However, the situation has been transformed by the careful attention that Dr. Renée H. Jaeger has given to the detail of the scientific sections of the manuscript — and that not only in relation to the references, but also the description and arrangements of parts. She has, in fact, edited the work in consultation with me and has drawn structural formulae where they were deemed to be necessary. I wish to express my deepest gratitude for help which vitalised my project.

I am also grateful to Professor W.D. Ollis, F.R.S. for extensive help with the chapter on brazilin, and to Dr. E.D. Morgan for help with the structures needed for a section on alkaloid biogenesis.

Throughout the work the object has been to locate the sources of novel developments and to show how different investigations have been connected by incident or bifurcation.

I wish to draw particular attention to the development of my theoretical ideas, which started with a theory of partial valencies and, on the advent of the electronic theory, to a general classification of conjugated systems on the electronic basis.

Great Missenden, January 1975

Chapter I

Family and Schooldays

My great-grandfather, William Robinson (Billy) (1772—1845), was an enterprising and successful tradesman. He learned the drapery business in Nottingham, but in 1794 he established himself in Chesterfield. In addition to the ordinary stock-in-trade he made "Dutch" gloves and clay pipes on a reasonably large scale. In 1796 he married Ann Bradbury, a member of a family living in the village of Combes near Chapel-en-le-Frith. There is an outcrop of steep rock called Castle Naze on the mountain side above the village on which I practised rock climbing on many occasions but without any knowledge of the fact that one of my forebears had lived in the valley below.

My grandfather, John Bradbury Robinson, was the third son of "Billy". He established himself as a retail chemist in Belper, but moved to his home town Chesterfield in 1828. He married his cousin, Martha Bradbury, in 1825. My grandfather was a naturalist much interested in native plants and birds. He had an inventive turn of mind. One of his diaries describes a rotary engine motivated by the impact of steam on blades, evidently a form of steam turbine. He was a man of ruthless energy but, as in some other such cases in the family, this was not combined with exceptional ability in business.

Soon after coming to Chesterfield he purchased a small factory building and commenced the manufacture of chip willow boxes which were required as containers for ointments. In 1841 he went to America without making any arrangements for the continuance of his business during his absence. Undoubtedly he was not in good shape either in mind or body and had hoped to profit from his experiences in the land of opportunity. He visited business houses and secured orders for boxes, but in the following year decided to return to Chesterfield. Fortunately his wife had managed to keep the business going. In the entrance hall of our home, which later became the nucleus of the "Works Welfare and Social Centre", there was a large case of brightly coloured stuffed birds brought from America

Great-grandfather William Robinson.

by our grandfather. I deduce from this that his circumstances were never actually in a desperate condition.

My father, William Bradbury Robinson, was born in Belper. Evidently he did not regard the family business as something which was so good that he must pursue it. At the age of 16 he wished to make a career on the seas but was eventually dissuaded from this by his mother. He then applied himself with great energy to the improvement and extension of the family business. In due course he became a pioneer manufacturer who invented quite a number of the machines used in his factories. He was the first to make a mechanical linting machine, to automate the cutting of cotton bandages, and to mechanise the production of cardboard pillboxes. Later he worked hard to produce disposable sanitary towels for women, and his aim was to bring the price down to a penny each. Quite late in life he invented machines for this purpose, and these articles are still produced in enormous numbers by the methods which he introduced. This was probably his greatest contribution to industry and hygiene. His factory in Chesterfield was one in which all the different processes of the textile trade were carried out. Later on it was found better to take advantage of the specialised work of manufacturers in Lancashire and elsewhere. His ambition to do everything in one place was found to be uneconomical.

He visited America on two occasions, once in the brig "Portland" which took him to Charleston. His brother Charles, younger by 18 years, was born during the time of this voyage and was hence called Charles Portland. Nowadays there is a Portland Works at Chesterfield as part of the firm of Robinson & Sons Ltd. In later years my father gave my uncle a half share in the business and afterwards they jointly gave my step-brother William Bradbury a third share.

My father was a tireless inventor and went every day to his mechanics shop where he had a small skilled staff. On one of my school vacations I was offered a golden sovereign if I could make a machine which would perform the following task: to take a roll of cotton wool wrapped in a gauze tube causing the end of the roll to move a certain distance along the table, then stop under a sharp knife which would cut the roll. The knife should go upward and the cut roll would be rolled up and dropped into a bin. The main roll would start again and the process would be repeated. The wool in its tube was about ½ inch thick and the width of the material was of the order of two feet. I had a groove cut in a plate of hard metal and of such a shape that it controlled the operation both of the roller bearing the material and the knife. The machine worked well and was kept running for a number of years — the golden sovereign was eventually incorporated in a brooch for my wife. This was my first and last contact with mechanical engineering and if I had not taken to chem-

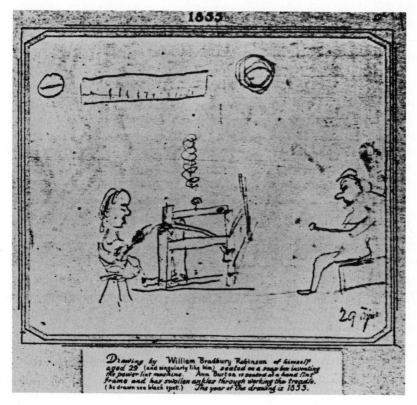

The lint machine.

istry I think I would have been pleased to continue with machines, as it certainly gives great satisfaction to see a thing one has designed actually working.

Early days

I was the eldest of my father's second family and born in Derbyshire at Rufford Farm near Chesterfield, and I have a very clear recollection of events in my first years of life.

After moving to New Brampton, at the age of three, I appear to have made my first scientific observation when I told my mother that ladybirds always climbed up a stalk, and never down, resting and flying off at the top. One further triviality is perhaps worthy of mention from both the psychological and chemical points of view. In the course of a children's party I was given a box of chocolates. These chocolates had highly characteristic odours which I have always remembered. It is not quite the same as that due to vanillin but is found when vanillin is associated with the size used in making cardboard. Unquestionably this substance results from the reaction of the vanillin with a constituent of the size, and I have found from recent enquiries that its chemical nature is still unknown.

My father's first wife was Elizabeth Lowe (d. 1871) and they had seven surviving children. His second wife was Jane Davenport (d. 1950) and they had two sons and three daughters. The children of my father's first marriage were: Martha Annie (Arna), b. 1851; Jemima (Mimie), b. 1853; Mary (Polly), b. 1855; Elizabeth (Lily), b. 1857; Maria (Lynie), b. 1859; William Bradbury, b. 1863; and Hannah Louisa (Louie), b. 1867. Kate, b. 1858, John Bradbury, b. 1861, and John Charles, b. 1866, the last named died in infancy.

Looking back, it appears remarkable to me that we all managed to survive our rather boisterous childhood. The rein was held very lightly and we seem to have been allowed to do almost anything, however adventurous, so long as it did not involve damage to property or harm to other people. I made a climb up the side of the house which included a rather neat chimney, formed partly by a stone pillar extending from the first to the second floor, and there were some rather risky rambles over the roof. The winters were longer and much more severe than nowadays. This involved the usual dangers of thin ice. There was also some tobogganing to be done on tea trays, which was not without its special interest. Our companions in these sports were usually our first cousins.

My first school was Miss Wilke's Kindergarten, of which I have a clear recollection. On the opposite side of the road was the Chesterfield Grammar School which I later attended. The Headmaster, Mr. Mansell, was an excellent teacher. I remember the thrill which followed his enunciation of the word geometry in a class which was supposed to be learning the elements of Euclid. For some time I stayed in his house as a weekly boarder. In due course Ralph, the son of Mr. and Mrs. Mansell, married Madge, the daughter of my half-brother William.

When I was a young child, a Christmas party and family reunion was a regular feature; very varied interests were represented. Martha

Annie was a spinster who lived in an extension of our home at Field House, New Brampton, Chesterfield. Mimie had married a barrister practising in London. Polly's husband was John Pearson, a master potter and a much respected citizen of Chesterfield. Their son Theo continued and extended his father's work both in the manufacturing business and in local administration. He received the Freedom of the Borough of Chesterfield at the Meeting of the Council at which I was similarly honoured. Lynie and Lily married J. Morton Clayton and J.G. Clayton, respectively. The brothers managed a tannery and were active in municipal politics. I owe a great debt to Morton, since he introduced me to alpine mountaineering. His brother was an excellent musician and I can hear now his masterly rendering of (Duetto) No. XVIII of Mendelsohn's "Lieder ohne Worte"; equally memorable was the way he manipulated his long cigar simultaneously. Louie married Dr. Giddings of Nottingham. The party was enlivened by the presence of grandchildren who were just a little older than us, the second batch. Hanna (Babs) Clayton, the daughter of Lynie and

The family: Father, Mother, myself, Victor.

Morton, and Hilda Crawshaw were two lively girls who were distinctly easy on the eye. William's son Frank was a handsome youth who tragically fell in the 1914—1918 War; his sister Madge is probably the largest individual shareholder in Robinson & Sons Ltd.

The second family consisted of myself, b. 1886; Florence, b. 1888; Victor Owen, b. 1891; Cecily Bradbury, b. 1893; and Dorothy, b. 1895. Victor had a son and two daughters who between them gave him a considerable number of grandchildren. Florence and Cecily did not marry. Florence was active in the firm of Robinson & Sons as Welfare Supervisor. She also served as Mayor of Chesterfield, with Cecily as her Mayoress. Dorothy and Cecily gave nursing service at the Endle Street Hospital during the First World War, and Cecily continued this activity at Queen Mary's Hospital, Hong Kong until the Colony was occupied by the Japanese. She was Matron in the Stanley Internment Camp and took an active part in combating an outbreak of cholera. Dorothy married Alex Bell and had a son, David, who, along with his wife Lilian, was killed in a motor accident, and Dorothy was left with the care of two grandchildren. Victor served with great distinction in the First World War, having been mentioned several times in despatches and having gained three bars to his M.C. In the Second World War he was in charge of enemy plane spotting over a rather important region, from Preston to the Southern Midlands. He was for many years Chairman of Robinson & Sons Ltd. and his wise conduct of the affairs of the Company led to considerable expansion of the business. At the present time I am told that it is the largest private company in Britain. Until quite recently it was a rather poor second to Pilkingtons, the glass manufacturers, but they are no longer in this category.

Victor was not only a national but also a local patriot and was often engaged in schemes designed for the good of the neighbourhood. One such always struck me as having the character of an incident which might have occurred in a novel by George Birmingham. In my brother's library there were several volumes concerned with the history of Derbyshire families, and in one of these he found a crest of the Derbyshire Linacres. This, he persuaded himself, was very similar to that of the Royal College of Physicians, founded by Linacre in the reign of King Henry VII. Linacre Hall was submerged in Linacre reservoir and my brother thought he had sufficient evidence that Thomas Linacre was the nephew of the head of the house. From this it was a small step to assume that he visited his uncle at

Linacre, which was a very small village a short distance from Old Brampton. Naturally there was no real evidence of this and we know very little about Thomas Linacre before he visited the University of Padua as a young man of 22 years. He was a Fellow of All Souls College, Oxford, and is reputed to have been the first to teach the Classics with the use of the English language. Later he founded the Royal College of Physicians in the reign of Henry VII and his connection with Oxford and the R.C.P. is well documented. However, my brother, like a hero of *Spanish Gold*, did not allow inconvenient trifles to stand in his way and he found a kindred spirit in the Vicar of Old Brampton Church, with whom he started a fund for some improvements in the fabric of the church and for the preparation of a plaque in memory of Thomas Linacre. Assistance was sought from members of the medical profession and from All Souls, and the result was a ceremony in the church, with delegates wearing academic robes. I heard the Bishop of Derby declare in resounding tones "It is very probable that Thomas Linacre worshipped within these walls". My comment is that it certainly is "possible" but that "probable" goes rather beyond the actual evidence at our disposal.

Schooldays

At the age of twelve years I attended Fulneck School, Pudsey Greenside, about midway between Leeds and Bradford. This was organised by the Moravian Church in Britain, and the majority of the masters were candidates for the Moravian ministry. My father had two reasons for sending me there: firstly, because a Mr. Albert Bingham, one of his commercial travellers described as being of remarkable rectitude, had been educated at Ockbrook, another Moravian school near Derby; secondly, two of my first cousins had been at Neuwied, a Moravian School in the Rhineland. Although there must have been many boys who came from Moravian homes at Fulneck, in my time there was probably a majority who did not and the atmosphere of the school was secular in its educational aspects. Amongst the distinguished pupils at the school was Herbert H. Asquith. For the information of those who have not studied the subject, I ought to say that the Moravian Church was the first Protestant Church in Europe and preceded the Lutheran. They were second only to the Jesuits in their missionary activities and three important Moravians were John Huss, the earliest pioneer, the educational philosopher Comenius, and Count Zinzendorf, who was a distinguished hymnologist. The school, which also had a section for girls, consisted of a building with a chapel separating the two schools. There was a long terrace which ran the whole length, with a neutral zone in the middle. At the end of our terrace was a large gate on which the equivalent of wickets could be indicated by chalk. We played cricket at lunch and other intervals by bowling in succession against the batsman, and the proof that the wicket had been hit was the chalk mark on the ball. The window of the Headmaster's study was some sixty yards down the terrace, and on one occasion I remember very well his head popped out and, clearing his throat in a characteristic way which all the boys could imitate, he said "Now boys, no slogging, only hard play". It is curious how one remembers the most ridiculously small things; for example, the Headmaster was walking along the terrace and he happened to see a very small boy called Lawrie and said to him "Well Lawrie, I see you are back again", to which the reply came "So it would appear, Sir, so it would appear".

The school had excellent playing fields and was on a hill-side above a deep valley, on the other side of which there was the picturesque old-world village of Tong. Some weeks before Guy Fawkes Day the weekly walks became "chumping" expeditions to gather material for the bonfire. The fireworks which the boys were allowed to have for November 5th were contained in little toilet bags, and I remember that on more than one occasion a boy had his hoard stolen from him by what we called the "Collups". One of the Masters with some of the older boys would then organise a punitive expedition, but I do not know what happened on these occasions as I never participated.

In my opinion the standard of teaching at Fulneck was remarkably high and, although it was certainly a rough experience in parts, I am very glad that I had it. My brother Victor remained at the school after I had left for Manchester and in one of his news letters said that they had been visited by the usual evangelist. He said that, as far as he knew, all the boys had been reconverted with the exception of James II. I have often wondered what happened to that sturdy individualist.

My father and uncle were both very influential Congregationalists and they took a large part in building a chapel of that denomination in Chesterfield. This was a very short distance from our house in New

Brampton. I mention these details because one of the ministers at the New Brampton Chapel was a Reverend John E. Simon who had some kind of a relationship with Lord Birkenhead. He was a brilliant preacher and, I think, a man of considerable intellectual power. It was the habit of ministers in the church to come to my father's house to discuss such interesting topics as "the meaning of prayer" and so on, and possibly partake of some refreshment as well. This usually occurred in the study/library and I, sitting on the library steps and eating my frugal supper, would hear a great deal, and I am afraid I found reason to scoff; in fact, I was what is called a "free thinker" at quite an early age. However, I played draughts and chess with the visitors, also from a somewhat early age, and got on with them exceedingly well as human beings. The Reverends A. Foster and J.E. Simon, particularly, impressed on my father the desirability of sending me to the University and I have these gentlemen to thank for influencing my career in this vital respect, for I do not believe that I would have had the chance without their advocacy. My father, of course, expected me to go into the family firm which, by the way, is still run as a family firm although it is a relatively large one. He had attempted to construct a bleach work on the information supplied in Chamber's Cyclopaedia. This had not been an outstanding success and he was therefore very anxious, when I went to the University, that I should enter the Chemical School. However, in my last year at school I received individual tuition from J.H. Blandford, who had taken the mathematical tripos at Cambridge with some distinction, and who took me under his care and taught me some of the more elementary parts of the higher mathematics, such as co-ordinate geometry, differential and integral calculus, in the first stages. I wanted therefore to be a mathematician, but my father's wish was clearly expressed and I decided to accept the inevitable and become a chemist.

At about this time, perhaps a few months later, I wrote a letter as a contribution to a discussion, published in *The English Mechanic and World of Science*, about what happens to the energy of a spring when it is dissolved in acid. I came to the obvious conclusion that the potential energy must be transformed into its equivalent of heat.

Towards the end of my last year at Fulneck I took, with some trepidation, the matriculation examination of the Joint Board of the Universities of Manchester, Liverpool, and Leeds. I felt myself rather inadequate in certain subjects, but the examiners evidently "tempered the wind to the shorn lamb" in view of better performance in physics and mathematics.

After leaving Fulneck I went to the University of Manchester.

Chapter II

Undergraduate Period

When I became an undergraduate at Manchester University I first lived as a boarder in the Moravian College which was in charge of the Reverend Leonard G. Hassé. Most of the small number of students had come from Fulneck; they included Ronald Hassé, a mathematician, and William T. Waugh, an historian, both of whom were later appointed to Chairs in their respective subjects. Living in the College involved daily commuting and later I joined Waugh in "digs" for a short time. When my brother left Fulneck we took apartments in Buxton, from which there was an excellent train service. Buxton is a well-known spa in the Peak District of Derbyshire, about mid-way between Manchester and Chesterfield. It rises to an average of 1000 feet above sea level and was a good centre for walking in the hills and dales and, on occasions, for tobogganing in winter. This pleasant life ended when my brother finished his course at the Manchester School of Technology.

The laboratory at Manchester had been built during Sir Henry Roscoe's tenure of the Chair of Chemistry at Owen's College. The First Year Laboratory for the Honour School of Chemistry is called the "Roscoe Laboratory". I found that one of my fellow students in the First Year was Ashley Dukes. We recognised one another immediately because we had been Captains of the 2nd XI Cricket teams of our respective schools in Yorkshire, I at Fulneck School, Pudsey Greenside, and he at Silcoates, Wakefield. The memorable circumstance was that we had both been bowlers rather than batsmen, and had dismissed each other for a duck apiece. Dukes took a great interest in student affairs and edited a magazine. However, in the final examination, three years later, he was awarded Class II Honours and immediately decided he would not pursue the profession of chemistry. He had a hard time for some years and spent a year in Germany studying the language and literature, and later took up a post as secretary to one of the political Brights of Rochdale. I had some pleasant excursions with him, especially on a hill which overlooks the town, which in those days was not distinguished for the complete cleanliness of its vegetation. He became more and more interested in the theatre and, after starting his work by making translations from the German, he achieved some reputation as a playwright and dramatic critic. He also introduced me to George Bernard Shaw, but the great man was far from scintillating on that occasion and, so far as I remember, said nothing of any interest or importance. One of Dukes' best known plays was *The Man with a Load of Mischief*. He wrote a small paperback book entitled *The Drama*. In 1918 he married Marie Rambert (Dame Marie since 1962) and in 1927 they acquired a Church Hall in Notting Hill Gate, which was used, in the first instance, as a Ballet Club; later it became the Mercury Theatre (1933) and also housed the Rambert School of Ballet. Dukes died in 1959 at the age of 73.

A student who came in at about the same time, perhaps a little later, was Cecil J.T. Cronshaw, who had had some previous laboratory experience. The demonstrator in the laboratory was Dr. Norman Smith; it was his habit to provide the students with solutions for analysis which contained mixtures of salts, and these were in large aspirator bottles above his desk. Cronshaw was given one of these solutions to analyse, but he turned to Norman Smith and said "Would you like to have the result now — or must I pretend to analyse the solution first?" After Smith had remonstrated with this piece of impertinence, Cronshaw said "You know, it is pretty well known throughout the laboratory what is in those aspirator bottles and I think you ought to change them". For this misdemeanour he was reported to Professor Dixon, who was the senior Professor of Chemistry, and I do not quite know what happened, but Cronshaw came out smiling. A few years later he told a story which I always claimed was apocryphal, but honesty compels me to admit that it has a certain ring of truth, nevertheless. He said that when he was passing through Perkin's private laboratory on his way to the Schunck Library, he distracted my attention from a combustion and the rubber stopper at the end of the combustion tube was slightly displaced; I do not think it came out altogether but it was loosened. I quickly tightened it and, according to him, said "I do not think I have lost very much". He had a brilliant career in the British Dyestuffs Corporation and in I.C.I., becoming Chairman of the Dyestuffs group of that combination.

In the days of British Dyes, the Government appointed Field Marshal Sir William Robertson to the Board, as a representative, and the Field Marshal came to Huddersfield to survey his territory. He was taken by Cronshaw to various plants, including the ammonia plant for the production of ice, large quantities of which were used in the preparation of azo-dyes. He asked the young man in charge to explain what was happening, and he received a rather detailed account of the physics of the processes. Robertson said "Well what is it for?" "Oh", said the young man, "it is to make ice for the plants". "Oh", said the Field Marshal, "you mean to say that it is just to make water into ice?" "Yes, indeed", said the young man. "Well, you damn fool", said Robertson, "why couldn't you tell me that to start with?"

Another incident followed the discovery of phthalocyanine, which greatly interested the large German dyestuff companies. Cronshaw went over, I think to Frankfurt, in order to discuss whether the German firms could collaborate in any way in the development. He reported that he was introduced into a room where there was an immense mahogany table with one or two very serious looking, well dressed figures at the far end. After they had exchanged polite preliminaries and the Chairman had told Cronshaw, who was leading a small group, what he wished, he added "Well, how much will it cost us to join with you in the development?" Cronshaw, in mock surprise, said "Did I hear you aright, are you offering us money? That is what we get from a bank". "What do you want then?" said the Chairman. Cronshaw replied "A share in some comparable new development of yours!" There is no record of the outcome of this preposterous suggestion.

The Second Year Laboratory was adjoining, and parallel with, the Roscoe Laboratory and was presided over, in my day, by Drs. G.H. Baily and W.A. Bone, two men of just about as different character as could be imagined. Bailey wrote a popular textbook devoted to the chemistry of metals, but I really do not recall any especially important research which he carried out. Bone wore flamboyant waistcoats and had a somewhat Mephistophelean air, but he was an extremely kind man and especially interested in children. He was for many years patron or chairman of a large children's hospital. His language was sometimes appropriate to his dress. There is a story that, when he was very ill, he was extremely annoyed with his surgeon, who had promised success and had not achieved it. Bone had made an arrangement to pay for a successful operation only and informed the surgeon that he intended to stick to it, and this produced something of a scene, after which Bone turned to the nurse and said "I wonder if you would mind reading me the test match scores?"

After Manchester, he proceeded to Imperial College, South Kensington, where he established an important school of research. I cannot forbear from mentioning that the authors of one of his papers in the Journal of the Chemical Society were Lean, Bone and Stocking.

The second year courses were not regarded by the students as being of supreme interest and many of us looked forward to the third year, when we would have an opportunity of studying practical organic chemistry in the Schorlemmer Laboratory. One of my fellow students was Peter Sandiford, who came from Hayfield, Derbyshire, and who was a very strong socialist. He insisted on taking me round Germany in 4th class railway carriages. We went up to the Isle of Rügen, down to Berlin and Dresden, and to the Thüringerwald, and certainly did what Sandiford thought was necessary, and that was, to get a good idea of how the poorer classes in Germany thought and worked. In the 4th class railway carriages there were no seats, you took a suitcase and sat on it if you could.

Sandiford was equal with me at the head of the list in the Final Examination. He later went to Canada, as a Professor, I am not sure of what, but it certainly was not chemistry; it might have been the English language. He died rather prematurely in middle age.

Another student was Rhona Robinson, who also achieved a 1st Class Honours degree and quickly distinguished herself as a very well-known militant suffragette. Later she worked as a research chemist in the Clayton Aniline Company which is, I believe, a branch of Ciba Limited, Basle.

CHEMICAL COURSES AT MANCHESTER IN THE HONOUR SCHOOL OF CHEMISTRY

A very short synopsis of the courses in the Honour School of Chemistry, 1902—1905, may be of interest as affording a comparison with modern practice.

I have already mentioned earlier that H.B. Dixon was the senior Professor of Chemistry at Manchester University. He was a pupil of Professor A.G. Vernon Harcourt, a most influential teacher at

Oxford University, who may justly be called the grandfather of Oxford Chemistry. Sidgwick, Hartley, Elford, Chattaway, Chapman, Andrea Angel, and many other names that were to be numbered among the famous of Oxford Chemistry were reared in Vernon Harcourt's school; five became Fellows of the Royal Society and his pupils' pupils provided nearly all the Heads of College Laboratories in years to come. For forty years he and his pupils maintained a small but active school of chemical research, a school which studied the general laws of chemistry and produced the practical applications that our universities are sometimes accused of neglecting. Vernon Harcourt himself was one of the first pupils of Benjamin Brodie, who occupied the Aldrichian Chair in Chemistry at Oxford and, in his early days, had his laboratory in the cellars of Balliol College.

Dixon's early career was at Balliol College, Oxford; he was a rowing blue and an alpinist. Like many Oxford scientists, notably N.V. Sidgwick, he was a classicist and an authority on the works of Homer. We were given to understand he composed Greek poems which had something of the thunder-roll of the Master. Dixon was a pioneer of the study of gaseous explosions. He discovered and explained the lag period before the waves started. The explosions were made in long tubes and were photographed. This pioneering investigation provided the scientific basis for the work of the Committee on the Safety of Mines. During my undergraduate days in Manchester he was also active in research on many other problems in inorganic chemistry, such as the synthesis of water and of hydrogen chloride, and the atomic weight of chlorine. One of his collaborators in the latter research was E.C. Edgar, and I have the following story from him. A top ranking European physical chemist visited the laboratories and asked Edgar what the main difficulties in his work were. The answer was that it was extremely hard to remove all traces of hydrogen chloride from the chlorine used. "But", said the visitor, "can't you do it by washing the gas with dilute sodium hydroxide?"

Professor Dixon lectured on the non-metallic elements in a highly interesting manner and with special attention to their position in topics which were being developed by research at that time. This was far from a mechanical drill, and it was a most stimulating experience to follow these lectures which included many personal recollections, giving a sense of contact with famous personalities of the generation of distinguished older chemists when Dixon himself was a student at Oxford. I vividly recall that one of Dixon's excellent lectures to

Invitation to Students' Dinner for Professor H.B. Dixon.

first year Honours Chemistry students dealt with ozone and included an account of Brodie's classical work on this topic.

In the second year, G.H. Bailey lectured on metals and their compounds and, looking back, one can appreciate how dull that subject can be without the light shed on it by electronic theory. The high point in my second year was the introduction to W.H. Perkin, junior. His course in organic chemistry roughly corresponded to Perkin and Kipping's well-known text book and was a miracle of clear exposition; as a matter of fact, one realises now that it was achieved to a large extent by brushing away all the little difficulties that might arise, and keeping ones eyes firmly fixed on the main immutable truth. To Perkin, organic chemistry had a mathematical simplicity and it was unnecessary to explain anything; in fact, what other chemists might regard as requiring immediate investigation, Perkin would regard as a kind of decoration and colour given to the narrative. He was, however, ready to take all stereochemical differences fully into account. I think this is the right place to record that attendance at Perkin's lecture course decided my future career; I was fascinated by the beauty of the organic chemical system. Indeed, I am disposed to agree with Sir Frederick Gowland Hopkins, who once declared that the system of organic chemistry is one of the greatest achievements of the human mind. In the second year the students usually took a course in German, and in the laboratory the whole available time was devoted to quantitative work of various kinds. There was also a practical course on electro-chemistry under R.S. Hutton. In the third year there was an advanced course of lectures in organic chemistry and a course on a special subject, which in my case was the chemistry of dyestuffs, with practical work arranged by J.F. Thorpe.

Bone and Wheeler worked independently with their own junior collaborators, for a considerable period of years, and both became Fellows of the Royal Society and received numerous honours. There was also a course on the history of chemistry, delivered by W.A. Bone in a most interesting manner. W.A. Bone (and later, R.V. Wheeler) followed up Dixon's researches, added his own innovations and contributed much to our knowledge of the processes occurring in the explosion wave and, more generally, to the reaction undergone by gaseous substances under various conditions. It should be added, that those of us who stayed on to do research were able to attend a special advanced course of lectures.

I remember particularly one such series given by Chaim Weizman on various topics as, for examples, Büchner's work on the addition of ethyl diazoacetate to aromatic hydrocarbons, and also on Baeyer's studies of reduction of the isomeric phthalic acids. Students were recommended to study these and similar papers in the original literature. The practical work in the third year consisted in making organic preparations and in identification of organic substances given as unknowns. This was called "Spotting" and there was no definite plan of action that could be laid down; it was a matter of observation of the behaviour of the substances with reagents, under a variety of conditions. The quantitative work in the third year consisted in carrying out combustions, estimation of nitrogen by Dumas' method etc. The advances over the last 70 years have naturally made great changes in the curriculum in the universities' Chemical Schools. Inorganic chemistry has been reconstructed on the basis of the Periodic System and knowledge derived from application of many new techniques. It has become a molecular structural science and involves the use of the principles of stereochemistry. Organic chemistry had been illuminated by the electrical theories of structure and reactions, and expanded by the use of chromatrography on the preparative side, X-ray crystallography, ultraviolet and infrared spectroscopy, and nuclear magnetic resonance (NMR), hitherto chiefly proton magnetic resonance, but now ^{13}C NMR is assuming more and more importance. In fact, there have been examples quite recently of X-ray crystallographic studies of natural products where the computer has been fed the data and has finally written out the molecular structural formulae. As computers capable of such work cost between 1 and 2 million pounds it is unlikely that they will become the standard equipment of many chemical laboratories. Commenting on this kind of situation at the I.U.P.A.C. Meeting in Australia in 1964, I remarked that a knowledge of a structure of a complex organic compound is certainly desirable, but not sufficient in itself; we must also know as much as possible about the transformations that the molecule may undergo, and in general its likely behaviour in more complex systems. This naturally applies with particular force to substances of physiological importance, but it is also necessary in other connections, for example the industrial, that we should know as much as possible of the chemical behaviour of the molecules as well as of their structure. I consider that three years spent in following a course such as that provided by Manchester University is still desirable after, naturally, various sections of it have taken into full account the progress made to date. Something like Dixon's lectures on the non-metallic elements is still needed, though the various topics treated might be different, and those that were retained could be made much more interesting as the result of discoveries made in the past three quarters of a century. I am afraid I despair of finding a successor to Professor Perkin. His simple and perhaps rather blinkered approach is hardly possible today, since almost all teachers would wish to discuss the teaching of organic chemistry from the point of view of electronic mechanisms. One can only hope, however, that the students are not to be bogged down by a too mathematical exposition, since the main facts and ideas can be so easily illustrated using a simple symbolism. Lectures on the metals nowadays tend to become essays on coordination chemistry and should be an important part of the syllabus. Unfortunately, I do not believe that this subject has been satisfactorily presented in a textbook of reasonably small size. Such a work should deal with the catalysis by metallic complexes, as well as the general chemistry of the metals and their compounds.

The history of chemistry has been crowded out of the syllabus, but it should certainly be re-introduced in view of its value in providing links between sections of development which might otherwise appear to be isolated. There is much human and social interest in the history of science, and this certainly applies to the development of chemistry. There is, however, a danger that enthusiastic teachers will stress the human and social implications and forget to say much about the science itself. I have, for example, noted a tendency to over-emphasise the social aspect of scientific development in some of the excellent radio talks given under the auspices of the Open University. One such lecture was to be on "The Cell", but this important subject was not reached, as far as I could tell, because the description of Sir Hans Krebs' effort to become established in this country occupied the whole of the available time. It is obvious that, nowadays, lectures on advanced organic chemistry may form part of a course, but the material selected now will be quite different from that which is appropriate in the first and second decades of the century. The practical work, suited to the present state of development, will still involve some qualitative and quantitative analysis, but by no means so much as heretofore. The students must be made to understand the principles of the spectroscopic apparatus which they may use for themselves. More probably, in present circumstances, and when it comes to the conduct of research, they will rely upon an expert to operate the apparatus. The laboratory courses will also include practice in column and thin layer chromatography, and certainly in preparation on a very small scale. In the third year a few larger scale preparations may be undertaken, and these may well be a series of substances in order to assist work in progress in the laboratory.

A.F. Edwards, the chief steward, was a remarkable man from several points of view. He was well known to the students on account of the skilful way he performed the experiments in Dixon's lectures; he was also the best dressed public figure in the department, and was but the outward sign of an unexampled correctitude. Every person working in the laboratory, in any capacity, had an account, and I never heard that anyone challenged the accuracy of Edwards' calculations. Neither did I see one of his experiments fail. He was a keen temperance reformer, and photographed groups of those who had achieved Firsts in the Hon. B.Sc. examinations. These pictures were thrown onto the screen in lectures which he gave, and the successful candidates were invited to sign a statement to the effect that they had never found the use of alcohol essential to their studies. If this was meant to imply that the said students never partook of alcohol I think it may be regarded as an unusual deviation from the "straight and narrow path".

The practical work in the third year was in the charge of D.T. Jones. He was a most enthusiastic initiator of research but, unfortunately, was extremely easily discouraged. I was picked on as a junior collaborator in a kind of chemical Blitzkrieg, the object of which was to make a bicyclobutane derivative. I do not wish to exaggerate, so I will merely say that he produced at least two new ideas each week and asked me to try them out. In addition, we attempted new reactions of ethyl diazoacetate, but I was never encouraged to vary the conditions. The uniform lack of success in these trials did not worry me unduly, as Jones' ideas were all in the nature of very long shots and even in those days seemed to me to be very unlikely to be successful. Actually, bicyclobutane derivatives have only relatively recently been obtained.

The third year course culminated in examinations in all subjects, theoretical and practical. Any questions could be asked in respect of the content of lectures, but this did not prove too onerous in view of the fact that candidates were not required to answer all the questions. The External Examiner in 1905 was Professor S.F. Kipping. We had a three days practical examination in which a problem was posed for investigation and a substantial amount of menthylamine hydrochloride had to be prepared from a given amount of menthol. This was a good test, because the menthol had to be oxidised to menthone, which was converted into its oxime, and the latter reduced by sodium and alcohol to the base isolated as the desired hydrochloride. Kipping used menthylamine for the resolution of certain racemic acids into enantiomorphs and used the occasion of this examination to increase his stock of this material. Naturally, he kept a watchful eye on the process and I had reason to be grateful for this as I was writing up my results in the small balance room next to the laboratory when the External Examiner came in rather hurriedly and said "Is that your menthylamine chloride which is in the basin in the graph cupboard?" and I replied "Yes, I was about to go into the laboratory to turn off the gas", to which he replied "That is a good thing, because you will get very few marks for the cinder you are about to produce". I tried to reassure him, but not, I feel, with full success. It was a small incident but had I charred the menthylamine, as suggested, it might have demoted me in the examination list and I might then

W.H. Perkin, jun.

have opted for my father's factory, rather than for a place in Perkin's private laboratory and a career in organic chemistry.

Frederick Stanley Kipping (1863—1949)

F.S. Kipping was the eldest son of James Stanley Kipping who was a very strong chess player and on one occasion even defeated Paul Morphy, the world champion. Frederick Stanley was not a particularly strong chess player, but the gene reappeared in one of his sons who was a world famous composer of chess problems.

In 1879 the Kipping family moved to Platt Fields, Manchester, and F.S.K. became a student of science at Owen's College. At this stage he concentrated on zoology and found Schorlemmer's lectures on organic chemistry so little to his taste that he cut the majority of them and played billiards instead. However, in 1882 he took a post as a chemist in the Manchester Gas Department, but even this did not incline him much to the study of chemistry. In 1886, on the advice of his friend Dr. Adolf Lichman, he went to Munich, and there, by a lucky chance, he was allotted a bench and came under the supervision of W.H. Perkin, jun. who had already been four years in Adolf von Baeyer's Institute and conducted the course devoted to research in organic chemistry. This association of Kipping and Perkin was life long, both on the scientific and personal sides. After returning to England Kipping spent some time in assisting his father in chemical manufacture, but in late 1887 he was awarded the D.Sc. of the University of London; this was the first occasion when this degree had been granted in the Chemical School. A little later he accepted a post in W.H. Perkin's department at the Heriot-Watt College in Edinburgh. He was promoted there, but his real opportunity occurred when H.E. Armstrong offered him the post of Chief Demonstrator in the Chemistry Department at the Central Technical College of the London Institute. There he was able to direct the work of junior colleagues, one of whom was Arthur Lapworth, and he became a member of a live chemical School. In 1897 he was elected F.R.S. and very shortly afterwards became Professor of Chemistry at the University of Nottingham where he pioneered the chemistry of silicon compounds.

In 1888 he married his cousin Lily Holland, the daughter of W.T. Holland, J.P., of Bridgwater, and granddaughter of C.A. Duval. Kipping, Perkin and Lapworth married three sisters, and it appears that Perkin met his future wife during Kipping's engagement. Lapworth, who was considerably the youngest, later completed this noteworthy trio. Only the Kippings had a family.

Kipping will chiefly be remembered for his work on complex derivatives of silicon, but he carried out a considerable amount of miscellaneous work, for example the preparation of indan-1-one. He was skilful at the bench and maintained the highest possible standard of accuracy.

Before I conclude this chapter I would like to say a few words about one of my favourite forms of entertainment. In my undergraduate days and as a young lecturer in Manchester I was very fond of the Music Hall, where I enjoyed the performances of Harry Lauder, Gracie Fields, and all the great comedians of the Windmill Theatre, the Tivoli, and the Ardwick Empire.

At the old Hippodrome on the Palatine Road in Manchester I was very impressed by a couple named the Zancigs who did a "mind reading" act. Mr. Zancig would roam the auditorium asking for articles — at random — from the audience which he would then ask his wife, who was blindfolded, to describe or otherwise identify. I was amazed at the accuracy of their work and in order to trip them up I once gave Mr. Zancig a brazilin formula to identify. To my astonishment, apart from one or two minor mistakes in description, they got it right. It was only at the end of their career that Zancig admitted it was all done by a complicated code which they never revealed.

The Hippodrome was a large enough theatre to stage a full scale circus. Great features of entertainment in Manchester were the pantomimes, in fact Manchester could almost be described as the home of pantomime as there were many schools there for the young aspiring performers. Pantomimes were given at the Theatre Royal, the Palace Theatre, Deansgate Theatre, the Gaiety, Ardwick Empire, and other establishments.

After our marriage, Gertrude and I were regular attendants at performances of the Gaiety Theatre where Miss Horniman was the impresario for Sybil Thorndyke and Lewis Casson, among others. Unfortunately, in later years the Gaiety became a cinema. However, its function as a repertory theatre was taken over by the Rusholme on the Palatine Road, beyond the University. A prominent actress at that time was Thea Holme.

I was also a great devotee of Gilbert and Sullivan and went often to the performances at the Theatre Royal. It was an additional source of amusement to me that the students knew and demanded the right number of encores for each of the popular numbers. In fact, a jolly good time was had by all.

Chapter III

Postgraduate Research at Manchester (1905–1912)

William Henry Perkin, jun. (1860—1929)

W.H. Perkin, jun. was my first teacher of descriptive organic chemistry. He had a simple outlook on the subject, which he treated as a system in which the parts were related by reactions. However, he never paused to consider the underlying mechanism of organic chemical reactions. For him, chemistry was still the science for transformation of materials and these could be represented by changes in structural formulae. Synthetic and other reactions could usually be explained by drawing rings round reactive moieties, with consequent changes in the binding of bonds. A full obituary, in three parts, was published by the Chemical Society in 1932, and I will only refer here to a few biographical details, since reference to Perkin occurs at various points in these memoirs.

He was the eldest son of Sir William Perkin, who at the age of 18 years discontinued his work as a junior research collaborator of A.W. Hoffmann at the Royal College of Science, in order to exploit the discovery he had made of the dyestuff, later called mauveine. He overcame all formidable difficulties and developed processes for manufacturing nitrobenzene and aniline, as well as processes necessary for the conversion of aniline and its homologues into triphenyl-methane dyestuffs. The problems involved were largely those of chemical engineering, and Perkin's pioneering efforts were the foundation of the organic chemical industry. The story of this brilliant achievement has been frequently told, and need not be recalled in full detail.

Perkin is said to have made a profit of £40,000 (needless to say worth more than that now), and then returned to academic life. I met him on two occasions in his son's laboratory. The raison d'être of the visits was to arrange a home for the equipment with which he determined magneto-optical rotatory powers. This was a subject which he had made his own and had published a paper of record length. I do not know what the outcome of his visits was, but I never heard that the subject was taken up by anyone in the Manchester Laboratories.

The Perkins were very musical and there was a family orchestra. W.H.P. played the violin, using a Guarnerius which was lent to him by his uncle. Later, when he went to study in Germany, he was not allowed to take this violin with him and he turned to the piano, on which instrument he was a brilliant, though not inspired, performer. Having on several occasions stayed in his house, I can vouch for the fact that his practice commenced at 5 a.m., though at one time he had a dumb piano. He had a near perfect technique, but little musical expression. Although it is not mentioned by Dr. A.J. Greenaway, I know that during my time in Manchester, Perkin was accompanied by Dr. A. Brodsky, the First Violinist of the Hallé Orchestra, and the conqueror of the difficulties of Tchaikovsky's Violin Concerto in D minor. In recognition of this feat Tchaikovsky subsequently dedicated the concerto to Dr. Brodsky. In Oxford, Perkin continued his organisation of chamber music. One of his musical colleagues was a pupil of Brodsky, Mrs. Briggs, and another was Professor R.A. Peters, the biochemist. In Manchester he organised a trio and quintet, and frequently had the assistance of professional musicians from the Hallé Orchestra. Arthur Lapworth often played the violin in performances of chamber music, with Perkin at the piano; on these occasions a composition by Mozart was usually selected. Perkin was not a great reader, and travelling one day with him from Oxford to London, I saw him attentively studying a book; it turned out to be a volume containing some of Beethoven's later string quartets. Apart from his chemistry and music, Perkin's chief interest was gardening. He specialised in growing carnations, chrysanthemums and delphiniums, but he was also a general purpose gardener, though I do not recollect having noticed that he cultivated alpine plants to any extent. These activities appeared to fill his whole available time. His periods of service on councils of learned societies and Government committees were regarded as rather unwelcome disturbances of his research activities. He was President of the Chemical Society from 1913 to 1915. Perkin took great interest in the infant dyestuffs industry and in his capacity as consultant to the British Dyestuffs

Corporation he established research units at several centres, including one in his own laboratory at Oxford. No detailed description of Perkin's research will be attempted. The memorial notices, to which reference has already been made, are:

1. The personal side, by A.J. Greenaway.
2. Early work, by J.F. Thorpe, covering a synthesis of carbon rings, the chemistry of camphor, and the synthesis of the terpenes, among other topics of alicyclic and aliphatic chemistry.
3. By R.R.; this deals with the work on berberine, cryptopine and other alkaloids, brazilin and haematoxylin, and topics of similar nature.

Perkin went to Würzburg in 1880 to study chemistry under Johannes Wislicenus. He received the Ph.D. on the basis of a thesis describing the condensation of n-heptaldehyde under the influence of alkalis. Later, in 1882, after a short intermission in England in his father's laboratory, he went to Munich to work with Adolf von Baeyer. His story was that he met a man in the grounds, whom he took to be a gardener of some kind, and asked him where he should find Professor Baeyer, and received the surprising reply "I am Professor Baeyer". Here, he found the scientific atmosphere most congenial and indeed some of those who worked in the laboratory at the time are famed for their contribution to organic chemistry; one of them was Johannes Thiele.

Between 1883—1893 Perkin carried out a masterly series of synthetic studies of closed carbon chains. The general view held by his contemporaries at that time was that only 5- or 6-carbon rings could exist and, consequently, his claims to have produced 3- or 4-carbon atom members were strongly criticised, especially by Fittig. In his Pedler Lecture Perkin himself gave a lucid account of his progress of the investigation. The critics could have had a stronger case than they actually put forward, if it had been realised that Perkin had wrongly interpreted the results (themselves quite accurately recorded) of the condensation of ethyl sodio-acetoacetate with trimethylene bromide. He thought the product was a cyclobutane derivative, but actually it contained a 5-ring of 4 carbon atoms and 1 oxygen atom. This would have been a splendid argument for the critics, but before they woke up Perkin had carried out a similar experiment with sodiomalonate, and this proceeded normally and unquestionably afforded a cyclobutane derivative. This classical study was followed by work on camphor which supported the Bredt formula and, with the co-operation of J.F. Thorpe, led to a second synthesis of camphoric acid. Much later, Perkin applied the Grignard reaction to the synthesis of terpin hydrate, terpineol, dipentene and limonene, carvestrene and sylvestrene, in a typically well planned campaign. He took advantage of the fact that a ketone is more reactive than an ester towards the organomagnesium derivative, and the requisite intermediates were either made by known synthetic reactions or by reduction of aromatic acids, and for the latter purpose the acids were frequently reduced with boiling amyl alcohol and sodium. This produced some iso-valeroate, the rather unpleasant odour of which was found to be highly persistent. Research students were forced to leave their lodgings and an inquiry heard in the senior common room was "Has anyone seen or smelt Perkin?" The last stages of this elegant work were being put through at the time when I entered Perkin's laboratory, and shortly afterwards W.J. Pope and O. Wallach collaborated with Perkin in providing proof of the correctness of van 't Hoff's prediction of a structure which would show molecular asymmetry, though not containing an asymmetric carbon atom, as usually understood.

The part of Perkin's work in which I later became involved started with a study of the structure of the alkaloid berberine, which was largely undertaken during the period 1887—1892 when he functioned as the first Professor of Chemistry at Heriot-Watt College, Edinburgh. Goldschmidt had already established the molecular structure of papaverine by oxidising the base with alkaline permanganate, separating a variety of substances so produced, and establishing their structure by further experiments. When the information obtained in this way was considered together, the structure of the alkaloid was revealed. Perkin adapted this method to the case of berberine and deduced the correct ring structure from the results. However, one of the products of oxidation, namely berberal, was synthesised, but the last stage of the reaction was misinterpreted. I noticed this error some years later and its correction allowed the two methoxyl groups of the alkaloid to occupy the position in the isoquinoline ring corresponding to that which they occupy in the meconyl group of hydrastine. The latter base is a congener of berberine and the relation of the two alkaloids was later proved by converting hydrastine into berberine (see scheme at the top of page 29).

A natural sequel after the berberine work was the examination of cryptopine and protopine. He obtained large supplies of these alkaloids through the generosity of T. & H. Smith & Co. of Edinburgh.

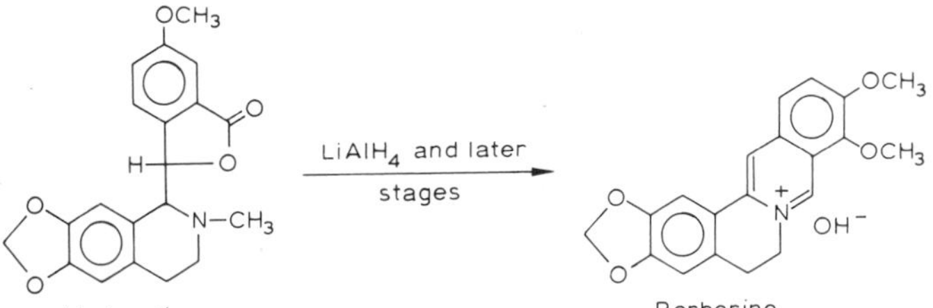

Hydrastine

Berberine

LiAlH₄ and later stages

The first paper published in 1916 is one of the longest ever accepted by the Chemical Society and contained results of outstanding interest. Cryptopine was disclosed as a substance containing a 10-ring fused with 2 benzene rings. The N-methyl group lies opposite a carbonyl and a link between these two can be established and the fundamental structure is that of an epi-berberine. Protopine (like bicuculline) has two methylenedioxy groups; its chemistry follows closely that of cryptopine.

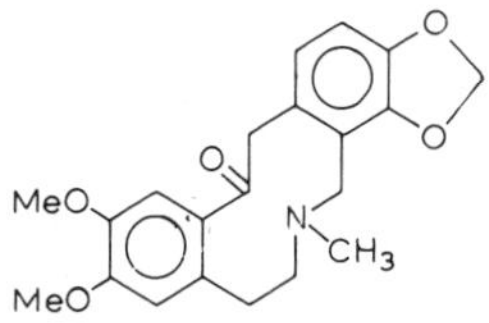

Cryptopine

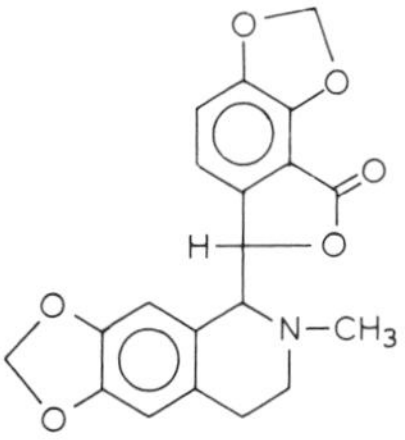

Bicuculline

The long series of studies of brazilin and haematoxylin started in 1883, but must have been subject to some interruption since publication appeared from 1899 onwards. The method chosen again was that of permanganate oxidation, and study of all the projects was subjected to ramifying further investigations. The final results were put together as in a jigsaw puzzle. In order to moderate the action of the oxidising agent the phenolic groups were protected by methylation. The substances were correctly recognised as having a ring system containing chroman and indane structures, but the proposed fusion of the rings was incorrect and, furthermore, brazilin and haematoxylin were presumed to be secondary alcohols, whereas this function is in fact tertiary. At this stage no satisfactory explanation of the oxidation of trimethylbrazilin with chromic acid was given.

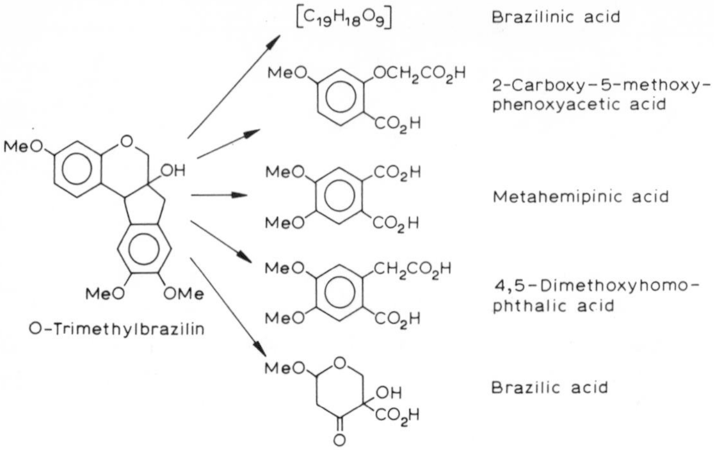

$[C_{19}H_{18}O_9]$ Brazilinic acid

MeO OCH$_2$CO$_2$H CO$_2$H 2-Carboxy-5-methoxy-phenoxyacetic acid

MeO O OH

MeO CO$_2$H MeO CO$_2$H Metahemipinic acid

MeO OMe

O-Trimethylbrazilin

MeO CH$_2$CO$_2$H MeO CO$_2$H 4,5-Dimethoxyhomo-phthalic acid

MeO O OH CO$_2$H O Brazilic acid

The further development of the chemistry of brazilin and haematoxylin is treated after the next paragraph and in chapter X.

Perkin's main experimental interest started in Manchester and continued throughout his whole Oxford period. This was the chemistry of strychnine and brucine, which suited him down to the ground; the new substances obtained crystallised well and he was able to make excellent use of his remarkable skill in bench techniques, which included the choice of reagents, the way in which they were applied, and the eventual isolation and crystallisation of the products. The line which he chose to develop personally was that of alkylation followed by decomposition of the quaternary salt with bases. Tafel's strychnidine and brucidine were also used as starting points. As an example, N-methylstrychnidinium methosulphate is converted by alcoholic sodium ethoxide into ethoxydihydro*chano*-N-methyl*neo*strychnidine; on treatment with hydrochloric acid the ring is reconstituted and N-methyl*neo*strychnidinium chloride is produced on thermal decomposition, and this yields *neo*strychnidine. Catalytic hydrogenation of strychnidine and *neo*strychnidine afforded the same dihydrostrychnidine. Thus, the opening of a ring in the quaternary salt is accompanied by migration of a double bond. This work ramified in many directions and was continued with considerable success. One of Perkin's collaborators, O. Achmatowicz, continued to work independently at the University of Warsaw. The problem of the molecular structure of strychnine was, however, solved by work along other lines.

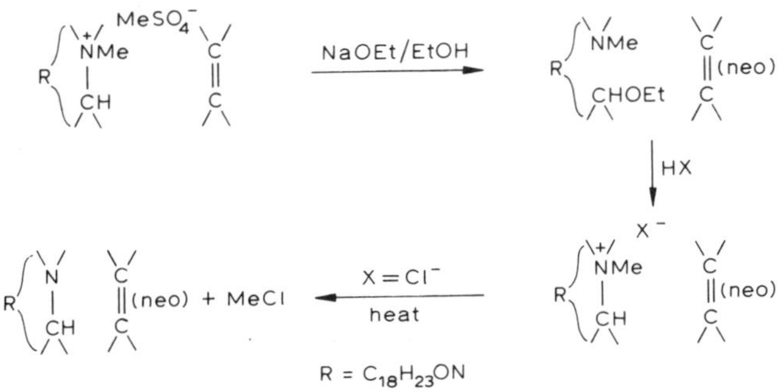

R = $C_{18}H_{23}ON$

Perkin had already carried out a long series of research studies of the oxidation of trimethylbrazilin with permanganate and had obtained a number of acids as a result, and gave the correct constitution to most of them, but not to the chief one, the most important one, which was brazilinic acid, which contains all the carbon atoms of trimethylbrazilin itself. I was extremely interested in this problem, because after reading through the work of Perkin and his suggestions, it seemed to me that there was something very wrong in the interpretations. The CH groups of the Perkin formula turned up in the oxidation products as CH_2, which is surely very unusual for permanganate oxidations at the ordinary temperature. It is true that one could obtain keto-acids which might lose carboxyl very easily and then get oxidised into carboxylic acids, but this would hardly fit the particular case of the brazilin compounds; so I went to Perkin one morning and suggested an alternative formula which avoided this difficulty and showed the CH_2 groups which are found in the oxidation products. Perkin was very interested and advised me to do some further work on the subject. The further work, which I had also proposed, was to synthesise brazilinic acid and brazilic acid according to the structures which were now proposed. In the case of brazilinic acid only, this was different from the structures given by Perkin, because he had already arrived at the correct interpretation of brazilic acid.

Two syntheses of brazilinic acid [3] solved the problem of the constitution, but to our chagrin we found, after we had done this work, that we had been anticipated some time ago by A. Werner and P. Pfeiffer, who had published the same suggestion of the constitution of brazilin in a short paper. However, these authors had not solved the whole of the problems, by any means; they had got a completely wrong conception of the nature of trimethylbrazilone, the oxidation product of trimethylbrazilin with chromic acid, and we decided to go ahead and finish the work until we were satisfied that we knew all about it. Incidentally, the synthesis of brazilic acid had not been accomplished, but that of its anhydro-derivative was carried out as follows [3]:

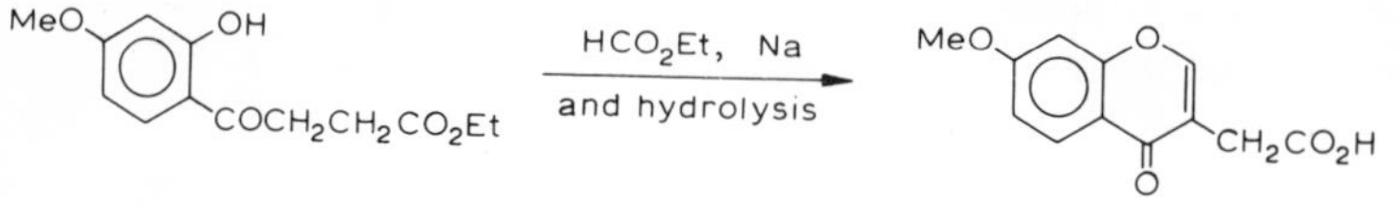

Anhydrobrazilic acid

The above synthesis of anhydrobrazilic acid was, in fact, the first of a 3-substituted chromone and served as a model for subsequent syntheses of isoflavones.

The synthesis of dimethoxyhomophthalic acid [2], another of the oxidation products of trimethylbrazilin, was an important stage in our progress because I decided to make it from dimethoxyindan-1-one, and the preparation of this substance eventually led to the discovery of the pyrylium salts synthesis, as mentioned below. Dimethoxyindan-1-one was made from vanillin, which was methylated by methyl sulphate and sodium hydroxide in methanolic solution. The aldehyde was condensed with ethyl acetate, with the help of granulated sodium. After hydrolysis of the ester, the dimethoxycinnamic acid was reduced in the usual way with 3% sodium amalgam. On acidification of the solution the hydrocinnamic acid separated in the form of small pellets which contained a certain amount of water, even when dried in the air. In this form the acid was dissolved in warm benzene and phosphoric anhydride was added. The mixture was then treated for a period on the steam bath. The reddish-purple complex was destroyed, as such, and on the addition of water dimethoxyindanone could be recovered in good yield from the benzene solution. It was obviously desirable that some water should be present in this process so that, in effect, we were using polyphosphoric acid. When this was realised, the flask was always swilled with water and drained, before the benzene solution of the acid was placed in it. I have mentioned this procedure in some detail, because it was the earliest recognition of the value of polyphosphoric acid as a condensing agent.

This dimethoxyindanone easily formed an isonitroso derivative which, by the action of PCl_5 and subsequent hydrolysis, gave the dimethoxyhomophthalic acid.

The most important synthesis in this phase was, of course, that of brazilinic acid, because this compound has all the carbon atoms of the brazilin skeleton. A very small yield was obtained by condensing the anhydride of metahemipinic acid with methoxyphenoxyacetic ester. The metahemipinic acid was obtained conveniently by permanganate oxidation of the isonitrosodimethoxyindanone.

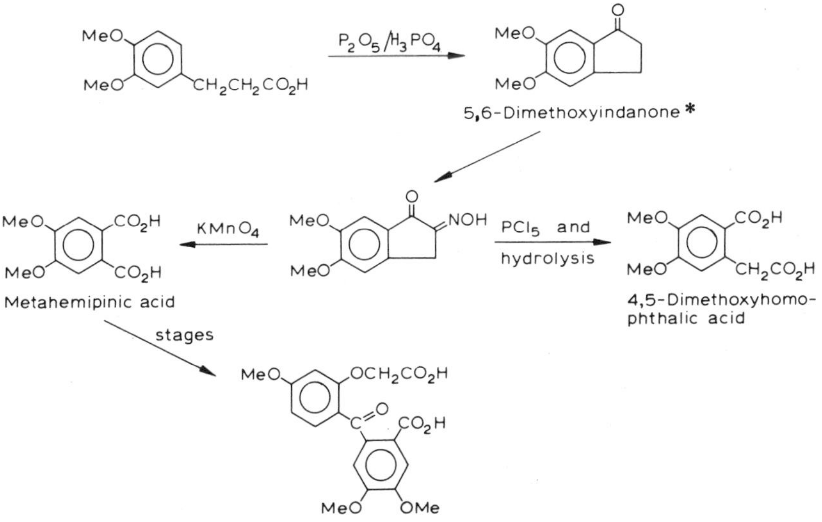

MeO, MeO CH₂CH₂CO₂H — P_2O_5/H_3PO_4 → MeO, MeO (O)

5,6-Dimethoxyindanone *

MeO, MeO CO₂H CO₂H — KMnO₄ ← MeO, MeO NOH (O) — PCl₅ and hydrolysis → MeO, MeO CO₂H CH₂CO₂H

Metahemipinic acid

4,5-Dimethoxyhomo-phthalic acid

stages

MeO, OCH₂CO₂H C=O CO₂H MeO OMe

Brazilinic acid

* W.H.P. and R.R. (loc. cit.) gave m.p. 115° for this substance, due to a clerical error which was discovered some years later. The correct m.p. is 120° and J.A. Barltrop kindly agreed to include the correction in a publication of his own (J. Chem. Soc. 1946, 961).

A better synthesis of brazilinic acid was the one shown at the top of p. 34, in which the lactone of dihydrobrazilinic acid was used as an intermediate. This lactone had the rather pleasant property of giving a brilliant crimson colouration in sulphuric acid, which disappears to a colourless solution within a short time. No doubt there is a quinonoid structure which becomes unstable when the substance is sulphonated.

There was in the laboratory a German who was a retired manufacturer, named Paul Engels. He presented, as a rule, the most extra-

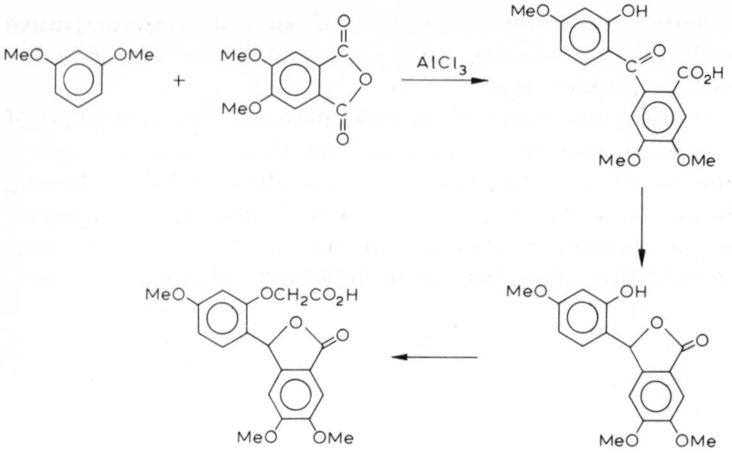

Lactone of dihydrobrazilinic
acid

ordinary picture, because he was working on the methylation of brazilein and got the alkaline solution all over his face and hands and his white laboratory coat. He worked with great enthusiasm in a downstairs room, usually called the cellar, which had a stone floor. The material was brought to Perkin, who worked it up to a highly crystalline trimethyl ether of brazilein, which formed a magnificent formate, crystallising in garnet red needles. The trimethylbrazilein itself was also a very beautiful substance of large orange prisms, the crystals of which were measured by Dr. T.V. Barker. Unfortunately, this and other valuable specimens, brought from Manchester, were all destroyed in a disastrous fire in my laboratory at Sydney University two years later.

Perkin carried out with his own hands a remarkable series of experiments on the action of hydrogen peroxide on methylated brazilein derivatives. The carbon shared by the benzene nuclei is broken away by oxidation and the products were further methylated, the results agreeing with the constitution, as shown below.

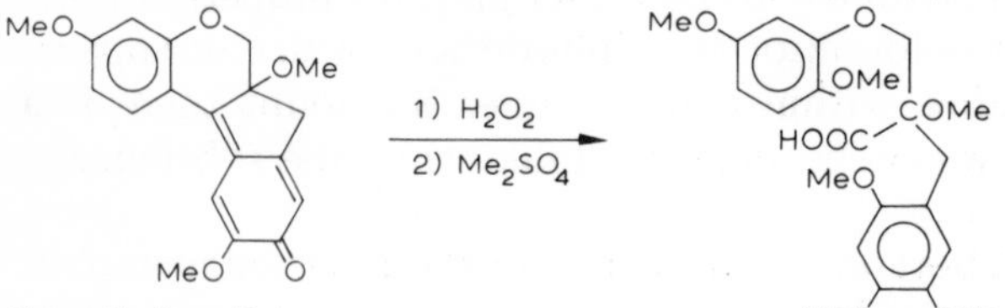

Trimethylbrazilein

Perkin realised that the oxidation of aurin with hydrogen peroxide in acetic acid solution would proceed along similar lines and he proved this, since the products were hydroquinone and p-hydroxybenzoic acid. Perkin had already shown that phenylhydrazine is able to reduce trimethylbrazilone to deoxytrimethylbrazilone, which is simply the removal of two oxygen atoms from the 9-membered ring with formation of fused rings. This substance proved important in the later history of the subject.

Before going on to other topics I thought it desirable to have a look at the possibility of making the older brazilin skeleton, at least in order to see what its properties were. This led to the important step of condensing the monomethyl ether of resorcylaldehyde with the dimethoxyindanone, which had already been prepared. When the dimethoxyindanone and the aldehyde were condensed by means of hydrogen chloride, an orange substance was obtained which was recognised as an oxonium salt [4]. In the presence of alkali a substance of the type of salicylideneacetophenone was produced and this, by the action of acid, also went into the oxonium salt. This oxonium salt was not identical with a substance of similar composition and properties which could be obtained from the methylation of brazilein. The following scheme will, perhaps, best explain this point:

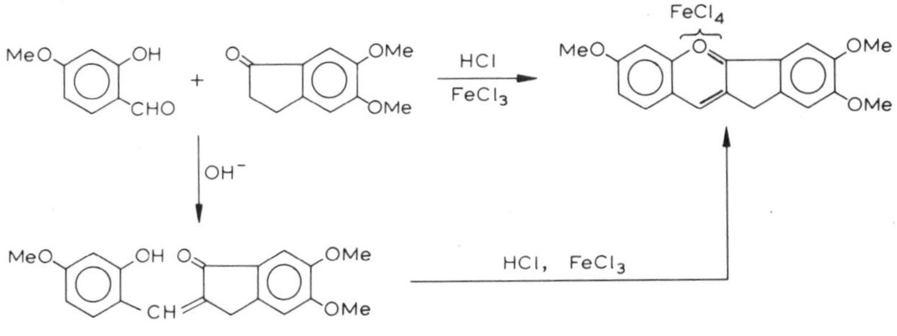

This proved that the original Perkin formula was incorrect — rather an unnecessary proof — because of our synthesis of brazilinic acid. However, the consequences of the contact with this kind of chemistry were of considerable importance. A.G. Perkin had shown that brazilein and analogously, haematein, are converted by sulphuric acid into what he called *iso*brazilein/*iso*haematein sulphate. These substances were obtained in methylated form from the product of the methylation of trimethylbrazilein and tetramethylhaematein.

Somewhere at this stage in this development, I cannot recall exactly when, it was realised that these substances, at first regarded as anhydropyranol salts, were really analogous to pyridinium salts.

The group had been recognised by A. Werner, who called them oxylium; most of his examples were in the xanthylium series. We stepped aside from our brazilin work, for a short time, in order to establish the nature of these substances and their production from hydroxy-aldehydes and aromatic ketones. The case which we looked at was that of the condensation of β-resorcylaldehyde with acetophenone, when we obtained exactly the same substance as Bühler and Sicherer had obtained by condensing hydroxymethyleneacetophenone with resorcinol, in the presence of hydrogen chloride. At this stage we prepared a number of salts of this kind which we described as pyrylium salts [4], following a suggestion of Decker and Fellenberg, whose work synchronised with our own, and examples are shown in the scheme:

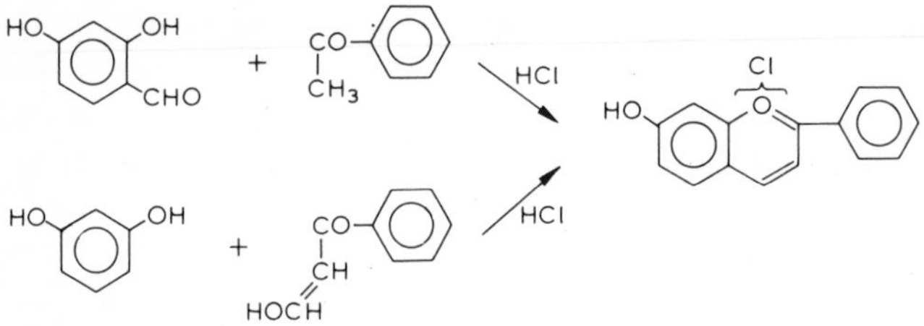

POST-GRADUATE WORK IN MANCHESTER

I got into the habit of working at night, until perhaps 3.00 to 3.30 a.m., and coming in rather late, surprising Perkin with the fact that I was able to do anything at all. Two other nightbirds were D.L. Chapman (who later became a distinguished Fellow of Jesus College, Oxford) and Dr. Ida Smedley. Chapman's brother, Sidney, was Professor of Economics in the University, and D.L.C. complained to him of the extremely low pay accorded to demonstrators in the university laboratories. Well, for example, when I was first appointed a demonstrator my salary was the princely sum of £120 per annum. However, D.L.C. got very little encouragement from Sidney, who said that he believed in underpaying scientists because it kept their brains active. The other night-bird, Dr. Ida Smedley, was the daughter of a rather well-known Baconian, and her sister was Constance

Smedley, the novelist. Ida Smedley early developed a strong interest in the biochemistry of fats. She had originally been a student of Henry E. Armstrong. Ida Smedley was a personal friend of my late wife, Gertrude Maud.

The research students working with Perkin formed a Tea Club, and this was very often a forum for quite interesting discussions.

Another very important friendship was formed in those early days at Manchester, namely, with Arthur Lapworth. When we found how close our interests were, we were always discussing theoretical questions and Armstrong described it as "Lapworth and Robinson playing noughts and crosses again". He did not believe a word of it and said that he would never be hung in chains, not even conjugated chains.

The first task which Perkin asked me to undertake was the preparation of ethyl piperonoylacetate [1] by adaptation of the elegant methods used by L. Claisen for the synthesis of ethyl benzoylacetate. He gave me a 5 kilogram bottle of piperonal, adding that he thought it would probably be enough for the purpose! The oxidation with permanganate was carried out in Winchester quart bottles, but the yield was always somewhat lower than can be obtained in analogous reaction with veratraldehyde. When I complained of this to W.H.P. he said "Do one more oxidation and you will get enough". The chloride of the acid, made with phosphorus pentachloride, turned out to be a hard solid which could be powdered. The Claison procedure gave excellent results, and a reasonable large quantity of the keto-ester was prepared. I was advised to continue the investigation in the direction of a preparation of a series of coumarins by means of the Pechmann condensation. Perkin pointed out that the products would not be unlike the naturally occurring dyestuffs and said "We will make a series and send them to my brother Arthur, who is a dab hand at all that sort of thing". However, I was attracted by the possibility of using piperonal in another direction, which was the exploration of some synthetic lines which had a bearing on the chemistry of brazilin. These quickly gave promising results in which Perkin himself was very interested and consequently the coumarin never saw the light.

The early synthetic work bearing on the brazilin problem is described on page 33. Dr. E. Schunck's laboratory and library were re-erected in a position adjoining Perkin's private laboratory and when I entered the latter, Perkin had a number of research students in the Schunck. These included F.W. Kay, J.L. Simonsen, who was a year senior to me in the Honour School of Chemistry, as well as Kenneth Fisher, who had taken a doctorate at the University of Jena, and was invited by Perkin to synthesise sylvestrene; "a fickle jade" he called her. Fisher was an extremely lively person — he gave a wonderful impersonation of Harry Tate and reproduced native dialects in most amusing forms. He once took me for a 30 mile walk on Cheshire roads, a more trying test of foot and footwear than any excursion in the mountains. In later years Fisher became Headmaster of Oundle School. His son became well-known for his nature studies, especially of birds, and also as a broadcaster on these topics.

In the course of one of my late sessions in the laboratory I completed a synthesis of protocotoin. This benzene derivative is piperonoylphloroglucine trimethyl ether. I made the substance by condensing 1,3,5-trimethoxybenzene with my newly acquired piperonoyl chloride with the aid of anhydrous ferric chloride. The reaction went very well and the product was easily crystallised, and it was found to have the correct melting point. It was stated to give an intense green solution in nitric acid; this I confirmed and was gazing lovingly at the beautiful colouration, when the contents of the tube shot out and went into my eyes. The material used had been placed on porous porcelain and no doubt still contained alcohol used for the crystallisation. I remembered that a piece of rubber tubing was attached to the swan neck immediately on my left, and I lost no time in washing my face with a good stream of water, after which I swabbed the eyes with very dilute ammonia solution. I recall this incident with one purpose in view, that is to mention the kindness of Professor Perkin, who visited me shortly after the accident. As a matter of fact, I cannot recall having published any account of this synthesis. The substance is described in Beilstein's Handbook and, nearby, the eye falls on certain naturally occurring α-pyrones. In the course of digression from other work, I made preliminary experiments on the synthesis of one of these and condensed ethyl propiolate with ethyl benzoylacetate. The product having the anticipated structure is a well crystallised substance which gives a blue-violet colouration with ferric chloride in alcoholic solution.

In my seventeenth year my father added a storey to an outhouse of our house in New Brampton, Chesterfield. This was equipped as a laboratory in which I attempted a rather grandiose set up, designed for atom smashing. It consisted of a coil, capable of giving a 6 inch spark. The electrical supply was obtained from accumulators which were kept fully charged. The discharge, under reduced pressure, was also kept running as constantly as possible and gases could be taken off for spectroscopic examination whenever it was so desired. Needless to say, I got no results, which I attributed at the time to the fact that further work along these lines was prohibited because of an alleged nuisance. I did, however, manage to do one thing in this laboratory, and that was to effect a synthesis of terebic acid, by the action of methylmagnesium iodide on ethyl acetosuccinate. After working up in the known manner, the product had the correct melting point, but no elementary analysis was carried out. One day I mentioned this to Simonsen, who expressed an interest and said that he would like to repeat the synthesis and extend it. This he did, and published a paper on the synthesis of terebic, terpenylic and homoterpenylic acids. At my request, he did not mention my unfinished work.

We decided to co-operate in the study of the chemistry of barbaloin [7]. Simonsen made very pure specimens of acetyl derivatives in order to establish the molecular formula of the substance. He also oxidised the acetyl derivative with chromic anhydride and obtained a good yield of diacetylrhein. It was already known that barbaloin could be hydrolysed with formation of aloe-emodin. This has the composition of methyldihydroxyanthraquinone and at the time of our work it was regarded as a positional isomeride of emodin. We showed that triacetylaloe-emodin could also be oxidised by chromic anhydride with formation of diacetylrhein, and this proved that aloe-emodin and rhein are related to each other as carbinol and carboxylic acid, $R \cdot CH_2OH$ and $R \cdot CO_2H$, respectively. It was later found that chrysophanic acid is $R \cdot CH_3$. We prepared the dimethyl ether of rhein and converted it through the acid chloride and amide to aminodimethoxyanthraquinone. After replacing the amino group by hydrogen, we obtained a dimethoxyanthraquinone which was at first thought to be the dimethylisochrysazin. Later, it was found by Oesterle that chrysophanic acid is a methylchrysazin. The orientation of the substituents was determined by later synthesis. We realised that barbaloin could not possibly be an ordinary arabinoside since it is far too resistant to hydrolysis. We suggested a constitution in which the sugar moiety was involved in the ring structure. It is now known that barbaloin belongs to the interesting class of C-saccharides.

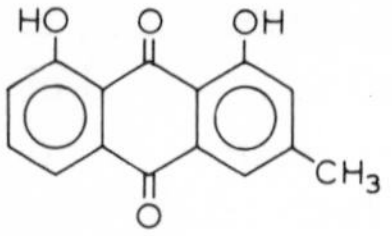

Chrysophanic acid

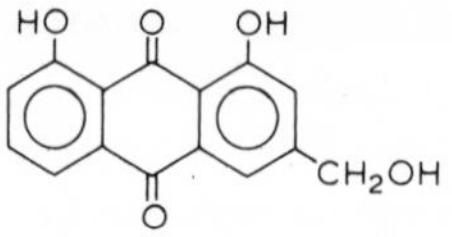

Aloe-emodin

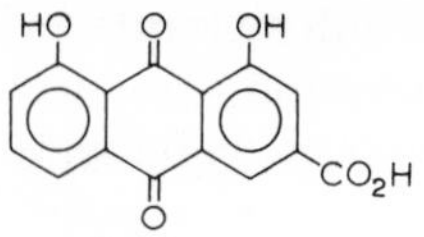

Rhein

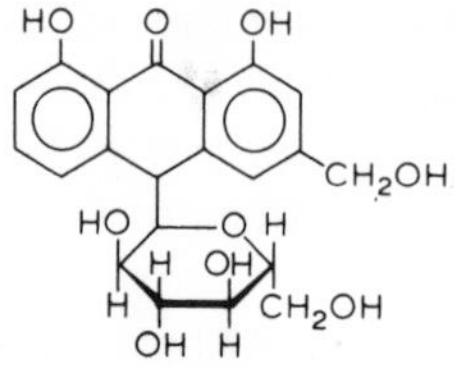

Barbaloin

John Lionel Simonsen (1884—1957)

J.L. Simonsen was born at Levenshulme, Manchester; his parents were naturalised British subjects of Danish origin and he had relatives of professorial status in Copenhagen and Stockholm whom he frequently visited. Their interests were mainly biochemical. Simonsen's topic of research in the first years was the synthesis of norpinic acid, a degradation product of pinene obtained by Baeyer in the course of classical investigations. The objective was not reached, but a large number of new reactions and new intermediate products was obtained. Later, success followed on a very interesting line of argument. Pinene contains, it is true, the cyclobutane ring which is retained in norpinic acid, but this cyclobutane in pinene is bridged by three carbon atoms connecting positions 1 and 3, the diagonal of the 4-ring. This means that all the carbon atoms of the system are members of a cyclohexane ring, and this fact doubtless makes an important contribution to the stability of the system. Accordingly, it might be possible to introduce a bridge across positions 1 and 3 of a cyclohexane. This is exactly the method eventually used for the synthesis of norpinic acid. Among other observations made in the course of this work was the fact that acetone will condense with hippuric acid in the presence of acetic anhydride and sodium acetate to an oxazolone derivative. I have a clear recollection of the pleasure with which he exhibited a specimen of the product which was used, many years later, for the synthesis of penicillamic acid. Simonsen was the first Schunck Research Fellow in Chemistry. In 1910 he became Professor at the Presidency College, Madras; in 1919 he became Chief Chemist of the Forest Research Institute and College at Dehra-Dun, and in 1925 he became Professor of Organic Chemistry at the Indian Institute of Science at Bangalore. He returned to England in 1928, and in

J.L. Simonsen.

1930 he was appointed Professor of Chemistry in the University of Wales at University College, Bangor. During the whole of this long stay in India, and for some years in England, he devoted his outstanding experimental talent to the study of essential oils largely of Indian origin. Especially noteworthy was his discovery that carene was an important component of Indian turpentine. This threw light on certain transformation series, among which was the biogenesis of sylvestrene. Another series of investigations concerned the reactions of the sesquiterpene longifolene. Throughout this work the isopentane rule was found to give reliable guidance, but Simonsen discovered a case in which the rule is broken. I thought the reason for this might be a rather plausible molecular rearrangement, and later work proved that this does indeed occur. During the period of his stay in India, Simonsen became the first authority on the subject of terpenes, and he wrote a compendious work in four volumes. However, the subject has expanded enormously in later years, largely, I am sure, because of the impetus given to the subject by Simonsen. Indian chemists have been, and still are, in the forefront of the wave of progress in this field and are now assisted by the use of physical methods, which were not available to Simonsen and other workers of his period. At the present time we are witnessing a remarkable new advance, made possible by the study of nuclear magnetic resonance in compounds containing ^{13}C.

When in India, Simonsen helped in the organisation of the scientific aspects of government in many different fields. During the First World War he was Controller of Oils and Chemical Adviser to the Indian Munitions Board. He took the first necessary steps to organise the Indian Science Congress and was certainly influential in paving the way for the establishment of national scientific institutions in India. After his return to England he became Director of Research in the Colonial Products Research Council, and in that connection made a visit to Nigeria in company with Sir Ian Heilbron. In 1944 Simonsen and I, in company with Alexander King of the D.S.I.R. and, at that time, head of the B.C.S.O. in Washington, visited the U.S.A. and the Caribbean on behalf of the Medical Research Council and the Colonial Products Research Council. In the Colonial Products Research Council in Washington, our work was largely co-ordination of the British and American Committees on the synthesis of new antimalarials. These were a large number of substances, partly modelled on atebrin and plasmochin, but other groups of heterocyclic bases were also explored. The discovery of paludrin in the I.C.I. laboratories came at a later date.

We then visited Puerto Rico, and were much interested in the efforts that were being made to remodel the University of San Juan on the lines favoured by Hutchings, President of the University of Chicago. Essentially, this provided for a very general education for two years and specialisation only in the third, and possibly a fourth year. We were told that higher study and research would be introduced in the next session, and when I suggested that it might be a good thing to invite help from the U.S. in starting this scheme, the reply was, that this would be quite unnecessary and that the teachers at present in the University would be quite capable of initiating research. I do not know with what success this jump into the deep end was made.

The industries of Puerto Rico at that time were not developed far beyond the making of cement, furniture and, naturally, agriculture. In the south of the Island we visited a remarkable communal enterprise in sugar farming (see p. 48). In Trinidad, apart from playing a kind of golf-croquet on the Governor's extensive and rough lawn, we were able to initiate some important projects. We confirmed the view, which had been expressed by others, that the Imperial College of Agriculture in Trinidad was not fulfilling all the hopes of its founders, but we proposed the organisation of a Microbiological Research Institute, which was built and directed by Dr. Thyssen, seconded from the Chemical Laboratory of the D.S.I.R. at Teddington. One result of Thyssen's later work was the biological production of ergosterol, and also of a yeast rich in protein. This, however, was found to be nauseous, so far as human consumption was concerned, and I do not know how it fared as food for animals.

We were also influential in establishing a Sugar Research Association. Incidentally, we visited the refinery at Trinidad where an advanced production of fuel for aircraft was in operation. We also saw the Great Lake of Bitumen. As a kind of vacation we visited the Virgin Islands and, in particular, St. Thomas. On arrival, we were met by the Danish chauffeur of the acting Governor, who told us that, unfortunately, our plan to stay in the residence could not be proceeded with and he would take us to Bluebeard's Castle, which turned out to be a small hotel. The reason for this was that, in the previous week, a U.S. destroyer had come to St. Thomas and the native staff of the acting Governor's residence promptly disappeared.

In Bluebeard's Castle we met the Chief Justice of the Island, a coloured gentleman, who explained with some gusto that he had the right to determine when the Island's Parliament should meet. He explained that he usually thought of 1 a.m. as appropriate.

We were due to visit Jamaica, but no planes were available as, for one reason or another, they had all been grounded. We therefore had a few days at our disposal and used these to visit British Guiana. As it was known that this State was mosquito infested, it seemed appropriate that an antimalarial experiment should be made there. We met the Deputy Governor and also representatives of the Government and Industry of the Colony. The malariologist explained that he did not believe in attempts to control malaria by chemicals, but only by engineering methods. However, we discussed the procedure among ourselves and, very briefly, with Sir Ian Heilbron in London and also with Professor Buxton. The latter proposed the method which turned out to be completely successful. The malarial region is about seven miles deep, from the coast towards the forest, and the mosquitoes bred in pools of water in this area. Buxton proposed to put a solution of D.D.T. in xylene into bottles which could be inverted so that the water was in contact with the xylene solution, but the D.D.T. was only very gradually released. After some time the mosquitoes were completely eliminated and gradually the malaria disappeared also. It only remains to add that our Italian malariologist was completely converted and wrote an enthusiastic report on the subject, but there was one curious result. The malaria had produced a very high death rate among infants, and when it was conquered the survival rate rose so that the population of Georgetown increased to such an extent that a serious social problem was posed. This was probably one of the factors leading to the political troubles which occurred in the following years.

Simonsen was appointed Knight Bachelor in 1949, and became F.R.S. in 1932; he also received the Davy Medal in 1950, and Honorary Doctorates of Birmingham, St. Andrews and Malaya. In 1913 he married Janet Hendrie, an eminent surgeon and specialist in malaria. He had many distinguished Indian students who continued, with great effect, his studies of Indian natural products, particularly in the terpene series. At Bangor, one of his students was E.R.H. Jones, later Sir Ewart Jones, and my successor as Waynflete Professor of Chemistry at Oxford University (1955).

Simonsen was a neat and skilful experimenter and the important results described in his numerous papers were largely the result of his personal work at the bench. He had many qualities that contributed to his success as an administrator; perhaps the most important were clearheadedness and the ability to make quick decisions. I always found him a very good friend, and I am sure he helped me without necessarily bringing the fact to my attention.

The social occasion in Perkin's entourage was the meeting of the Tea Club in the afternoon and this brought, at one time or another, most of his collaborators together.

On one occasion I organised a walk through Cheedale and Cowdale in Derbyshire, and this stimulated Robert Storey (a rugby footballer) to write some doggerel verses which I have carefully preserved, but will not inflict on my readers. However, he does mention the names of eleven participants who included the Misses Smedley, Walsh, Dobson and Bamford, and also Mrs. Weizman, attended by A.N. Meldrum, E. Hope, F. Thomas and J.L. Simonsen.

A.N. Meldrum was a pupil of W.P. Wynne, himself a student of H.E. Armstrong. He was an extremely careful experimenter; his independent work at about this period included, for example, the condensation of acetone with malonic acid in acetic anhydride (wrongly interpreted, as transpired later). He also explored the condensation of isomeric cresotinic acids and chloral with the help of sulphuric acid. Later, reference is made to other members of the party.

Unfortunately the aforementioned expedition ended in disaster, as its members were almost drowned by very heavy rain, and I was never able to induce my friends to repeat the experience. The mass invasion of Derbyshire dales was not repeated, but Miss Walsh and I devoted many weekends to rock climbing on the millstone grit edges of the Peak District. After our marriage this was continued as mentioned below.

Chaim (Charles) Weizmann (1874—1952)

The biographers of Weizmann were obsessed by the philosophic questions involved in his Zionism and it is difficult to extract hard fact from the haze of enthusiastic appreciation with which they have surrounded their beloved subject. I cannot vie with them in the analysis of Weizmann's motivation and in the assessment of his place in the political aspects of Zionism. I was intimate with him in the early Manchester days, but discussed organic chemical questions

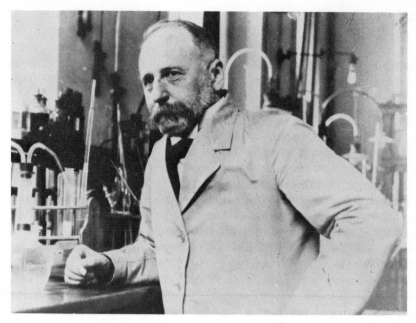

C. Weizmann.

more frequently than the National Home. I gather that his views on the latter were essentially pragmatic, that he was convinced of the justice of the cause and determined to do what he could to advance the practical realisation of the objective. Indeed, his philosophy was quite a simple one and he was content to await an opportunity which, as we know, was eventually presented to him. I shall attempt no biography of this complex character, but shall rely on memories of personal contacts.

I entered the private laboratory of Professor William Henry Perkin, jun. as a post-graduate student in September 1905, and shortly afterwards Perkin, who was carrying out an experiment, was interrupted by a laboratory assistant who said that a foreign-looking gentleman wished to speak to him. Although Perkin had been greatly annoyed by this invasion of his privacy, he stayed away for almost half an hour, and when he returned, rubbing his hands, he said, "Robinson, I think we have got a good man". Weizmann was appointed Lecturer and Administrator, his charge being the Schorlemmer Laboratory in which practical organic chemistry was taught to third year students of the Honour School of Chemistry.

Weizmann introduced the idea of giving these students some practice in research of a very simple kind, and at least one paper was published as a result. It described a synthesis of a number of benzophenone derivatives, using the Friedel-Crafts reaction. One of the coauthors was Walter Norman Haworth (p. 131). When the new Morley Laboratory was built Weizmann had a private laboratory to which he admitted two or three research students; amongst them were Gertrude M. Walsh, my fiancée (p. 51), Henry Stephen (p. 63), and Maurice Copisarow (see entry in N.D.B.). He also gave a series of lectures on rather unusual topics culled from the literature, examples of which were Baeyer's reduction of the isomeric phthalic acids and Büchner's work on the addition of ethyl diazoacetate to aromatic hydrocarbons. The students loved him for his forthrightness and for the help which he was always ready to give them individually. Many years later we visited Weizmann, not long before his passing, in the President's House at Rehovot, and my wife raised a smile on the blind man's face when she reminded him of those days when he noticed the approach of a visitor, and he shouted "Shop"! During his Manchester period Weizmann was a consultant to the Clayton Aniline Company and collaborated with certain members of their research department. Perhaps the most noteworthy outcome of this was a series of papers on the synthesis of naphthacenequinones. Novel methods were developed in the course of this work, especially the use of boric acid as a condensing agent. Although some of the dyes and pigments produced had attractive properties, they do not appear to have been marketed.

The next development, some years later, was to equip a small laboratory for bacteriological work. I never knew why Weizmann decided to take up the subject of chemical change induced by bacteria, but he quickly developed his new interest along useful lines. The French bacteriologist Fernbach had shown that *Bacillus butylicus* was capable of changing carbohydrates into *n*-butanol and acetone, but this observation had not been developed beyong the test tube scale. Weizmann set out to do this and the first step would obviously be to obtain a specimen of the Fernbach culture. This was not possible by the obvious direct method, but Weizmann visited Vienna and brought back from a bacteriological laboratory in that city a culture, which was stated to be one of *B. butylicus*. Whilst he was away, one of his collaborators stated that he had obtained a culture from the surface of maize, which also had the properties of the desired organism. Apart from some unexpected disclosure, we cannot know the truth about this claim.

At an early stage in the First World War, Britain was threatened with a shortage of acetone, which was needed for the manufacture of military explosives. Weizmann offered his services to develop the Fernbach fermentation on a large scale, and received every encouragement from the British Government (1915). He overcame the problem of large scale culture of bacteria and their utilisation in the fermentation process, and thus broke new ground technically, much as Sir William Perkin had done earlier, when he put the manufacture of dyestuffs on its industrial feet. In both cases the chemical engineering must be characterised as pioneering. The production of acetone was carried out at Holton-Heath.

Many years later I had the opportunity to visit Lafayette in southern Puerto Rico, and it was astonishing to find there an organisation of sugar cane growers, each on a small scale, organised as a commune, something like a Jewish Kibbutz, with joint buying and selling of the different small-holders, and with many other co-operative features, including care of infants and schools. After a certain number of years, the farmers would be given a title to a certain share of the property. However, what was especially interesting was the fact that the sugary residues from the mills were taken to one establishment, where the Weizmann process for the manufacture of n-butanol and acetone was operated.

I happened to meet Weizmann, I am not quite sure how, when he greeted the Jewish Forces on their return from the First World War. He took me along on that occasion to the Midland Hotel, Manchester, where there was a most interesting large-scale luncheon, at which the political and religious aspects of Jewry were alternatively predominant. Weizmann delivered a characteristic speech, eloquent, inspiring and witty. He told his large audience to be proud of their race and, touching his nasal organ, said "You will not be able to hide it". Although I am not attempting in any way a biography of Chaim Weizmann, it is desirable to mention his ambition, often mentioned in early Manchester days, to establish an Institute devoted to Science within the Jewish National Home. This project was rendered possible, in the first instance, by the generosity of Israel Sieff and other members of his family, who provided funds for a Laboratory of Organic

Chemistry, erected in memory of his son Daniel Sieff. Daniel Sieff died in 1933, and Weizmann not only offered his sympathy in this bereavement, but showed a way in which Daniel might be memorialised.

I was privileged to write a short introduction to Ritchie Calder's *Hand of Life*, which was published in 1959. Speaking of Weizmann's beginnings of the realisation of the dream of a Scientific Institute in Israel, I wrote:

"Characteristically, Weizmann took his mourning friends into Hyde Park where, as they walked and talked, the plans for the Institute took shape.

Remember, this was 1933; the Nazi persecutions had already begun and eminent Jewish scientists were being hounded from their laboratories. Weizmann saw in an Institute in Palestine a possible refuge for many of them, but he saw also the possibility of creating a research centre which would serve the needs of the country and, at the same time, form part of the wider world of science. He inspired his friends with his ideas of the ways in which such an Institute could help to break down the walls which isolated one section of knowledge from the other. The comfort which he offered them was the opportunity to serve a fine purpose.

So the Daniel Sieff Institute was endowed and, in 1934, was built in the sandy wastes of Rehovoth, then called the 'Gateway to the Negev'. As Weizmann himself wrote in his autobiography: 'There was not a tree or a blade of grass . . . I had before my eyes the green lawns of the English and American universities, and the scientific academies, and thought that we would be showing a lamentable lack of aesthetic feeling if we merely planked down the buildings and did nothing with the surroundings'. It is difficult, indeed impossible, for anyone visiting the present Rehovoth for the first time, to realise that those lawns and gardens and groves were once a sandy waste.

The Daniel Sieff Institute was opened on April 3rd, 1934, by Richard Willstätter."

The Daniel Sieff Laboratory for Organic Chemical Research was the nucleus around which the Weizmann Institute of Science was crystallised. The organisation stands high among the research laboratories of the world and has been a centre of important research in mathematics and physics, all branches of chemistry and biochemistry, as well as the life sciences. I have been privileged to be a member of the Board of Governors and a Fellow of the Weizmann Institute of Science.

Weizmann's work, largely in collaboration with E.D. Bergmann, on the thermal decomposition of petroleum fractions was the scientific basis of a process (Catarole process) which had some vogue, until it was superseded by methods which afforded the lower olefins in higher yield. Two points are of major importance in this connection. In the first place, the process involved ordinary thermal cracking and its novelty, on the chemical side, was accordingly an open question. Secondly, the yield of the more valuable olefins was inferior to that obtained by other methods, which soon entered the field. The wide range of the products obtained in the Catarole process, though attractive at first sight, was found in the longer run to be an embarrassment. The Catarole process was, however, for several years the basis of the operations of Petrochemicals Limited.

Weizmann and his wife Vera (née Chatzman) lived, during their Manchester University period, in a house in Willoughby Road, off the Palatine Road, and Gertrude and I were frequent visitors at their home, both before and after our marriage. Mrs. Weizmann qualified in medicine, was an accomplished pianist, with a preference for Debussy, and had a charming personality. When we visited them, we often found Weizmann immersed in scripts which he examined in 'order to turn an honest penny; adding a book to the pile, he might say "Now I can call this chair my 'own". These rather lean circumstances did not last very long, because he was soon able to get a comparatively lucrative consultancy and, I am sure, acquired other resources, as his temporary financial embarrassment quickly disappeared.

The following dates are taken from a publication of the Government of Israel, 1952:

Chaim Weizmann

1874   Born in Motol, Russia.
1886   High School at Pinsk.
1895   Studied in Berlin.
1898   Doctorate (*summa cum laude*) at Fribourg, Switzerland.
1901   Lecturer in Chemistry, University of Geneva.
1904   Lecturer and Demonstrator in Organic Chemistry, University of Manchester.

1906	Marriage to Dr. Vera Chatzman.
1915	The development of the Fernbach fermentation as an industrial process for the production of acetone.
1917	Was influential in securing the famous Balfour Declaration in favour of a Jewish Home in Palestine.
1921	President, World Zionist Organisation.
1948	President of Provisional Government.
1949	Elected First President of Israel. Opening of Weizmann Institute of Science.
1951	Elected President of Israel for second term.
1952	Died at Rehovot.

Gertrude Maud Walsh (1886—1954)

Gertrude Maud Walsh was the daughter of Thomas Makinson Walsh and Mary Emily Walsh of The Hollies, Winsford, Cheshire. After graduation, Gertrude worked in Weizmann's private laboratory and as a result, two short joint papers were published. She also taught chemistry at the Manchester High School for Girls. The Headmistress, Miss Burstall, was an educationalist whose reputation extended beyond the boundaries of the City of Manchester. Gertrude lived at Ashburne Hall, a residential college for women students of the University, both as a student and a tutor. I remember that one of the College songs went something like this:

5 o'clock is striking,
Ma may I go out?
My young man's a-waiting
For to take me out.
He takes me to the ocean,
He takes me to the sea,
He takes me to his mother's 'ouse
To 'av a cup o' tea.
Johnnie Brown of London Town
Is going to marry me —
Won't it be an 'appy time
When I sit upon his knee?

We were married in the early summer of 1912, and later in the same year we went out to Sydney, N.S.W. Here, and later at British

Gertrude M. Walsh (the first Lady Robinson).

universities, she did a large amount of experimental work on topics which I had suggested.

A paper on reactions of piperonylcarbinol describes the ready condensation of this substance, also of veratrylcarbinol, to sparingly soluble crystalline compounds [33A]. The reaction occurs very readily under the influence of acids; the alcohols lose a molecular proportion of water and the product is obviously a polymeride. I thought, and it will be agreed that this was the most natural explanation, that the substance was a dihydroanthracene. This appeared to be supported by a reaction with nitric acid, which gave a bis-nitro-veratrylmethane, which could be independently synthesised from diveratrylmethane. By treatment with hydriodic acid to remove the methyl groups and distillation over zinc dust in a stream of hydrogen, a small yield of dihydroanthracene was obtained. We were disturbed by this poor performance which threw some doubt on the dihydro-anthracene structure. Accordingly, when we left Sydney for Liverpool, I asked Dr. F. Keffler, an expert in calorimetry and other physical methods, to be kind enough to determine the molecular weight of the supposed tetramethoxydihydroanthracene by the lowering of the freezing point method. As in the other experiments, the veratryl derivatives were preferred to the piperonyl derivatives because the methoxyl groups confer greater solubility and lower melting point on the relevant substances. We also prepared corresponding derivatives from ethoxy-, methoxy- and diethoxy-benzyl-alcohols. Keffler used a new solvent for the lowering of the freezing point, namely thymol, which is commercially available in a quite pure condition in large crystals. He returned all three substances as dimers. Later, at Sydney, we condensed cyanocatechol ethers, e.g. veratronitrile, by means of a cold solution of chlorsulphonic acid in chloroform, and obtained good yields of compounds we considered might be dimers. Keffler was asked to study the molecular weights of these and confirmed the dimeric hypothesis in each case. We were naturally quite satisfied with this, but the properties did not by any means fit the concept that they were anthraquinone dimerides. Subsequently, Quilico showed that the condensation products of the alcohols are trimerides. Similarly, those of the nitriles are *sym*-triazines.

The only reasonable explanation of Keffler's results is that he accepted my statement that one of our compounds was a dimeride, possibly the dehydration product of veratrylcarbinol, and calculated the constant for thymol on this basis. Naturally, all other determinations made using this constant would be one and a half times too great. Of course, being human, I like people to believe in me, but certainly not to that extent. I mention this story in case there might be some kind of a lesson in it, not to accept any authority in the laboratory except that of an independent experiment. I readily acquit Keffler, who was President of the Students' Christian Union, of any intention to deceive, but by accepting my view of the nature of the substance, instead of determining the depression of the freezing point of thymol with substances of known molecular weight, he certainly saved himself a little trouble.

We studied the formation of cyanomeconin from opianic acid and also made the nitropiperonyl- and nitroveratrylglycolic acids [34]. When either of these was heated in nitrobenzene solution they decomposed smoothly with formation of azo-acids, the nitro groups having oxidised the hydroxy-acid to a lower carboxylic acid. Azoxy-veratrole could be readily mono-nitrated and the result was interpreted in terms of unsymmetrical structure for azoxy groups [36B]. This result was a novel confirmation of the work of Angeli. Another piece of work that Gertrude carried out was on the nitration of p-iodoanisole [36A]. Among the products of this reaction are 4-nitro-2-iodoanisole and 2,4-diiodoanisole. Iodine in nitric acid was found to be a powerful iodinating agent. The diiodoanisole was probably obtained via p-iodoanisole. The formation of the nitro derivative is doubtless due to a replacement of the iodine atom in the p-position to methoxyl by nitroxyl. The p-nitroanisole is then iodinated in the 2-position by the nitric acid/iodine mixture. This view was confirmed by actually carrying out the latter reaction, i.e. by converting p-nitroanisole into its two iodo-derivatives by reaction with a mixture of iodine and concentrated nitric acid.

A considerable series of experiments was made on the improvements of the synthesis of long chain acids, especially those with oxo groups in various positions [80]. The syntheses followed several methods, some of which are analogous to Claisen's method for ethyl benzoylactate; the sodio-derivative of a β-keto-ester, which may be 2-substituted, was condensed with acid chlorides of varied structure in a neutral solvent, such as ethyl ether. The diketo-esters so produced are progressively hydrolysed so that eventually only the 2-carbon atom of the original ethyl acetoacetate remains. The following illustrates the sequence of reactions:

$$CH_3(CH_2)_n\overset{\overset{\displaystyle COCH_3}{|}}{CH}CO_2Et \ + \ ClOC(CH_2)_mCO_2Et \ \xrightarrow[\text{ether}]{\text{Na in}} \ CH_3(CH_2)_n\overset{\overset{\displaystyle COCH_3}{|}}{\underset{\underset{\displaystyle CO(CH_2)_mCO_2Et}{|}}{C}}CO_2Et$$

$$\xrightarrow{\text{1) } OH^-;\ 2)\ H^+} \quad CH_3(CH_2)_{n+1}CO(CH_2)_mCO_2H$$

Lactarinic acid: n = 10, m = 4
10-Ketostearic acid: n = 6, m = 8

Another useful method was the mono-alkylation of such substances as ethyl cyanoacetate, using an excess of the ester with an alkyl halide and potassium carbonate as a condensing agent, the whole being refluxed under reduced pressure [69A]. The yields were variable, but in many cases quite excellent and disubstitution was minimised. In the course of this work on fatty acid compounds the first synthesis of oleic acid was carried out (see p. 157). Four different ketostearic acids, synthesised by our methods, were submitted to Dr. Shearer of the Royal Institution, to see if X-ray methods alone could serve to determine the position of the carbonyl groups. The result of this test was that three of the acids were correctly characterised, and in the fourth case the chemical crystallographers got the carbonyl one place removed from its correct position, probably due to the change of angle between the molecules of the fatty acid and the crystal axis. This was the first example of determination of a structural detail solely by the use of X-ray crystallography. We have travelled far along this road since those early days and at the present time, 1974, several examples of the determination of a complex structure by X-ray crystallographic methods, combined with the use of highly sophisticated computers, are on record. However, such computers, costing something of the order of one and a half million pounds, are not likely to be generally available.

Another thing which Gertrude did in the course of this work was to synthesise a fatty acid with a very long *n*-carbon chain; this and other developments in the series are described on p. 159. It may be added that the method and stage of hydrolysis of the condensation products, mentioned above, have been considerably improved by (Mrs.) R.H. Jaeger, whose work has, however, not yet been published.

Further reference to the work of G.M.R. and to incidents in her later life will be found in Volume II of these Memoirs. Nevertheless, I cannot postpone an acknowledgment of the very great help which she gave me at all stages of my career. Looking back, I can see how she subordinated her interests to mine, was always such a ready collaborator in scientific work, and cheerfully followed my chief vacation activity, namely mountaineering. She was an excellent hostess, both for small parties of friends and for larger gatherings of research students and staff of the Department, and she commanded to a remarkable degree the affection, loyalty and respect of those she came into contact with.

Lest I should be regarded as a biased reporter, I might perhaps be allowed to quote the following extracts from her obituary notices. Thus W. Baker wrote (Nature 1954, 173, 566): "Her contributions to chemical knowledge have been substantial in spite of many pressing calls on her time and energy ... It is in the dual role of an indefatigable research worker and a kindly hostess that she will long be remembered. In particular, the younger members of the teaching staffs and their wives have reason to be profoundly grateful to her; she found time to take a personal interest in them and their families, which lasted long after they moved elsewhere.

Lady Robinson's scientific papers, mainly in the Journal of the Chemical Society, record work carried out in the Universities of Manchester, Sydney, Liverpool, St. Andrews, London (University College), and the Dyson Perrins Laboratory, Oxford. The first two, with Dr. C. Weizmann, were published in 1910 and 1911 under her maiden name of Walsh. Many of the later papers were published jointly with her husband. In work on certain derivatives on catechol ethers the important discovery was made that asymmetrical substitution occurred in azoxy compounds, thus adding proof to that earlier provided by Angeli of the asymmetrical structure of the azoxy compounds themselves. Another series of papers of considerable novelty dealt with nitrogenous pseudo-bases, and the mechanism of Fischer's indole synthesis. Still another series described the development of new methods for the synthesis of high-molecular weight fatty acids, notable among which was a variation of the acetoacetic ester synthesis for the extension of the carbon chain by twelve carbon atoms at a time; this elegant process culminated in the synthesis of n-triacontanoic acid in 1934.

Lady Robinson published numerous papers on the anthocyanins and their separation by distribution between two partially miscible solvents, a method which was virtually a forerunner of modern partition chromatography. More recently still, her interest in these compounds led her to undertake a very difficult task, namely the investigation of the leucoanthocyanins, in particular peltogynol. She took an active part in the work on penicillin during the Second World War, and it is perhaps not generally known that she was the first chemist to prepare synthetical material with genuine antibiotic character of the penicillin type.

Lady Robinson's name is assured of a lasting and honoured place among those organic chemists who have made major contributions to their science."

J.L. Simonsen, after describing her scientific work and interests, had this to say about Gertrude (J. Chem. Soc. 1954, 2267): "It might be thought that this intense scientific activity would have fully occupied Lady Robinson's time. This was, however, far from being the case. She shared to the full her husband's scientific and other interests. She was a skilled climber and travelled widely with him. Any account of her life would be incomplete without a reference to her social gifts. She was a born hostess. Those who had the privilege of being her fellow students in Manchester will still recall with pleasure her invitation to dances at Ashburne Hall, the Women's Hall of residence. Later in the succession of universities in which her husband was professor she took the deepest interest in the welfare of the wives and children of his staff. She seemed never to forget a name or a face.

The full opportunity for her to excercise her great gifts came however in Oxford. There, in her beautiful home or at Magdalen College, she showed gracious hospitality both to Oxford friends and to the numerous visitors from home or overseas. No scientific conference in Oxford was complete without one of her delightful parties. Her unique qualities were recognised last year by the University of Oxford when they conferred upon her the Honorary Degree of Master of Arts. Her undoubted pleasure in receiving this degree was more than shared by her innumerable friends."

George Barger (1878—1939)

I first met George Barger at a cocktail party in the Smedley's London home and we were introduced by Ida Smedley. George, very characteristically, acknowledged this by saying: "Are you Perkin and Robinson?", to which I replied that I was part of that combination. His main interest at that time was the joint research with H.H. Dale (later Sir Henry Dale) on the biologically active

George Barger.

amines which are substituted β-phenylethylamines, of which adrenaline is typical. This classical investigation was carried out in the laboratories of Burroughs Wellcome. In 1909 he entered the academic field by his appointment to the Goldsmiths College as Head of the Department of Chemistry, and in 1913 he became Professor of Chemistry at Royal Holloway College. In 1919 he was appointed as the first Professor of Chemistry applied to Medicine in the University of Edinburgh. In 1937 he became Regius Professor of Chemistry at the University of Glasgow. The decision to move from Edinburgh to Glasgow must have been a very difficult one to make as it involved a loss of close contact with many friends and relinquishment of control of a Department which he had built up from its first beginnings.

During his London and Edinburgh period we became close friends and took every opportunity to discuss problems in the alkaloid group, which were of mutual interest. For many years I functioned as his External Examiner in Edinburgh, enjoying the hospitality of his home for the better part of a week, during which the examinations were held. Barger was a rather stern examiner and in the *viva voce* examinations was, I am afraid, rather apt to lead the erring candidate astray by posing supplementary questions. Some of the results would have amused me but for the fact that my colleague attributed the breakdown of the candidate to my inhumanity! This would be hardly worth mentioning except that it was such a firm tenet in George's philosophy that right was right and wrong was wrong, and there could be no compromise between them.

During the examination period we were in the habit of making a traverse of Arthur's Seat before the morning session, and on other occasions we took longer excursions in the Highlands. George was not a rock climber, in the strict sense, but he was quite a good scrambler. The route, such as the Cirque, the highest of the Teallachs above Dundonnell, was the kind of thing he enjoyed most of all.

One of the earliest of Barger's researches which I was privileged to take an interest in was thyroxine. We discussed together the probable course of the iodination of tyrosine and Barger devised experiments designed to test abnormal substitution which might have occurred. In this work he was ably assisted by his favourite student, Charles Harrington. Unfortunately, as I thought, he developed a strain of paternal generosity in that direction and this led him to fade out of the picture and contribute the success of the operation to his student. There is no doubt that Harrington worked very hard on the project and that his laboratory technique was probably superior to anything that Barger could manage, at that time, but it was Barger who conceived the underlying idea of the abnormal iodination of tyrosine.

I was specially interested in discussing with Barger his work on the structure of alkaloids. At the I.U.P.A.C. Meeting in Madrid in 1934, which I attended with him, he suggested that the second half of the molecules of the indole alkaloids, such as yohimbine, is derived from a substituted phenylethylamine (the first half coming from tryptophan). At that time I, along with most other chemists, accepted this idea. It was later elaborated as the "Woodward Fission", which also seemed reasonable, but Nature as an organic chemist surpasses our wildest imaginings, and Allan Battersby has proved a suggestion of A.F. Thomas to be correct. The scheme seemed unlikely to be the basis of the biosynthesis because the starting points are not structurally related in a simple manner to the products.

George and Florence Barger had two sons and a daughter. Harold, the eldest boy, was correct and normal in every way and in due course became an American Professor. Evert, when I first met him, was a brilliant young man brimming over with life and energy. I feel that he got from his mother, Florence, a broad political sympathy with the less fortunate among the community, and from his father a habit of orderly thinking. When an undergraduate at Oxford, he had a visiting card printed "Evert Barger, Journalist" and this slight extravagance showed his firm intention to devote himself to some aspects of public affairs.

In 1966 my wife Stearn took a taxi from Soho Square and found that a previous occupant had left an envelope containing papers on the seat. We found that they were papers relating to the estate of Florence Barger, and of course I suspected they must have been left in the cab by Evert Barger. By a complex process of investigation I found that Evert Barger was living in France and working on a commission of the United Nations.

When George Barger was appointed Regius Professor of Chemistry in the University of Glasgow, his position in the world of science was adequately recognised for the first time. Unfortunately he occupied the Chair for two years only and, hence, did not have the opportunity to develop the wider interests which he had at heart.

Henry Edward Armstrong (1848—1937)

No chemist could evolve during the early decades of the twentieth century without feeling the influence of H.E. Armstrong, Professor of Chemistry at the Central Technical College, South Kensington,

London, from 1884 until 1911, when the "Central" was absorbed by the Imperial College of Science and Technology. Armstrong was a great teacher and early publicist in the cause of science — a man possessing strong convictions which were energetically expressed. He contributed much to the progress of chemistry in some directions, and at the same time did his best to put the clock back in others.

In descriptive organic chemistry his studies of orientation in the formation of substituted naphthalenes was a major contribution to theoretical science and also to its industrial applications. This work was continued with patience and success by William Palmer Wynne. Armstrong was perhaps the first chemist to realise the potential importance of a knowledge of crystal structure; here, the banner was carried by another student, probably the one he regarded with the most favour, namely, William Jackson Pope. In collaboration with Barlow, the idea of crystal shape being an outward sign of an ordering of the molecules, was very clearly stated in an attempt to deduce the nature of this marshalling from goniometric and molecular structural data. Unfortunately, Pope and Barlow were just a little too early; Laue's brilliant suggestion that the spacings in crystals should be capable of diffracting X-rays, and the implementing of this suggestion by the Braggs, gave a practical method for the actual determination, not only of the marshalling of the molecules, but of the molecular structures themselves. Parenthetically, it may be remarked that improvements in the methods, especially in the use of computers, have led to a situation such that a full molecular structure can be computed using the X-ray diffraction diagrams from a single crystal.

Armstrong did not accept Arrhenius' theory of electrolytic dissociation in solution and this led him into serious error, in many directions. He was a student of Kolbe, who wrote in the journal, which I believe he edited "A certain J.H. van 't Hoff, a lecturer in the Veterinary College at Utrecht, has, it seems, no taste for exact science. Mounted on his horse Pegasus, evidently borrowed from veterinary stables, he thinks he can see the atoms arranged in everlasting space". Armstrong had a great respect for the opinion of his teacher, who was also not enamoured of the theory of Arrhenius.

Many of Armstrong's public utterances in general, and on scientific education in particular, reveal that he was an advocate of the theoristic method, which is somewhat analogous to teaching the young to swim by throwing them in at the deep end. Students were encouraged to think things out for themselves, though they might be given a little guidance on the lines of thought they should pursue. The idea works well with the more intelligent pupils and, without adopting the system in the manner contemplated by some enthusiasts, it is certainly a good thing to give them the opportunity "to think it out for themselves" in suitable selected cases.

H.E. Armstrong rented "Manestey", a house on the west end of Derwent Water, and just after I had been appointed junior lecturer in the University of Manchester, he invited me to come and stay with him for a few days. He met me at Keswick with a horse drawn cab, and said not a word until we were near to the door, then he barked "I suppose you think you know what sulphuric acid is". I understood the situation and replied "I know what it is supposed to be, but perhaps when we get to Manestey you will explain what it really is", which he did, though I fear I do not recall the details except that it involved polymerization of the molecules. Next day we went over the Honister Pass, calling at Gatesgarth Farm. The rooms there were covered with certificates of awards gained at agricultural shows for their particular breed of sheep. In the visitor's book there was a poem, reputedly written by an Oxford don, and the following is a quotation from it:

With what humility and reverence deep
We should observe so many first-class sheep.
For sheep or men we love first classes,
Only the coaches love the passes.

(It should be explained that, in this clever play on words, the coaches find it more lucrative to tutor men taking pass degrees because there are so many more of them.)

We went on to Green Gable and Great Gable, descending to the Sty Head Pass, and so home again. The weather was fine but Armstrong carried an ice axe, which somehow made me think of Mark Twain's ascent of the Riffelberg. The more I knew of Armstrong the better I liked him as a person. His spitfire characteristics were the outward signs of strongly held convictions. He was always on the side of the angels, although it is true that no angel would express himself in the manner of Henry Edward Armstrong.

A good account of Armstrong's public work, especially in the field of nutrition, was given by Sir Frederick Keeble in his obituary notice in the Proceedings of the Royal Society, No. 9, Jan. 1941, Vol. 3.

Armstrong was influential in founding "The Catalyst" Dining Club. The title shows no great humility because the catalyst is the small amount which makes a reaction go. The implication could have been that the members of the club were those whose efforts were essential to the organisation which they served. When I became a member, the dinner meetings were held in the Ivy Restaurant. I recall an occasion when Armstrong appeared in a multi-coloured dress-waistcoat, probably yellow, purple and green (but I am not quite sure of this), representing Caledon Jade Green and its leuco-compounds. This was designed to advertise the triumph of the British industry (Scottish Dyes Limited) making this new and valuable dyestuff. Many of the meetings of this club were of great interest; the members were important figures in the chemical industry and in the chemistry departments of universities. There has been a long series of distinguished guests.

Henry Stephen (1889—1965)

Henry Stephen entered the School of Chemistry at the University of Manchester in 1908. After holding a graduate scholarship, and later a Baeyer Fellowship (1912), he stayed in the Organic Chemistry Department at Manchester until 1926, when he was appointed to the Chair of Chemistry at the University of the Witwatersrand, Johannesburg, South Africa. During this period he carried out much important research and devised what became known as the Stephen reaction for the conversion of nitriles into corresponding aldehydes. This process, which works particularly well with aromatic nitriles, depends on reduction by means of stannous chloride and hydrogen chloride with subsequent hydrolysis of the aldimine hydrochloride produced. In 1914 he was awarded a travelling fellowship, but could not take advantage of it owing to the outbreak of war. In collaboration with J.E. Meyers (later Sir James, a Principal of Manchester College of Technology) he identified "mustard gas" as $2,2'$-dichlorodiethyl sulphide, and Stephen and Meyers then synthesised the substance by treating ethylene with sulphur dichloride. It is of interest that this process was for a time replaced by the use of sulphur monochloride (S_2Cl_2), a reaction developed by Sir William Pope. Later, a return was made to the Stephen/Meyers method. After transferring his activities to South Africa, Stephen developed a fine school of teaching and research in organic chemistry at the University of the Witwatersrand. He returned from the Chair in 1954, and accepted an invitation to become the first Executive Editor of *Tetrahedron* (Pergamon Press) in 1956. The Head of the Press, Robert Maxwell, gave the new International Journal of Organic Chemistry the strongest possible support, so that it became one of the most important media in the world for the publication of original communications. Such success would certainly have been impossible without the effective work of its first Editor, Henry Stephen, who was joined by his wife Theodora (cf. Vol. II). Dr. T. Stephen has functioned as Editor of *Tetrahedron* from 1965 to the present time (1974) and the excellent work which the journal has done, and the success that it has enjoyed, is largely due to her unremitting effort.

Jocelyn Field Thorpe (1872—1940)

J.F. Thorpe was one of my most highly valued teachers during the early years, and a good friend and colleague later on. He was born in London in 1872, and his farther, a barrister of the Middle Temple, reputed to be a Devonian, advised him to give up the engineering studies, which he had been pursuing for several years, and devote himself to chemistry. He knew very little about the latter profession, but had been told by a friend in Fire Insurance that the prospects in this field were quite good.

Thorpe attended courses at the Royal College of Science, became fascinated by organic chemistry, and thereafter spent two years as a research student at the University of Heidelberg, in Victor Meyer's laboratory. While in Germany he took the opportunity to work for a period in the laboratories of a dyestuff manufacturer. This was turned to good account when, in 1895, he joined the Chemical School at Manchester University, since he was able to organise highly attractive practical courses designed to illustrate the relation between structure and colour in various classes of dyestuffs. He occupied the small Levinstein Laboratory, had his own working bench at the end, and a battery of dyeing pots and ovens completed the equipment. Each student was provided with a different dyestuff, but all the specimens were closely related. After a little lecture on the method of preparation, the dyeings were made and subsequently cut up and distributed, so that each student could see what the effect of the different substituents was; for example wool might be dyed with a

J.F. Thorpe.

whole series of alkyl- or aryl-substituted rosanilines. I enjoyed this course immensely. Thorpe collaborated with Perkin in a novel synthesis of camphoric acid. Much later, when we were both consultants of Imperial Chemical Industries, we went to the Dyestuffs Group Research Committee (D.G.R.C.) monthly meetings, of which he eventually became Chairman.

On the way from St. Pancras to the Central Station, Manchester, we always did out best to solve "The Times" crossword puzzle, and discussed the problems of the Research Group as well.

Many important discoveries were made during the tenure of our consultancies, and perhaps the most significant was that of phthalocyanine. A greenish-blue deposit occurred at some point in the plant manufacturing phthalimide at Scottish Dyes Limited, Grangemouth. This was scraped off, analysed, and found to have the formula $C_{32}H_{16}N_8Fe$, and on oxidation with nitric acid it was converted into phthalimide. I wrote down the structure at once and said that it was obviously an industrial chlorophyll. Thorpe was very excited about this and advised that some of the more academic aspects should be studied by R.P. Linstead. This was done with great success and, at Blackley, Wyler contributed important and novel methods of preparation.

Thorpe was a master of organic synthesis and discovered many new methods. Of particular importance was the Thorpe reaction which is a ring synthesis, analogous to the Dieckmann reaction, but using nitriles instead of esters. Thus, o-xylylene dibromide reacts with potassium cyanide with formation of a dinitrile readily converted in alcoholic solution with a trace of sodium ethoxide into an iminonitrile, which can be easily hydrolysed with formation of indan-2-one. This mode of cyclisation occurs in homogeneous solution and was used by Ziegler in his synthesis of large carbocycles, using the method of high dilution. Thorpe stumbled, just once, when he thought that the C-methylation of Komppa's intermediate in the synthesis of camphoric acid must have given a methoxy derivative (J.F. Thorpe and G.L. Blanc, J. Chem. Soc., 1910, 97, 836, 2010). However it was later shown that this substance is indeed an enol; it affords the C-methyl derivative as claimed by Komppa (K. Aghoramurthy and P.M.E. Lewis, Tetrahedron Letters, 1969, 1415).

Thorpe was an extremely prolific and successful investigator; it has been said that he made two new substances every day. I was frequently fascinated by watching him carrying out a vacuum distillation using a Perkin triangle, and his use of this piece of apparatus was certainly the most skilful that I ever witnessed.

No attempt is made to cover, in any satisfactory way, the whole of

Thorpe's distinguished career, but it must be mentioned that he made a detailed study of glutaconic acids and showed that they may be represented as containing part valencies.

A favourite starting material in his synthetic studies was ethyl cyanoacetate. The intermediate products were imines which often underwent tautomeric change into amino derivatives and heterocyclic bases. It was a rich field and even now has not been cultivated to the extent it deserves.

Thorpe was a good cricketer in his early days and functioned as wicket keeper in the Manchester team. Later, he was plagued with the result of some injury to his leg and walked with a limp. He was an excellent conversationalist and after dinner speaker, a bon viveur with pronounced aristocratic tendencies. He was a Fellow of the Royal Society, Longstaff Medalist 1921, Davy Medalist 1922, President of the Chemical Society and Institute of Chemistry, appointed Professor of Organic Chemistry at the Imperial College of Science and Technology in 1913.

I had the privilege of being an External Examiner of many of the candidates for Ph.D. who he had supervised.

Lord Rutherford (1871—1937)

In the period approximately 1905—1907 Professor Arthur Schuster organised short lectures and experimental demonstrations to keep interested persons up-to-date with the sensational developments arising from the study of radioactive elements. The topics arose largely from the work of Ernest Rutherford, who succeeded to the Professorship in 1907. He continued these exciting talks, and I remember particularly a very significant one which was given on the large angle of scattering of α-rays after bombardment of a solid surface. The large angle of deflection of the α-particle could only be explained by its penetration deep into the constituent atom of the material bombarded, so that the repulsive effect of the charged nucleus on the α-particle would be great enough to explain the effect. The conception of the atom consisting of a very small positively charged nucleus surrounded by electrons at various levels and with relatively large amounts of empty space followed directly from these experiments. This Rutherford atom was mathematically treated by Niels Bohr by using quantum mechanical principles. Bohr worked for a time in the Physics Laboratory, in close association with Rutherford, and the model resulting from the combined experimental and theoretical work became known as the Rutherford-Bohr atom. The work of the School was very much interrupted by the outbreak of war in 1914, but although many calls were made on Rutherford for advice to Government Departments, he still found time to pursue his researches. In this period Professor H. Geiger invented his well-known counter for individual charge particles, and this has been of outstanding assistance in varied studies involving radioactive elements; for examples, the whole subject of biogenesis in plants has been elaborated by the use of radioactive tracers, which have been followed along the phyto-synthetic routes with the help of the Geiger counter. George de Hevesy, another of Rutherford's co-workers during the Manchester period, discovered the radioactive isotope of carbon ^{14}C, which has been frequently used in experiments on plant biogenesis, although it is true that other tracers such as deuterium and radioactive tritium have also been employed. Radiocarbon is, however, more reliable than tritium, due to the propensity of the latter to undergo exchange with hydrogen. I can make no attempt to estimate or even indicate, in detail, the vast output of fundamental research which Rutherford carried out at Manchester University and, later, in the Cavendish Laboratory at Cambridge. Many of his research colleagues were awarded Nobel Prizes. These were Soddy (atomic disintegration and isotopes), Bohr (quantum mechanical theory of the atom), de Hevesy (radioactive tracers), Cockcroft and Walton (the first atom smashers), Chadwick (discovery of the neutron), George Thomson (wave properties of the electron), and Blacket (cosmic rays and magnetic phenomena). Rutherford himself received a single Nobel Prize; he certainly qualified for a plurality of these awards. It would be out of place to attempt any elaboration of the vast importance of the research output of Rutherford and his School, but it is safe to say that it is unequalled in the history of science.

I was privileged to see something of Rutherford at home in Manchester, and Frank Pyman and his wife were fellow guests on more than one occasion. In the period between the Wars, I met him at the Pen-y-gwryd Hotel, not far from which he had a country cottage. The landlord of the hotel, a Mr. Lockwood, was a wellknown figure, who had a hobby of carrying out water works behind the hotel on the route to Glyder Fach. He had formerly been a civil engineer in Burma. He was the discoverer of "Lockwood's Chimney" which I found chiefly notable for the mass of loose rock and rubble which one was compelled to dislodge on to the next man on the rope. Lockwood told us that he believed that Sir Ernest was supposed to be a great scientist, but he could assure us that he was not a good motor mechanic, as his car was continually out of order, and he showed no capacity whatever to put it right. This triviality fits the conception of the total world of men and manners, in which no man is a hero to his valet. There is no general standard of appreciation, and I have to admit that when the radio is running I invariably switch off at a threat of a discussion on sociology (inter alia — inter alia). Having made this damaging admission, I wish to say that at the top of my list of scientific heroes I find Ernest Rutherford and Louis Pasteur.

Arthur Lapworth (1872—1941)

Arthur Lapworth's father, Charles Lapworth, was originally a school teacher at Galashiels, and self-taught in geology in his spare time. His pioneering work on stratigraphy was started by studies of the graptolites which occurred in the rocks of the vicinity. He later became Professor of Geology at the University of Birmingham, and resolved a controversy regarding palaeozoic Welsh rocks, in which Sigdwick, Professor of Geology at Cambridge, was involved.

Arthur Lapworth's undergraduate and early post-graduate work was carried out at the Central College of Technology in London, where he worked under the guidance of Henry E. Armstrong. However, he early showed unusual independence of spirit, for one of Armstrong's pupils, because he refused to show the Professor his thesis for the degree of D.Sc. Lapworth said "It is my work and I have no intention of changing it". I heard something about this incident from Ida Smedley (later Smedley-Maclean), who was also a research student in Armstrong's Department. Parenthetically, she was given the task of purifying m-nitraniline, the bright yellow colour of which did not conform to Armstrong's theoretical views. He thought that o- and p-nitranilines owed their colour to quinonoid forms, but this idea could not be extended in the m-series. Ida Smedley said that he persisted for over a month, suggesting vacuum distillation, attempted conversion through salts and other derivatives, usually ending his visit to the bench with the remark "We must wash this nigger white". Lapworth was never quite forgiven for his temerity, but he

A.L. Lapworth.

was entirely justified in his action, since Armstrong's theoretical ideas did not, at that time, include acceptance of Arrhenius' theory of electrolytic dissociation.

In 1909 Lapworth left his Lectureship in the Goldsmiths College to become Schunck Fellow and Senior Lecturer in Inorganic and Physical Chemistry at the University of Manchester. I had the inestimable advantage of friendship with him, and unlimited opportunity for discussion, from that time until 1912, when I entered on my first Professorship at the University of Sydney. During that period he was possessed by his theory of alternate polarities which, though not a reliable guide in all circumstances, still provides a useful mnemonic for the behaviour of molecules of many carbon compounds in reactions.

On the chemical side Lapworth continued to develop his interest in the reactions of ketones, including α-, and β-unsaturated ketones. Prominent results from his earlier work in this field were the condensation of crotonic and oxalic esters with the help of sodium ethoxide, and his explanation of the mechanism of the benzoin synthesis. The first of these was an early example of a reaction type, later developed extensively by R. Kuhn and others, and also recognised as important in biosynthesis. It seemed possible that the explanation of Lapworth's reaction was the conversion of crotonic esters into isocrotonic esters, followed by oxalylation in the α-position. However, this does not appear to be the case and Lapworth's original interpretation has been upheld.

The explanation of the benzoin synthesis, shown below, came decades before its time. Its full implications were only generally understood many years later.

$$Ph \cdot CHO + CN^- \rightleftharpoons Ph \cdot CH(CN) \cdot O^- \qquad (I)$$

$$Ph \cdot CH(CN) \cdot O^- + H^+ \rightleftharpoons Ph \cdot CH(CN) \cdot OH \qquad (II)$$

$$Ph \cdot CHO + Ph \cdot CH(CN) \cdot OH \rightleftharpoons \begin{array}{l} PH \cdot C(CN) \cdot OH \\ | \\ Ph \cdot CH \cdot OH \end{array} \qquad (III)$$

$$\begin{array}{l} Ph \cdot C(CN) \cdot OH \\ | \\ Ph \cdot CH \cdot OH \end{array} \xrightarrow{OH^-} \begin{array}{l} Ph \cdot CO \\ | \\ Ph \cdot CH \cdot OH \end{array} + CN^- \qquad (IV)$$

During this early period Lapworth developed most aspects of his classification of his reagents on a polar basis, but I think this started before he came to Manchester, and was continued until about the third decade of this century. At that time I was working with Edward Hope on reactions of cotarnine and hydrastinine, and especially developed their facile condensation reactions with substances capable of providing anions. In harmony with the tautomerism suggested by the spectroscopic work of Dobbie, Lauder and Tinkler, Lapworth suggested that the condensation reactions involved the pseudo-base (ammonium hydroxide form). The anion derived from the substance condensed with the pseudo-base links with the unsaturated carbon, and the proton with OH⁻ to form water. This very simple and obviously correct theory is exemplified, as follows, in a part structure:

$$-CHO \;+\; HNR_2 \;\longrightarrow\; -CH(OH)-NR_2 \;\longrightarrow\; -CH=\overset{+}{N}R_2 \quad OH^-$$

$$\xrightarrow{\;H^+,\,X^-\;} -CHX-NR_2 \;+\; H_2O$$

I have written an obituary of Lapworth in which I paid more attention to his work as a whole, but I have here emphasised matters which had a considerable influence on my own thinking. He succeeded Perkin as Professor of Organic Chemistry at Manchester University in 1913, and when I returned from Sydney to take up the Heath Harrison Chair of Organic Chemisty in Liverpool, in 1915, I once again had the opportunity for close consultation with my friend, albeit largely by correspondence. In 1922 Lapworth became Sir Samuel Hall Professor and Director of the Laboratories in Manchester. This was a highly active period for both of us in the development of theoretical ideas. We were jointly and severally attacked by B. Flürscheim and C.K. Ingold, chiefly in the correspondence columns in Chemistry & Industry. After the end of 1925 Ingold, at least, saw the light. The events of this period are developed at greater length in Chapter XI.

Lapworth married Kathleen Holland, the youngest daughter of a pioneer radiologist of Liverpool. Francis Stanley Kipping and William Henry Perkin, jun., each married sisters of Mrs. Lapworth, who thus showed a partiality for organic chemists which has probably never been previously noted. Kipping was one of Lapworth's research supervisors at the Goldsmiths Institute, and the original source of his interest in camphene and camphor. The outcome of this was that by the recognition of the molecular rearrangement Lapworth removed an outstanding difficulty in the way of Bredt's structure for camphor.

Lapworth had many hobbies; he was an excellent violinist, his favourite composer being Mozart. He was fond of walking and climbing and I remember seeing some particularly fine photographs of ascents among the group of Dolomites above Rosenlaui. In later years his favourite recreation on vacation was fishing. He was the type of angler who sets out to catch a particular fish and usually succeeds. Although not a bird watcher in the modern sense, he knew and recognised the songs of all the wild birds, and I remember getting instruction from him on this subject in the course of walks round St. Andrews. Actually, I admired Lapworth's enthusiasm on these occasions more than the bird songs themselves, and I regret that his efforts in this particular direction were largely wasted. On the other hand, I did appreciate and, I hope, profit from his outstanding knowledge of the British Flora. He made his own cigarettes, but I recall occasions when he had some difficulty in finding his matches. The cigarette had to be taken from the lips, shortened, and the whole cycle repeated. At times the cigarette was a total loss; his active conversation contributed to the result. There must have been occasions when Lapworth was angry, but I cannot recall one, and I am quite sure he never did a mean action.

EARLY WORK IN THE GROUP OF THE ISOQUINOLINE ALKALOIDS

It was natural to extend our synthetic work in this direction, chiefly because many of the intermediates encountered in the brazilin/haematoxylin research obviously were suitable to act as starting materials for the attempted syntheses of isoquinoline alkaloids.

At first I worked on the case of papaverine and completed a synthesis along the following lines.

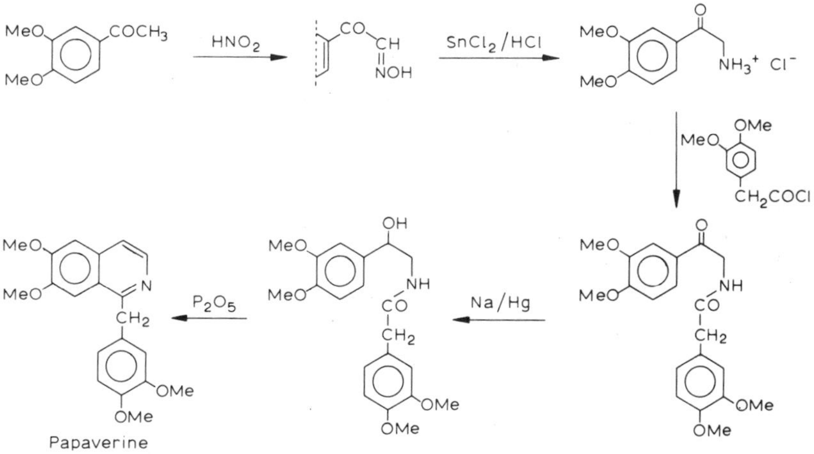

Perkin was not quite satisfied with it because the products did not show a colour reaction which was thought to be typical of papaverine. We now know that this reaction is due to the presence of small quantities of cryptopine in the alkaloids of opium, and is not characteristic of pure papaverine. Again, the penultimate intermediate, the hydroxy-amide, was not obtained crystalline, but as a thick oil. Perkin thought it much better to make further attempts to purify this substance and obtain it in a solid condition. However, all my efforts in this direction failed and, meanwhile, Pictet and Gams described the same synthesis (Ber. 1909, *42*, 2943). Otto Wallach, who came over to Manchester to take an honorary degree, was told of this incident and strongly advised us to publish, but Perkin never took any steps in this direction.

Some time later I noticed that the hydroxy-amide, which Pictet and Gams claimed as an intermediate, had the same melting point as the substance in which the hydroxyl was reduced to a hydrogen atom, that is to say, the dimethoxyphenylacetyl derivative. I had the interest, therefore, to repeat Pictet and Gams and found that, indeed, the reduction which they described did give a considerable amount of the phenylacetyl derivative. I do not doubt the Pictet/Gams synthesis, but they could not have succeeded with the pure intermediate as claimed, they must have used an oily mixture, as I had done myself. Later on I did some further work with these acylamino ketones, reducing one of them to an alcohol, which was crystalline. Strangely enough, Pictet wrote a paper in which he claimed that these observations were incorrect, but F.L. Pyman also repeated the work and found that my account of it was, indeed, perfectly accurate. As a consolation prize I developed a synthesis of oxazole derivatives [9,20] from these acylamino ketones; this has proved to be the best synthesis of oxazole derivatives and has been developed by many other investigators. Among the substances prepared in this way was a phenylnaphthyloxazole [20] which was intensely fluorescent in the solid state. Many of the arylsubstituted oxazoles show more or less fluorescence in solution, for example in benzene or sulphuric acid, but this solid-state fluorescence was unique for this substance, among those examined. The comedy of errors in the papaverine synthesis was completed by a claim of a series of reactions which were thought to proceed as shown on the left in the annexed scheme. This was incorrect and I published a paper in which a different mechanism was put forward [242].

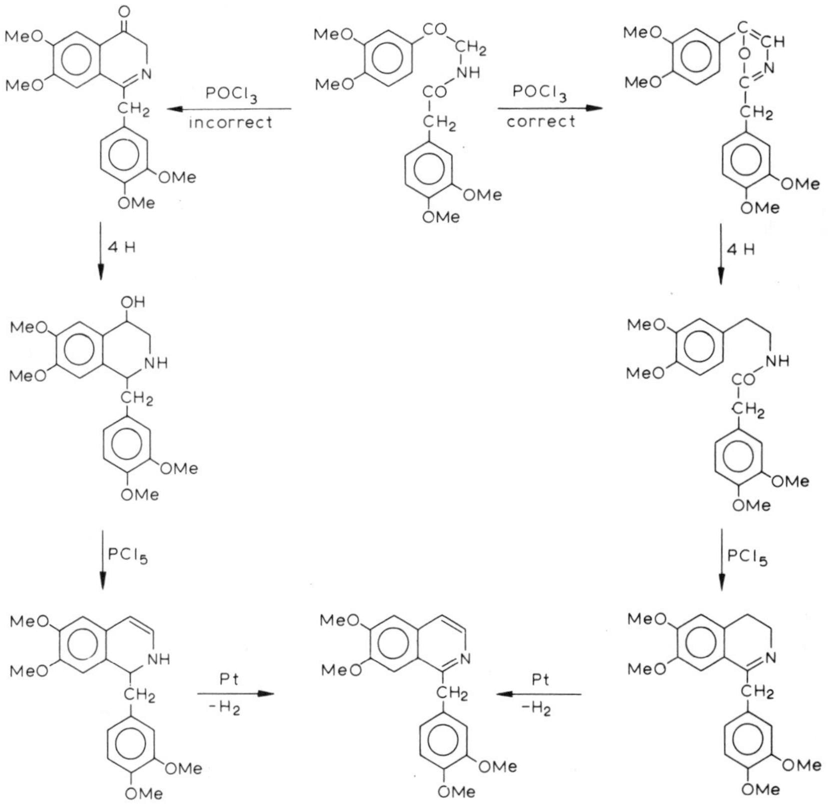

We then turned our attention to the phthalide group of iso-quinoline alkaloids, especially hydrastine and narcotine. Liebermann had condensed hydrocotarnine with opianic acid and obtained an isonarcotine in which the remaining free position in the aromatic ring of hydrocotarnine had been substituted by meconyl. We wished to use the methylene group of meconin as the receptor of the attack by cotarnine (contemporaneously synthesised by Salway), or hy-drastinine. It was thought that the methylene of meconin might be sufficiently active because it is in the *ortho*-position to carbonyl, and also because it is in a ring system. Direct condensation of cotarnine and meconin did indeed afford a small yield of optically inactive nar-cotine, also termed α-gnoscopine [12]. We were in possession of a considerable quantity of this *dl*-narcotine, which had been supplied by T. & H. Smith of Edinburgh. Its optical resolution proved to be difficult, but was ultimately brought about by the preparation of the bromocamphor sulphonate. I remember that the dishes containing the bromocamphor sulphonate were set aside at the beginning of a long vacation and that, on return, a crystal nucleus was found to have been produced in the gum. This was cut out, washed free of gum, and could be used to nucleate a fresh preparation and obtain quickly a considerable amount of the salt. This salt proved to be the salt of natural *l*-narcotine. However, the yield in this first condensation was very low and a more detailed study was made later, with E. Hope, during my second period in Manchester.

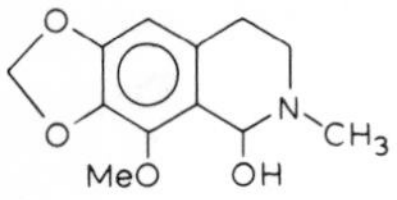

Cotarnine

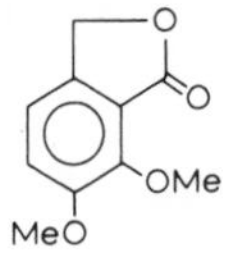

Meconin

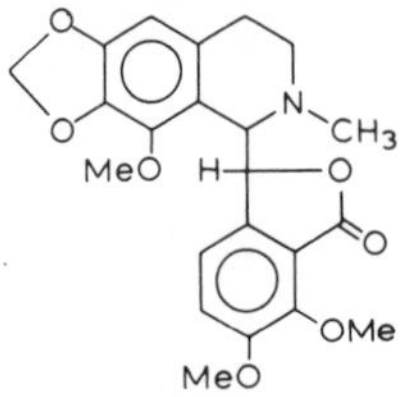

dl-Narcotine

Alkaloids of Peganum Harmala

Following his usual uncanny instinct for a good research topic, Perkin had acquired a considerable quantity of seeds of this plant, which grows in profusion on the lower Russian steppes. The bases contained harmine, $C_{13}H_{12}ON_2$, and harmaline $C_{13}H_{14}ON_2$, together with a small quantity of harmol, $C_{12}H_{10}ON_2$. O. Fischer had already shown that harmaline is dihydroharmine and that harmine contains a methoxyl group which can be hydrolysed by vigorous treatment with concentrated hydrochloric acid to the corresponding hydroxy-compound identical with harmol. We had also heated harmol with zinc chloride and ammonia and thus replaced the hydroxyl by an amino group. This amino-compound was then deaminated with formation of harman, $C_{12}H_{10}N_2$, the whole process being simply a replacement of the methoxyl group by a hydrogen atom. Harman was much later shown to be identical with the natural alkaloid aribine. Work in this field was commenced in my first period in Manchester; the seeds were triturated with dilute hydrochloric acid and the bases precipitated from solution by the careful addition of small volumes of aqueous sodium hydroxide. Harmine is a much weaker base than harmaline and was the first to separate on basification of the solution. The method worked well in practice and with careful attention the pure bases could easily be separated and subsequently crystallised. We made one further significant observation at Manchester, namely that harmine contains a reactive methyl group. When harmine was boiled with benzaldehyde it afforded benzylideneharmine and this, on oxidation with permanganate, yielded norharminecarboxylic acid; the latter on decarboxylation gave norharmine [21], illustrated by the part structures below. This intermediate acid gave a picolinic acid type of colour reaction with ferrous sulphate. It became probable therefore that harmine contains a pyridine ring with a methyl group in the 2-position relative to nitrogen. Norharman was obtained subsequently, but at this stage its existence was decuced by combining information from the O. Fischer degration with our own elimination of a methyl group from the nucleus. The further development was delayed until my return to England from Australia, and was the result of a lucky chance (p. 116).

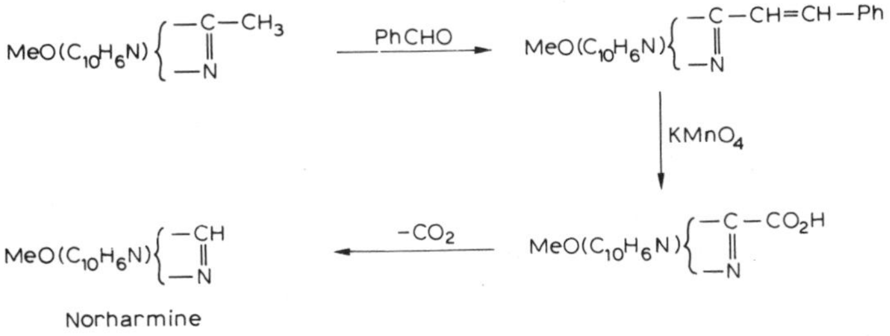

Norharmine

Chapter IV

Sydney (1912–1915)

We were married on August 12, 1912 and not long afterwards went out to Australia, to the newly founded Chair of Organic Chemistry, Pure and Applied, at Sydney.

We made a very leisurely trip, spending ten days at Chamonix, and a week in Florence, which included Christmas Day. There, we were pleased to be greeted by Samuel Alexander, Professor of Philosophy at Manchester University. Alexander was a very eminent scholar and, physically, might have served an artist as a model for Moses. He was also a most kindly man and showed, in many ways, his interest in the younger members of the academic community.

From Florence we went to Naples, also for a week, and visited Pompeii, firmly resisting the blandishments of a guide who wanted to take us to his native village on the slopes of Vesuvius. At Naples we boarded S.S. Scharnhorst, a ship of the Norddeutscher-Lloyd. The first stop was Colombo in Ceylon, and we had time for a visit to Kandy. This was our first experience of real tropics and we were greatly impressed with the beauty of the country where, according to the well-known hymn "Every prospect pleases and only Man is vile". I can certainly confirm the first part of this statement.

The first call in Australia was at Fremantle, but this was rather a hurried visit and we did not see the famous black swans of Western Australia. However, at Adelaide we stayed long enough to visit Mount Lofty, where we saw and heard large flights of a species of small parrots. Adelaide was the home of the Braggs, father and son. It was, and perhaps still is, a city in which English tradition persisted longer than in most other places on the continent. At Melbourne we visited the home of Professor Lyle, a physiologist, and after lunch experienced, for the first time, what a temperature of 105°F feels like.

In Sydney we took a flat at the very top of the Doctors' Building, Wyoming, in Macquarie Street; it overlooked the domain and botanic garden, and on the other side the Parramatta district. The custodian who showed us the flat strongly recommended it on account of the magnificent views one had of the fires that were constantly occurring in the Parramatta. The best, he said, were those produced by stocks of rubber tyres, and so forth. I am afraid we had good evidence, in the course of the next two to three years, to the effect that his recommendation was founded on fact.

Wyoming was practically monopolised by doctors. Some little time after we came to Sydney there was an outbreak of smallpox and revaccination was compulsory. As we had not yet consulted a doctor we plumped for the third floor of our building and were dealt with most expeditiously. Much of the vaccine used on this occasion led to strong reactions and there were rumours of amputation — we decided to stay with our third floor choice. We looked out to Rose Bay and the Head of Sydney Harbour; altogether it was a delightful position, with the possibility of a small garden on the roof.

Before appointment, I had attended a Committee in London; one of the members was Thomas Anderson Stewart, a physiologist. On arrival at the University in Sydney, Anderson Stewart took me aside and said "You are here on false pretences; you did not tell us that you did not play golf, and you also did not contradict me when I called you Robertson. In fact, I thought you were a Scot and I find that you are not, so that is false pretences". "I am very sorry", I said, "I do not know whether it would be possible to get naturalised at this late date". He said he did not think so and pretended to be very annoyed. Of course, it was just a joke, but there was a certain amount of truth in it; " kidding on the square" as the Americans say. The Vice-Chancellor of Sydney University was Sir Norman MacLaurin, and a well authenticated story is that at a dinner party a lady said rather playfully "You know Sir Norman, I believe that *ceteris paribus* you would always prefer a Scotsman". Sir Norman replied "*Ceteris paribus* be damned!"

I was a recipient of great kindness from many members of the University, and I would like to make a special mention of the Registrar, Henry Barff, who did everything possible to smooth a way, which was not always free from difficulty. During my time in Sydney I designed a new laboratory, which was actually built, but I never used it myself. Our own students in the science faculty were extremely well behaved and interested in their work; not so the medicals and the engineers, who regarded organic chemistry as somewhat of a nuisance and something which they had to do by regulation, but which they intended to forget as soon as they possibly could. Some of my predecessors had very great trouble with this unruly mob. It is said that an Italian organ was brought in to play for the audience and that missiles, including fruit such as oranges, were thrown at the blackboard, and pennies or other movable objects like metal balls, were rolled down the steps; in fact, every kind of insubordination and insolence was indulged in by these students. I had a certain amount of trouble, not as much as might perhaps have been expected, and usually managed to get a hearing.

The one University figure these sadists, along with everyone else, respected was Professor Edgworth David, a geologist, who had been on the Henry Shackleton Expedition to the South Polar regions. Actually David had no intention of going on this expedition, but he went down South to see them off, and at the last moment, having made no preparations whatever, he decided to accompany them. David was a man of the most attractive personality, highly respected by his academic colleagues, a well-known figure in the life of the city and state, and loved by the students. He was the only academic personality who escaped the severe leg pulling of songs composed for the annual Commemoration Day. Perhaps I may be allowed to reproduce one about myself, although I fear it may be incomplete. It ran something like this:

In year 1953, to the Halls of Chemistry
Came a stranger for Prof. Robinson inquiring.
Then up spoke a stude who said,
Sir, he you seek has fled
To a land of torrid heat and great perspiring,
For he scorned our n'Edward's aid,
And himself his skill displayed.
Of the dangers of this course we had often warned him.
Then he pointed to a spot,
Just a purplish kind of blot
On the ceiling, and said:
There behold him,
A bang blew high this learned snobbo;
One throbbo, then a blobbo was Robbo.

We saw the Australian regiment marching out to harbour for embarkation to Gallipoli, and a little later, the University staff organised itself into an O.T.C. with lessons in drilling and shooting. I believe that the best marksman was the physicist, Professor Pollack, who made a rather remarkable total score. I managed to pass the test with quite a good mark and with full marks on the lower ranges. We went into camp at Kiami, on the coast south of Sydney, and there learned other military disciplines, but our services were never called upon, though Professor David volunteered for Gallipoli, where it was thought his geological knowledge might be of some service.

Then, a very unfortunate occurrence at Sydney University was the complete gutting of my previate laboratory by fire, which involved the loss of all the specimens which I had accumulated up to that time. The fire was probably caused by incandescent carbon in the flue of a small fume cupboard, which fell on to the rubber of a connection to the gas pipe. This small private laboratory had some strategic significance in tussles between hordes of medical and engineering students, which occasionally occurred. They could perform some outflanking movement by going through the chemical laboratory. To do this they had to pass through the door of my private laboratory. My wife, on one occasion, turned away a mob of medicals, who used to take advantage of this facility, by simply saying "You cannot come here, this is Professor Robinson's private laboratory", and strangely enough, that worked.

I have to admit, possibly with shame, though I feel very little of that emotion, that I applied for the post in Sydney, in the first instance, because it would be an excellent base for the exploration of the alpine chain of the New Zealand Alps. This was my primary objective, not, I am afraid at that stage, the advancement of the science of chemistry.

We arrived in Sydney approximately at the same time as the new Professor of Botany, Anstruther Abercrombie Lawson ("Man, what a braw name!" said the students' magazine). Lawson was a great character and in his teaching was notable for extremely neat and artistic blackboard illustrations. He early showed some of his quality by claiming that his skipper had brought the ship into Botany Bay instead of into Port Jackson. He further claimed that he told the Captain not to be disheartened by this, because he was not the first great navigator who had made that mistake; the reference was of course to Captain Cook, who missed Port Jackson altogether. Later, we visited Lawson, and he us, because he had a flat in Quarry Street quite close to the Australia Club. On one occasion we found him there in a red velvet jacket, and on opening the door, he said "Ssh", and we said "What is it Lawson?" He then said "I will tell you later", and he went on rubbing a picture very carefully with his thumb, and he said, finally, "It's a Rembrandt!" His theory was that the Scottish families who came to Sydney in the early days, brought their belongings with them and, in many cases, there were some old masters among their household chattels. The truth of this is something that I cannot possibly estimate, but undoubtedly Lawson had quite a number of pictures in his room which looked like old masters, although none of them, so far as I can remember, was particularly attractive.

We went for many walks together in the Blue Mountains around Katoomba, Wentworth Falls, and other districts, and in the course of one of these journeys, but not one of those we took with Lawson, but another one, he discovered the prothallus of a fern called pmepteris, which had hitherto escaped the observation of botanists. Typically, he did not write about this at once, but he drew it in every possible way, and he purchased an estate in the Mount Wilson area, where he thought he should be able to find this fern in greater quantity, and this proved to be the case. His house in the Mount Wilson district was one which had many English trees, as well as the usual Australian vegetation. He went on and on and on, and never published this work. Finally, I went back to England and Professor Lang of Manchester asked me "How is Lawson getting on with his prothallus?" He said "You know, the only thing we want to know about it is, has it a root?" I said that I did not know, but that I would try and accelerate matters by discussion with Lawson when I got back but, unfortunately for him, an amateur South African botanist also discovered the prothallus of pmepteris and published it. Lawson published his much larger and more complete work and was elected an F.R.S. Whether on that ground or on others I do not know, but it is said that he celebrated so well that either at the time, or later, he succumbed, and we lost him. By this time, however, I had been succeeded by John Read, and then by James Kenner. Read took a great interest in Lawson, whom he described as Lawson of Pittenweem, because the theory had been spread that he was a son of one of the fishermen of that attractive village on the East Fifeshire Coast above St. Andrews. When the papers left by Lawson were examined, it was found that he was born in Glasgow, and this was a terrible blow to John Read, who never really recovered from the loss of his image of the fisherman's son.

I wish to pay a warm tribute to the memory of Henry George Smith. He started, I was told, as a painter and worked in the Sydney Botanic Gardens. Then he took some courses at the Technical School, Sydney, and largely taught himself. He formed a friendship with R.T. Baker, a botanist, and together they surveyed the pines and eucalypts of Australia, and wrote voluminously on both these topics. He took me on many journeys into the bush and told me a lot about the vegetation, especially the eucalypts, and the interesting connection between the chemistry and the venation of the leaves, which I believe he had discovered himself. From certain kinds of eucalypts he isolated several substances, namely eudesmin, aromadendrin, and others. Eudesmin was available in a larger quantity and we embarked on a study of it in collaboration (see page 89). H.G. Smith was, later on, a great help to John Read in his interesting studies of piperitone and other terpenoid constituents of the species of the genus. He was a remarkable and enthusiastic scientist and one wonders what might have happened if his early work had been carried out under more promising auspices.

Thomas G.H. Jones was one of my most active collaborators in Sydney and he afterwards became Professor of Organic Chemistry at the University of Brisbane.

Some notes on piracy in chemical research

Professor Charles Fawsitt was Professor of Inorganic and Physical Chemistry in Sydney, during my tenure of the new Chair of Organic Chemistry. He hailed from Glasgow University where he was a student of Professor Ferguson and, like his teacher, he was more interested in the historical and literary side of science than original research. He may have been discouraged by an incident which he related to me at Sydney and which I think worthy of record as a kind of a parable. He had a small room not far from the one occupied by F. Soddy. He was never a particularly enthusiastic research worker, but in those early days did some interesting work with urea and the physical chemistry of its equilibrium with ammonium isocyanate. For the conduct of this work he required a spectrometer, and after some difficulty managed to get one and duly installed it into his laboratory. Coming down two or three days later he found, to his great surprise, that it was no longer there. Hurrying to the laboratory steward he taxed him with the careless removal of this valuable instrument, but was met with the rejoinder "I think Sir, you had better look in Mr. Soddy's room", and in Mr. Soddy's room, which was accordingly inspected, there was the spectrometer as large as life and already coupled in some complicated way to another apparatus, which would make it difficult to remove. Complaining of this extraordinary behaviour of Soddy, Fawsitt was met with the reply "But my dear fellow, you know perfectly well that I can make better use of it than you can". I will not give illustrations of the application of this process of reasoning in organic chemical synthesis,they are only too obvious; possession of the great battalions, including distinguished foreign workers, ample funds, and splendid laboratories, enabled this kind of operation to succeed; indeed, one can say with Macaulay "And even the ranks of Tuscany could scarce forbear to cheer".

As a rule this kind of invasion of territory is carried out with fresh forces using new methods. It is not a question of copying so much as of unnecessarily occupying ground which somebody else is clearly tilling.

Sometimes, others have to complain of leakage. I am quite unable to confirm that the following has any real basis in fact, but the statement was made, so that one supposes there must have been some reason for it. Samuel Smiles had established the tetrahedral environment of quadrivalent sulphur (trialkylsulphonium salt) and lectured on the subject after his publication. He then referred to the fact that simultaneously with his own paper another had appeared, the authors of which appeared to be Messrs. Peep and Poachey (Spoonerism for Pope and Peachey).

When an organic chemist publishes what he thinks a general reaction, he not only does not resent its use by others, but should certainly welcome it. Even here, however, there is a possibility of too rapid follow up.

I am afraid the code of conduct which should be appropriate for an academic sphere has no chance of being adopted in industrial research. There the objective is to destroy the other man's patent, if you can, and should you be fortunate enough to put forward one of your own, you should make sure, as far as possible, that there are no loopholes which will allow others to use it. No consideration of ethics seems to enter into the patent world, insofar as that statement applies to the consideration of competing effort. There is, however, one aspect of patents in organic chemical topics which does seem to be unethical and against public policy, as at present conducted. It is possible to make claims of a general character where letters represent groups and types of groups, and where the number of substances claimed to be included under the patent is quite numerous and does not correspond to any experiments actually carried out. It seems to me that patents should be granted for specific substances which have been made, and that claims outside the range of those that have actually been made should not be allowed. Of course I am well aware that this opens the door to imitation by simply altering an unimportant group, say a methyl group into an ethyl group, but I feel there might be a middle way in which the claim might be for derivatives or their recognised equivalent. As it stands, the range of analogy permitted by the patent offices of the world goes far beyond this and includes cases so different from the original that they really should have required separate experiment in order to allow their inclusion in the claims.

SCIENTIFIC WORK AT UNIVERSITY OF SYDNEY

The hetero-enoid conjugated system

The description "hetero-enoid" is self-explanatory. From the beginning it was held to include enamines and enols, aromatic amines, phenols, and pyrrols. The first publication in this field of research concerned the C-alkylation of an enamine[35]. This was carried out as a model for a presumed biogenetic mechanism in certain alkaloids of the isoquinoline group. At that time a method for the production of the simple types of enamines had not been developed. Now, due largely to the pioneering work of Gilbert Stork, they are readily available in great variety and their reactions have been widely explored. However, in a review of this subject Stork appears to have overlooked this early example of the C-alkylation of an enamine. To find further examples of this reaction I turned to ethyl β-aminocrotonate, and this led me to suggest that C-alkylation of the C-sodioacetoacetate and similar reactions are the result of attack of the enolate ion by the alkylating agent [36]. J.N. Collie had shown in 1883 (Annalen *226*, 316) that the reaction of ethyl β-aminocrotonate with ethyl iodide, followed by addition of undried ether, afforded ethyl α-acetylbutyrate. I asked Collie, some years later, how he explained the reaction. He said that the yield was poor, and at the time he offered no explanation. The aminocrotonic ester is a reactive substance and undergoes various condensations, he said, accompanied by formation of alcohol and stronger bases. He thought that these might react with the imino form of the ester to give a substituted ammonium salt which could react with the ethyl iodide in a manner analogous to that characteristic of ethyl sodioacetoacetate. The simple idea of addition, followed by hydrolysis, had not occurred to him and he added ruefully, but with characteristic generosity "If I had thought of that, do you suppose I would have left the matter where I did?" Similarly, Conrad and Epstein (Ber. 1887, *20*, 3055) found that sodium attacked ethyl β-aminocrotonate in ethereal solution with formation of a sodio derivative. This reacted with methyl iodide with formation of sodium iodide and ethyl β-amino-α-methylcrotonate. The assumption was that the sodium had replaced the hydrogen in the α-position to the carbethoxy group. I later pointed out that a much more probable explanation is, namely, that the sodio compound is a derivative of sodamide and the alkylation is an addition to a hetero-enoid system. In order to avoid the dubieties introduced by the amino group in the aminocrotonic esters it was decided to use ethyl β-dialkylaminocrotonic esters. These substances do not form sodio derivatives on treatment with sodium in cold dry ether. Ethyl β-diethylaminocrotonate reacted with ethyl iodide to form an adduct which, on treatment with water, afforded ethyl α-acetylbutyrate and diethylamine hydriodide. The mechanism proposed was further strengthened by realising a case in which the α-carbon of the ester bears no hydrogen atom, but the alkyl group of the alkyl iodide employed appears in this position after hydrolysis of the adduct. The case illustrated below was selected because of condensation of methyl acetopropionate with ethylene diamine, which gave a crystalline product.

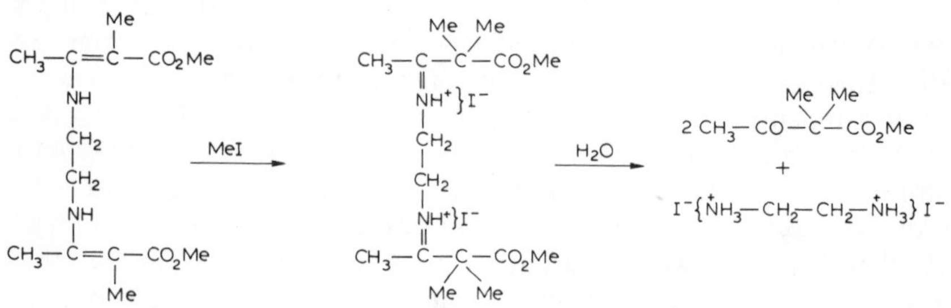

During this early period the basic ideas were expressed in terms of polarised partial valencies, but in a few years time, when the electronic theory of valency was adopted, the representation of the same ideas was much simplified (see chapter XI).

The C-alkylation of enolates

This follows by analogy, but it is a very convincing one. The well-known experiments of K. Meyer show that ethyl acetoacetate and many similar substances are completely changed in aqueous and alcoholic solution by alkyl metal hydroxides into enolate salts. Nevertheless, such salts are converted by alkyl halides into C-alkyl derivatives of the keto-ester. The explanation is probably that the anionic charge is distributed between oxygen and carbon in a fixed ratio under the circumstances of the experiment. Although the oxygen will bear the greater part of the charge, that which is distributed to carbon will confer organometallic character which will enable the process of C-alkylation to be started. This must disturb the aforesaid ratio of the distributed charge which will be restored and the cycle of processes repeated. Hence, the anionic charge of the enolate ion, because of its part distribution to the α-carbon, behaves in the outcome as if it were all on carbon in the first place, thus justifying the old-fashioned way of representing the process, or at least harmonising the latter with the later acquired knowledge that the sodio derivatives in question are essentially enolates.

Miscellaneous experiments largely with catechol derivatives

Work carried out at Sydney University, either in collaboration with R.R., or at his suggestion, has already been mentioned on page 53.

A number of catechol ether derivatives were prepared; for example, it was found that 4,5-dibromomethylenedioxybenzene is obtained in high yield on the addition of bromine water to a solution of piperonylic acid in dilute sodium carbonate solution. An interesting point is that test tube experiments at Sydney led us to the conclusion that the first reaction was displacement of the carboxyl group, followed by bromination in the nucleus. However, E.D. Morgan, working in the Egham Laboratory of Shell Research Limited, found that sodium bromopiperonylate was the first product, and the displacement of the carboxyl group by bromine the second process. Nevertheless, the test tube experiments made at Sydney were carried out under unrecorded conditions, and variables that could have affected the results were the temperature of the solutions, and the concentrations. Morgan's experiments were made under precise conditions and were so reproduceable that it is safe to claim that the bromination of piperonylic acid is the first stage, and it is followed by replacement of the carboxyl group by bromine.

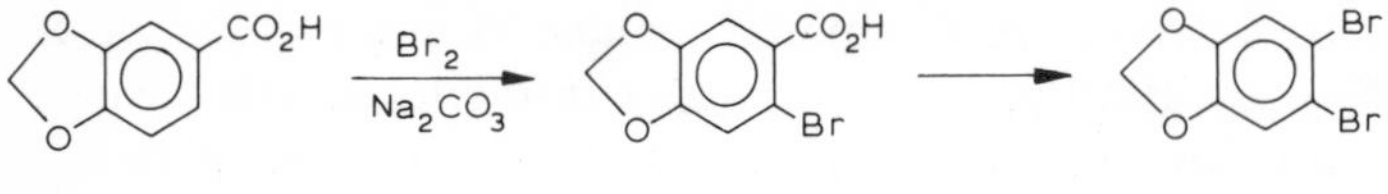

Veratric sulphamide (dimethoxysaccharin) was prepared; it is not sweet, but on the contrary, slightly bitter in taste. Many experiments were made with the object of determining the structure of disubstituted veratroles. For example, it was not known that dinitroveratrole is a 4,5-derivative, and the formation of this substance by nitration of 4-nitroveratrole was attributed to the neutralisation of the methoxyl in position-1 by the p-nitroxyl, leaving the methoxyl in position-2 to direct the substitution into position-5. The probability that the explanation was correct was greatly increased when it was found that 3-nitroveratrole yielded 3,4-dinitroveratrole on further nitration. Here, it is the 2-methoxyl which is deactivated, leaving the 1-methoxyl in control. The isomeric dinitroveratroles can be easily recognised by conversion — after reduction with an excess of zinc dust and hydrochloric acid — into the respective phenanthraphenazine derivatives; the 3,4- and the 4,5-derivative fluoresces green and violet, respectively.

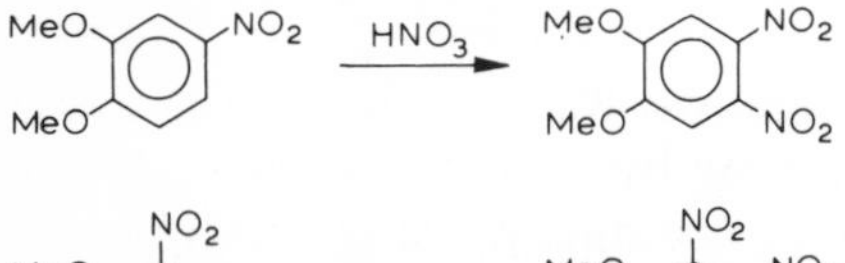

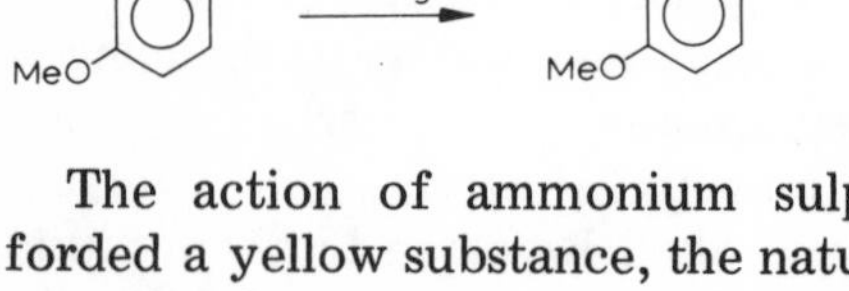

The action of ammonium sulphide on 4,5-dinitroveratrole afforded a yellow substance, the nature of which was misinterpreted as a result of an error in the calculation for nitrogen content. This was returned at double the correct figure due to a cancellation in the denominator of a fraction which was not matched by a similar operation on the numerator. The bright yellow substance obtained in high yield was later shown by Blanksma to be di-(4,5-dinitroveratryl)-sulphide.

Chemistry of eudesmin

As already mentioned, this constituent of the kino of certain eucalypts was discovered by H.G. Smith. On oxidation with permanganate it afforded veratric acid or, when the substance was heated with nitric acid (d., 1.42), it gave 4,5-dinitroveratrole in so high a yield that it was obvious that the molecule $C_{22}H_{26}O_6$ must contain two veratryl residues. Moreover, the substance is devoid of ketonic or hydroxylic properties and, apart from the veratrole nuclei, is saturated. It is therefore diveratrylfuranofuran. This was confirmed later when the full structure was ascertained. Eudesmin proved to be the first member of a group of substances to be recognised. They belong to the C_6—C_3—C_3—C_6-type and may well be derived from coniferyl alcohol dimer. Our investigation of aromadendrin remained unfinished when I left Sydney, but we had established that it was related to apigenin.

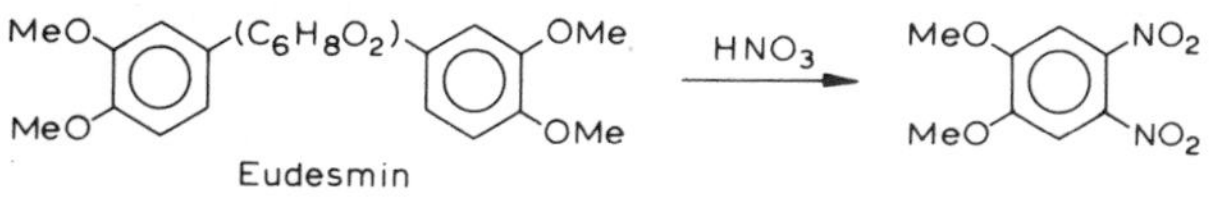

Eudesmin

Lawson was succeeded as Professor of Botany by J.G. Bentley Osborn whose wife, Kathleen, née Kershaw, I had met when living in the Moravian College at Fairfield near Manchester. I was more interested in her younger sister, Ada, but all to no avail. She married William T. Waugh, a friend of mine with whom I had "diggings" in Manchester. Waugh was a historian and burned a large volume of midnight oil in writing a book on the early Lollards. He was quite sure that there could be nothing much in the scientific work I was doing, chiefly I think, because of my devotion to chess and frittering away the time in various other ways. He eventually occupied a Chair in one of the Canadian Universities.

The Osborns were at Adelaide when we passed through on our

way to Sydney. We were delighted to see them because we had been fellow students at Manchester and we made many trips together in the Blue Mountains. Osborn was a general botanist and his knowledge of plants was extremely wide; for this reason and because of his attractive personality he was an excellent teacher. Some years after the death of his wife he remarried and settled in Adelaide.

John Read (1884—1963)

John Read was my immediate successor at Sydney. He was a great West Country man and a friend of Thomas Hardy, and was delighted to find a branch of a society of Somerset men in Sydney. He threw himself with great energy into the teaching work involved by his appointment and also carried out valuable research work on natural products, particularly piperitone. He became a close friend of Henry G. Smith.

One of Read's favourite stories was of the great Zider day when he reported that he asked the workers who got free drinks "How be the zider?" The reply was "It be just right". "How do you mean, just right?" "Well", came the answer, "if it was any better us wouldn't get it, and if it was any worse us couldn't drink it!"

In 1923 Read once more followed in my footsteps by becoming Professor of Chemistry at St. Andrews, and he remained in that position for the rest of his life. Before his appointment to the Chair in Sydney, he had acted as a private assistant to Professor Sir William Pope, who became Professor of Chemistry in the University of Cambridge in 1908. The Pope/Read collaboration produced important results, but many of these could not be published. A story, possibly apocryphal, was repeated in Cambridge in those days, to the effect that after a dinner in Hall, Pope and Read would sit in front of the fire and neither would say a word for hours, until Read would look at his watch and say that it was time for him to leave.

He wrote a number of small books in West Country dialect, but to my taste they were inordinately sentimental. On the other hand, Read took a great interest in the history of alchemy and wrote several useful books on this subject. He also wrote an Introduction to Organic Chemistry, which is acceptable but not specially noteworthy in relation to what was already available.

Read's successor was James Kenner.

James Kenner (1885—1974)

After an undergraduate period at East Londen College (now Queen Mary College), James Kenner worked under Knoevenagel at Heidelberg, for his Doctorate. From 1909—1924 he was a member of the Chemistry Staff at Sheffield University, and from 1924—1928 he followed John Read as Professor of Organic Chemistry at the University of Sydney, and was himself succeeded by J.C. Earl of Adelaide. From 1928—1950 he was Professor of Technological Chemistry at the University of Manchester. Kenner is distinguished for his well developed chemical intuition, and his penetrative insight was especially directed to a clearer understanding of the mechanism of organic reactions. He considered such problems from the point of view of specific chemical properties associated with certain groups of atoms, rather than any generalised system in which reactivity was based on electronic constitution. Topics of research which he illuminated theoretically and experimentally were aspects of aromatic chemistry, especially the discovery of isomerism in substituted diphenyl derivatives, which he attributed to a restriction of free rotation. He also developed a new synthesis of diazo alkanes from intermediates derived from the nitrosation of adducts of mesityl oxide and secondary amines. After retirement from academic life, possibly in relation to his consultancy to the British Rayon Research Association, he attacked problems of degradation of carbohydrates, with interesting results. Kenner held strong views and could never suffer chemical fools gladly. He made a most important contribution to questions on the theory of organic chemical reactions.

Chapter V

Mountaineering

Although at school and in early college days I played soccer, hockey and lacrosse regularly, I found when the various pressures were removed that the out-of-doors activities I greatly preferred were fell walking, rock climbing and alpine mountaineering. No opportunity to indulge in these sports was missed and until I was about 75 years old two or three periods in a year were devoted to walking and climbing. I naturally started on the mill stone grit of Derbyshire, Cratcliff Tor and Robinhood's Stride. The Black Rocks of Cromford, Stanage Edge and Laddow Rocks on the Staffordshire Border were regularly visited from Manchester at the weekend. Longer holidays were spent in North Wales, the Lake District and many centres in Scotland. My first contact with the Alps was when my sister Florence and I visited Switzerland on holiday and she kindly waited for me to do a traverse of the Wetterhorn at Zermatt to climb the Untergabelhorn.

Next year and for a few years after this I was encouraged to climb in the Alps by a brother-in-law, Colonel Morton Clayton, A.C., who had made some notable ascents in the Alps, for example, the Gross Schreckhorn in winter and the Moming Pass. He introduced me to the delights of Arolla, where there is excellent rock climbing of not too great difficulty, and I remember particularly the traverse of the Aiguilles Rouges, Petite Dent de Veisivi, Mont Collon, Mont Blanc de Cheilon, and it was routine to leave Arolla for Zermatt, a journey which we always did in one day, our host M. Anzevui packing a bottle or two of champagne in the rucksacks. Nowadays, I believe the custom is to spend a night in the Cabane de Bertol as the trudge over the Col d'Hérens is certainly a long and arduous one if one does take it in a day. Having this district in mind I recall a bitterly cold day on Mont Brulé; the degree of frost was shown by the fact that a mixture of equal parts of red wine and tea in my rucksack froze solid. Morton Clayton sustained a couple of nasty frost bites and I think everyone was glad to get down again. The mountain is a very easy one under ordinary conditions.

In Zermatt we met, on several occasions, Edward Whymper, the pioneer of the Matterhorn, and once accompanied him on his annual walk to St. Niklaus, which he carried out as a kind of memorial ceremony. He was rather old and prattled on about the crime in the design of climbing boots. He said that the only safe kind of climbing boot was one with elastic sides, because if it gets wedged in a crack it is possible to withdraw the foot. At Zermatt, both during the period of companionship with Clayton and afterwards, I made many of the usual climbs — the Dufour Spitze of Monte Rosa, the Obergabelhorn, Dent Blanche, and a few minor peaks such as the Strahlhorn and Rimpfischhorn. Others were attacked from the Saas-Fée side and these were the Südlenz Spitze, Nadelhorn, the Mittelhorn, Egginergrat, and last of all Portjengrat and Weissmies. I made several attempts on the Matterhorn, but owing to bad weather never reached the summit. Once, with a guide named Julius Truffer, I got a long way up the Zmutt Arête, and Truffer told me that the main difficulty had been surmounted, but a terrific thunder-storm, which was really frightening, drove us back.

Morton Clayton's guide had been the elder Pollinger, famous *inter alia* for his ascent of the hitherto unclimbed Arête Dent Blanche, and for his remark on the summit "Wir sind vier Esel", after which this ridge was known as the Viereselgrat. Pollinger had several sons, amongst whom I met Alois and Josef; Heinrich, a son by a second marriage, was our guide and was engaged for about three weeks at a time at a flat rate whether we were able to climb or not, or whatever we did. Other members of the family were Hermann and Alexander. One of these, together with J. Brantschen, were my guides in an expedition which included the ascent of the Finsteraarhorn. We started early from the Concordia Hut, as the programme contemplated was a long one, and reached the summit of the peak in perfect weather. The climb by the rock ridge offers no difficulty. Snow began to fall, however, when we were still on the summit, and on reaching the Agassiz Joch the storm accompanied by a very strong wind had become violent. Normally the descent from the Joch is fraught with some danger from falling stones, but Brantschen judged that the conditions were such as to minimise this particular trouble. On the glacier below the Joch we were subjected to very strong gusts of wind which did not allow an upright posture and either completely stopped us in a crouching position or made progress very slow. Nevertheless, Brantschen steered us admirably through whatever difficulties there were and after some hours we reached the Strahlegg Hut. Here he complained of internal pain and went to sleep without removing any of his soaking wet clothes. In the morning it was obvious that he was very ill and he was taken by stretcher to the Schwarzegg Hut and later to Interlaken where he went into hospital. He died from this attack of peritonitis two days later. At the inquest it was disclosed that he always complained of food when away from home, and his condition in any case was serious. Nevertheless, the descent from the peak must have aggravated his condition.

After about 15 years Gertrude and I were accompanied by two research collaborators, J.G. Porter and Shinzo Murakami, in a journey from Ried to the Grimsel Pass via the Concordia Hut. The first part was an easy snow walk in drizzling rain and then we saw before us a track leading to the hut. There was however a Schrund (gap) which seemed to be filled at one point with snow. I probed it with my axe and nothing happened, then followed with my left foot and nothing happened. This snow bridge, by the way, was only four feet long. Consequently I thought it safe to carry on with my right foot, when the bridge broke and I went down into a crevasse, fortunately stopping some six or seven feet below the surface, but the rucksack which I was carrying was a decided inconvenience. This was made worse by the well-meaning efforts of my party who tugged hard on the rope which effectually prevented me from making efforts with my ice-axe which I had retained. After a time I found the tension on the rope relaxed and by using back and foot chimney methods I managed to scramble out of the crevasse. I found my friends still pulling on the rope which had settled itself in the snow by virtue of the phenomenon of regelation. It then appeared that the major consequences of the incident were the bruises sustained by my comrades by holding on to the rope rather than anything the chief culprit himself had suffered. A walk of a few yards took us to a place where the crevasse could be crossed. In the hut we found a very international group including a lady who took it upon herself to organise us, and insisted on a representative of each nation making a speech in honour of the Swiss mountains. Next day we went to Oberaarhorn Hut and walked up the peak for the sake of its magnificent view. I found that Murakami must have had some alpine experience but not so Porter. The route was iced and I found it necessary to cut steps for the greater part of the way down. Murakami took the responsible position in the rear and we then threaded our way through the large crevasses of the Oberaar Glacier and reached the valley where engineers were at work on the Grimsel Dam. They kindly gave us a lift in a locomotive to a neighbouring Hospiz. Here Porter and Murakami left us and as the day was still young, my wife and I decided to go over the Nägelisgrätli to the Rhône Glacier. I asked one of the local ladies walking in the road how to get on to the track to the ridge and received the reply "Ohne Führer geht's nicht!" Acting on general principles we took the best way to the ridge and followed it to the Schrund separating the mountain from the Rhône Glacier. This gave no real difficulty and we walked across the well-known level part of the glacier to the ice-grotto and so descended to the Victoria Hotel.

Our rock climbing in Great Britain, climbing in Norway and the Pyrenees, easier climbs in the Alps and Dolomites, and almost all our traverses of passes were guideless.

On the whole, climbing together was very successful but there were three or four occasions when we were undoubtedly lucky. I will mention only one of them which concerned the crossing of a ridge separating two arms of the Rhine; it separated the valley of Vrin from that of Vals. Unfortunately I took a demarkation line from the Siegfried map. I took it to indicate a path and followed beside a river — which took us to a water fall on the Vals side of the ridge. It was possible by traverses to reach the bottom of this, only to find that an extremely steep pine wood lay below. We had started late, underestimating the distance to be traversed. The weather then broke, and a thunderstorm raged in our neighbourhood for about half an hour; by this time light was failing and we had no path, so we tied ourselves to the trees which were on a very steep slope and did what was possible to keep awake by exercises and prodding each other. There was moonlight and early in the morning we saw an animal moving about twenty yards below us. We thought it was a fox; it seemed to be moving with such certainty in a specific direction that we deduced the existence of a path. We climbed down to this location and found, indeed, a narrow wood cutter's path. We turned to the right and in about an hour reached an occupied hut. All difficulty was now over as quite a good track led down to the village from the hut.

Much later Gertrude and I were on the Italian side at the Hotel Jumeaux and intended to climb the Matterhorn on that side. We had bad weather for a week, but it cleared away and a party of French guideless climbers came over. One of them was injured and was treated in the yard of the inn by an amateur surgeon named Josef. Earlier, at the Royal Hotel in Courmayeur, I had met Captain Farrar, who at that time was librarian of the Alpine Club. His companion, Miss Wills, was a direct descendant of Judge Wills, who by his climb of the Wetterhorn did so much to popularise alpine sport among the British. Captain Farrar had asked us what we intended to do, and when we told him that we proposed to attack the Italian side of the Matterhorn, he said "Oh well, if you are going that way you had better ask Camille Maquinaz to act as your guide. He is an extremely reliable man and a good companion". So, of course, when we arrived at the Hotel Jumeaux we sought out Camille who readily agreed to take us up Mont Cervin. However, the weather was bad and he thought he would give it a day in order to settle a bit, because the snow and ice had seriously affected the rope ladders, and this was the cause of the accident to the French climber. Just as we were ready to start off Captain Farrar arrived with Miss Wills and proceeded to explain that he was taking Maquinaz away to make an important climb on the Italian ridges of Mont Blanc. This, it now appeared, was an overriding obligation and apparently Maquinaz was permanently engaged by Farrar for this kind of operation. Farrar's suggestion that we should take Josef Maquinaz was meant seriously but not accepted by me as Josef had only one arm. It was, however, extremely hard luck on us, especially as we were near the end of our holiday. So I made appropriate protest and Professor Clarke, a physiologist from University College, London added his own words. Still, nothing could be done; the interest of mountaineering was at stake and so we had to lose our guide. In desperation Gertrude and I left the Hotel Jumeaux as quickly as we could and went over to the Great St. Bernard and up to Zinal, where we took a guide off the wall, paid an enormously excessive fee for provisions to the Hotel Diablons, and went up to the Cabane de Mountet.

I had always been attracted by Leslie Stephen's *Playground of Europe* and had followed his exploits wherever possible. For example, I had even gone to the extent of climbing the Jungfraujoch, which I found an extremely difficult expedition. Later we followed him to San Martino di Castrozza which is one of the most delightful resorts in the Dolomites. It is amazing what Leslie Stephen managed to do; he seems to have climbed the highest peak in the district direct from Primiero, which is a remarkable walk as well as a good climb. One of his best known climbs was the traverse of the Zinalrothorn. Anyhow we went over the Zinalrothorn next day, traversing it to Zermatt; it was the last day of our holiday and we were extremely pleased with it, and to some extent this made up for our disappointment.

After this we climbed in many mountain regions in Norway, the Pyrenees, and made journeys which connected up the whole of the Alpine chain from south of the Maritime and (Coldi-Tenda) Cottian Alps to east of the true Dolomites. Incidentally, we made some more prolonged stops, for example, in the Graian Alps where we climbed the Grivola and Gran Paradiso. We were coming back by a more northern route when it suddenly became impossible to continue. Apart from these journeys with a rucksack, we had holidays in centres, especially Cortina d'Ampezzo, San Martino di Castrozza, Karer See, the Ortler district, and Upper and Lower Engadine, and several points in the Pennine chain and also in the Bernese Oberland; in fact our vacations were alpine travels, rather than restful holidays in a single spot. We never got far with winter sports because our Christmas and Easter vacations were spent in the home mountains, rock climbing in Wales, the Lake District, or in the Scottish Highlands, and my only serious attempt to learn to ski was brought to a sudden end by an accident to my knee.

The latest climbs, after the death of Gertrude, were those of Table Mountain (1966) by a scrambling route which was a favourite of General Smuts (I was accompanied on Table Mountain by Dr. J.F. Elsworth and Mr. N. Eshton-Sordy), and a climb in the Yosemite (the Gun Sight) to which I was introduced by Alan Steck, son of a former Shell director, and Mr. Hastings, who occupied an important position in the Alpine Club of America. This gulley climb of about seven pitches is approximately as severe as some of the more difficult moderates, or easy difficults, in the British mountains. Alan Steck devised a special rucksack in which he proposed to transport a recent arrival in the family up the climb, but after the second pitch Mrs. Steck struck and told him that he had to accompany them back to camp, which he did. He then returned to the climb and reached the bottom of the last pitch just after we had completed it .

Our chief guide in New Zealand was Conrad Kain who is mentioned elsewhere. We also made climbs with the Graham family, especially Peter Graham who was guide in chief at the Hermitage Hotel — a little south of Mount Cook.

We spent all possible vacations, up to three months at a time, in New Zealand, touring and climbing in the alpine regions. I believe that the first attempt of Coronet Peak was made by Claud MacDonald, in 1850, but Conrad Kain took me up again in 1915, and Harold Sloman and a friend followed in our footsteps. Harold Sloman was

Headmaster of Sydney Grammar School and that we did not meet in Sydney was due to the fact that we left for Liverpool later in the same year. Coronet Peak is a remarkable wall of ice and snow which rises directly opposite to the Malte Brun Hut on either side of the Tasman glacier. We went on to make the first ascent of Mount Neeson, which is a mere walk from the top of Coronet Peak. I have been told that Coronet Peak has been used for the training of climbers ambitious to conquer Everest. Conrad Kain was Chief Guide of the Canadian Alpine Club and came to New Zealand to get climbing all the year round. He was a remarkably clever wielder of the axe and an excellent rock climber. He just looked at a peak and said "Oh well, we'll go up that way". He saw in rather good detail the route to be followed. We made several climbs with him, but nothing of great difficulty apart from Coronet Peak itself. My wife and I made the first guideless descent of Mount Sealey and were very amused, later, to find that Samuel Turner, the author of *Climbing in Seven Continents*, had taken the trouble to record a solo ascent of Mount Sealey. The mountain is extremely easy and it is hardly worthwhile to record either of these skips in alpine climbing in New Zealand. We ascended Mt. Edmont from the south and went down to Three Springs, and the next day went back the same way, which astonished the natives quite considerably. Mt. Egmont is not difficult, but it is a question, in many places, of two steps forward and one step back because of the volcanic slags which one traverses.

In a trip to Milford Sound, by the old method which involved three days and two nights in huts on the way, we were intrigued by a fellow traveller who was travelling very light. We were anxious to know what he had, and this was finally disclosed as a brush and a tin of shoe polish. At the other end of the walk, which is surely one of the most beautiful in the world, we had to explode a small stick of gelignite in order to attract the attention of Donald Sutherland who conveyed us to his accommodation house by motor boat. He was a remarkable character, who gave his name to the High Sutherland Falls of that route. He was rather in the habit of falling out with his wife, or female relations who were staying with him, and very often it was said that they did not speak for six months. He had a constant mechanical motion of freeing his arm from sand flies, which certainly are a real pest of the region.

Milford Sound is equal in beauty and grandeur to some of the best Norwegian fjords, but nowadays it can be reached very easily from

Queenstown, Lake Wakatipu, and a place called Paradise. For a long
time it was desired to find a route from the head of Lake Wakatipu to
Milford Sound and eventually a route was discovered which only involved rope ladders in two places. Now that this has been traversed by
road the whole round can be carried out, I believe, in a day.

I mention the visit to Milford Sound in this section because we
proposed to make an ascent of Mount Tutoko which rises above the
north head of Milford Sound. The party consisted of Gertrude, two
other visitors and myself. We started very early in the morning,
moving off in a north-westerly direction and ascending wherever it was
possible to do so. Apart from the difficulties of terrain which necessi-
tated rather long traverses, the chief trouble was the lush vegetation.
We emerged once or twice to view-points but never saw our peak
which I feel sure was quite remote from our circuitous route; nevertheless, though somewhat disappointed, we felt we had a grand day.
At that time the surroundings of Milford Sound could not be recommended to pedestrians but now that a road has been opened from the
head of Wakatipu to Milford Sound, it is possible that this formerly
impenetrable country side will be "developed".

Milford Sound has reminded me of Norwegian travels. We made the
usual trip from the Turtegro head of the Sognefjord over passes in the
Jøtunheim and a memorable excursion was from the Nordfjord over
the Jostedalsbrä. But our favourite resort was Øie on the Jørundfjord.
Here, for a change, we picked up a guide; most of our travel in Norway was guideless. It turned out that he was a commercial traveller
whose stock in trade was shirts; guiding was as much of a pastime to
him as a service to us. He walked on ahead, even when there was a
chasm to be crossed, one at a time, by hanging on to a bar attached
to a pulley running on a rope. However, we negotiated this safely and
caught up with him later on. At the summit he addressed Gertrude as
follows: "You will be pleased to hear we have made several records
today. In the first place I have at last discovered the easiest way of
getting up this peak; secondly you are the first lady to have climbed
the peak this year, and thirdly you are decidedly the oldest lady who
has ever climbed this peak!"

I visited the Pyrenees twice, once in company with my brother
Victor and we climbed some of the main peaks of the chain. We saw
traces of a bear and were told in the evening that it had attacked sheep.

A hut on the Spanish side just below the Vignemale was in the charge
of a Spaniard and his wife who entertained the guests with superb

dancing. We crossed from Gavarnie to a beautiful valley on the Spanish side; presumably the rocks were Dolomitic as they were bright red in the evening sun. The inn and the valley made some of Hilaire Belloc's statements about the Pyrenees more credible. On a second occasion in the Pyrenees I was alone and remember especially a visit to Andorra.

On one occasion we visited Hobart in Tasmania and walked up Mt. Wellington.It was a holiday for the Hobart people and it was surprising what a large number of them chose to make the ascent. It was a regular procession such as we have never seen on any of our home mountains. My most vivid memory was of a gentleman carrying a parrot in a cage. I asked him whether he thought the parrot would enjoy the view. He replied "It may seem strange to you, Sir, but we just couldn't leave him at home". It reminded me of a German I once encountered who was carrying a large heavy stone up the Piz Languard — enquiries as to the purpose of this elicited the reply that he got more exercise that way. Mention of Piz Languard — a notable view-point near Pontresina — reminds me that in my early 70's I walked up Piz Julier near St. Moritz accompanied half way by a young American. At the point where he left me I deposited my rucksack and although I saw no-one else on the climb, could not find it on the return journey from the summit. Much time had been lost, partly because I had to see that my friend reached the valley safely before I continued the ascent, and I stumbled down the approach valley in total darkness, my left leg sustaining some injury in the process. Next day I went up again to look for my rucksack and found it carefully stowed away behind a boulder by some well wisher whom I had not seen.

These reminiscences of my mountaineering days are, of course, far from complete, but I hope they convey something of the fascination the mountains always held for me.

Chapter VI

Liverpool (1915–1920)

The call to return to England, as first Heath Harrison Professor of Organic Chemistry at Liverpool University, was due to the good offices of Professor W.H. Perkin. I accepted with no hesitation because the opportunity for scientific contacts in Sydney were, at that time, relatively limited.

It turned out that we had ample time for the journey from Sydney to Liverpool and could regard it as a vacation. We spent a few days in Fiji and again in Honolulu, entering Canada at Victoria. There we visited several centres in the Canadian Rockies, spending the longest time at Lake Louise where, although it was off season for high climbing, we made several interesting excursions. Then we went by rail to Buffalo staying in a hotel, the lounge of which was a fine rotunda. Here Gertrude was approached by the manager who politely informed her that smoking by ladies in the lounge was not permitted. We were accompanied at this stage by a Maori officer who had volunteered for war service. He was inclined to be argumentative about the prohibition of smoking.

After seeing Niagara Falls we spent about ten days in New York and then crossed the Atlantic in the St. Paul, an old ship of the American Navy. This was a substitute offered for the liner on which our passage had been booked and which had been sunk by a German submarine. The masts of the St. Paul were covered with lights in the manner of a Christmas tree and we reached Liverpool without incident. However, we had to contend with bad weather and a ship which was not noted for its stability even in good weather.

The Chair which I was to occupy in Liverpool for five years was newly instituted, and the former Head of the Organic Chemistry Department was Dr. A.W. Titherley, who carried out some notable research and wrote an excellent practical book on organic preparations using small-scale methods; probably this was one of the first of its kind and it is still quite a useful textbook for semi-micro methods.

Titherley was convinced that the Earl of Derby wrote many of Shakespeare's plays. He wrote a detailed account of his researchès in this field, but I fear that it received very little attention from the cognoscenti; in fact, Sir Maurice Bowra told me, many years later, that he did not believe that there was any real basis for the suggestion about the Earl of Derby. Later, of course, the Earl of Oxford also came into the picture as a possible Shakespeare ghost writer.

The members of the academic staff of the University were: Edward C.C. Bailey, Professor of General Chemistry and, in effect, Head of the Department, and Professor William C.C. Lewis, Professor of Physical Chemistry, who occupied the relatively new Donnan Laboratory of Physical Chemistry. Bailey was an enthusiastic, ebullient individual full of new ideas and abounding in energy and initiative in experiments. Many of his schemes for synthesis of organic products from carbon dioxide have since been realised and it would be unwise to discount some of the claims which he made himself, such as the synthesis of coniine. He had the idea of chemical reactivity by opening up the force fields in the molecule and this I acknowledged in putting forward a very similar conception, in more definite form. Elsewhere (p.107) I have described the unusual activities of the advanced students in the practical chemistry laboratories and this development was entirely due, in the first instance, to Bailey, although naturally others, including myself, made contributions later on.

A very valued colleague at Liverpool was the Professor of Biochemistry, Walter Ramsden; he was perhaps our closest friend there and was a recognised pioneer in the development of surface chemistry. He had some peculiar ideas about research; thus, wishing to investigate the pharmacology of quinine and its derivatives, he looked for the best animal on which to make the experiment, and he found that the cheapest was undoubtedly the tadpole. At a dinner party in our house he unfortunately got a triangular piece of chicken bone stuck in his throat, which he tried to conceal for a long time, but eventually had to give in and he was hurried away to a dentist to have the offending fragment removed. He had it polished and mounted on a little pedestal and placed it on his mantelpiece. As typical of his quality, I might mention that he was asked by a lady sitting next to him at a dinner party, who was looking at a young couple on the other side of the table, whether he did not think it was wonderful to be in love. "Madam", he replied, "I would sooner be a canary". He was, of course, a confirmed bachelor.

I had a very happy time at Liverpool, and made many friends. Among others, we visited the older Muspratt, who had been a student of Justus von Liebig. Muspratt had a magnificent oil painting of the great pioneer in his study. I also came into contact with many members of the important milling and shipping firms, which reminds me of a somewhat amusing incident.

There had been a series of disastrous fires in the harbour, due to oil escaping and then bursting into flames. I was consulted on this and visited members of the Harbour Board who turned up in impressive uniforms, etc., and the situation was explained to me. Then I said "Does this oil burn, because, you know, it is not too easy to ignite a heavy oil?" and the answer was "Of course it does; that is what we are consulting you about". I said "Could we have a specimen of the oil here", and it was brought, and I put a lighter on to it and, of course, it did not burn; then I threw a few matchsticks into the saucer and the whole thing flared up. So I said "Gentlemen, that is the answer to your problem, it is not entirely the oil, but also the driftwood in the harbour acting as a wick, and what I advise is to remove the driftwood and perhaps to collect the oil in some form of separator". Both these measures were carried out and proved entirely successful, and there were no more fires at all. They then asked me rather diffidently what my fee for this exercise would be. I was quite innocent at that time of anything of this kind, so I said I was very pleased to help them, but if they wanted to signify their approbation of this service, would they mind making a subscription to the University library. This was the first, and the last time, that I made a mistake of that kind. My comment in this matter was talked about and one of my commercial friends chided me on what he regarded as the stupidity of my action.

That reminds me again, that I was in touch with Crossfield, the soap manufacturers, where the son of H.E. Armstrong, namely Edward Frankland Armstrong, was a Managing Director. I worked out for them a way of making n-octanol from ethyl caprylate using the Bouveault-Blanc reduction. The reaction was carried out with the addition of only one mole of ethanol in boiling xylene and the yield was almost quantitative. E.F. Armstrong had a pleasant home near Warrington, and what particularly interested me was his very fine rock garden.

Edward Frankland Armstrong (1878—1945)

After undergraduate years at the Royal College of Science and the Central Technical College, he worked for a doctorate with van 't Hoff at Kiel University. The subject of his thesis was the hemi-hydrate of calcium sulphate, the interest of which was related to the Stassfurt deposits, a major field of van 't Hoff's investigations. It is worth noting that F.G. Donnan was also a student in this laboratory and carried out similar work. However, Armstrong's leaning was towards organic chemistry, and at that time Emil Fischer was at the height of his reputation and consequently Armstrong gravitated towards Berlin; he was fortunate to obtain a position as assistant, and later demonstrator, in Fischer's laboratory. Although he only stayed in Berlin a little more than a year, his contact with Emil Fischer always remained as one of the outstanding experiences of his life. One experiment made by Armstrong deserves to be mentioned, not only because of the intrinsic importance of the result, but also because that outcome could be secured by the use of polarimetric measurements alone. The object of the work was to determine the stereochemical relations of the two known methylglucosides with corresponding glucoses. Under different conditions of crystallisation glucose can be obtained in two forms, α and β, having very different rotatory powers. In solution the two forms are inter-convertible (mutarotation) and an equilibrium between them is set up characterised precisely by the observed rotatory power, and there were also known two methylglucosides, also of divergent rotatory power, and such that it was suspected that one was α-methylglucoside and the other β-methylglucoside. No direct proof of this, however, existed. Armstrong demonstrated the relation by hydrolysing the respective methylglucosides by means of enzymes. One of them could be hydrolysed by emulsin from bitter almonds, but not by maltase from yeast, whereas the other of the pair was hydrolysed by maltase and not by emulsin. As the enzymes are active in neutral solution, mutarotation of the glucose produced is slow and something near the values for the α- or β-glucose were obtained in the two cases. On the addition of a drop of ammonia the mutarotation equilibrium was quickly obtained and, as expected, in one case the rotatory power moved to the right, and in the other case to the left. Of all experiments that have real significance this was surely the laziest.

In 1905 he started his distinguished industrial chemical career by becoming Chief Chemist to Messrs. Huntley and Palmers Ltd., biscuit manufacturers. In 1914 Armstrong became Technical Adviser to the Manager of Crossfield & Sons Ltd., and in the following year Technical Director. In subsequent years he became involved in various mergers, for example Lever Brothers and Brunner, Mond & Co. In 1925 he became Managing Director of the British Dyestuffs Corporation. This interest was continued even after he relinquished the post in three years time. Whilst at Crossfield there is no doubt that Armstrong made considerable contributions to the large-scale production of simple organic chemicals by catalytic methods, but I believe that his contribution to the budding dyestuffs industry in Britain was quite unimportant.

Professor S.B. Schryver, in his book entitled *The General Characters of the Proteins* (1909), mentions the following in a footnote: "H.E. and E.F. Armstrong have suggested that the main polypeptide can assume a spiral form, and have constructed models. In this case the more reactive groups might be represented as the freely moving groups external to the spiral. The stereochemical configuration would probably also affect the reactivity of the amino and carbonyl groups; adopting the Armstrong configuration it is conceivable that those which are external to the spiral would be reactive, and those protected by groups of other atoms inert."

Professor A.C. Chibnall (Chemistry & Industry, July 29th, 1967), who drew attention to this interesting footnote, proceeds: "To the best of my knowledge this remarkable and prophetic conjecture has been altogether lost sight of, due, I imagine, to the strange and indirect way it was presented, for a search has failed to reveal any communication whatever from the Armstrongs themselves, and Schryver unfortunately did not bring out a revised edition of his monograph in the early 1920's, like his fellow authors of the 1909 series."

E.F. Armstrong's son, Alexander, came to work with me at Oxford many years later. He was a most attractive young man, both from the physical and intellectual points of view, and we had great hopes that he would turn out to be the best of the distinguished line of Armstrongs. He did complete a small piece of work with me (see Vol. II), but on a holiday in the Alps a tragic occurrence put an end to his promising career. An avalanche swept down and almost engulfed a close friend of his. Alexander escaped, but went to the help of his friend and was probably buried by a second fall. I know of few tragedies in the Alps which have affected me, personally, so deeply.

The period in Liverpool coincided with the beginning of a concerted effort to build a larger dyestuffs industry in Britain. Perkin was a consultant to British Dyes Limited and British Dyestuffs Corporation, but although we continued collaborating on other matters, we did not do so in the dyestuffs field. The Earl of Wilton established a research scheme which was under the direction of Dr. F.W. Atack, a good industrialist, and I joined this scheme and carried out some researches under its aegis. In later years I was surprised to be awakened in the middle of the night by a telephone message from Canada, and to hear the drawl over the telephone "This is Atack, there are twenty-four Atacks now". I have quite forgotten what the rest of the conversation was about.

Towards the end of my five years in Liverpool, Herbert Levinstein came to the laboratory and offered me the Directorship of Research at British Dyes Limited, Huddersfield. After prolonged thought, and taking of advice, I accepted this as it seemed very much in the national interest that I should do so. Levinstein was a man of most optimistic temperament and his instruction to me was "You know Robinson, we have to be cleverer than the Germans and what I want you to do is to make a red sulphur dye". I told him that I thought there was one in Friedländer's thioindigo. "Oh no", he said, "I do not mean the indigos, I mean sulphur dyes such as are dyed with sodium sulphide in the ordinary way". I looked this problem up, to some extent, and then reported that so far as I could see, all sulphur dyes to-date were blue, or some dark colour around blue, and that there was no evidence that anyone could produce a red sulphur dye of the usual type. It seemed to me rather like knocking one's head against a brick wall, and Levinstein reluctantly agreed that it might be rather difficult.

He made a habit of going to mountain resorts and carrying out some climb or other which was supposed to be one of the more difficult in the district. For example, at Cortina d'Ampezzo he selected the Punta di Fiammes by the Pompanin Kamin. This peak is at the extreme left, looking from Cortina, of the Monte Cristallo range, and the conspicuous cleft up its face is very easily seen from the village. When I went up I had the same two guides, namely Barbaria and Pompanin, and they told me that Levinstein had more or less become jammed into the chimney, but he was a great sportsman and took it very well. This is one of those climbs which ends at the top, because a porter brings round your boots and you change from your scarpetti and walk down into the valley. On another occasion Levinstein went to Wasdale Head and demanded audience of the Dolomites guide who was employed there at that time. He said he wanted to do a rock climb, and when asked what it was he wanted to do, he answered "Walkers Gulley". The guide shook his head and said "No, that is the place where stones are always falling". As a matter of fact, this peak, or this climb, is above the Screes and is hardly worthwhile on account of these falling stones. Otherwise, I think it involves no very serious difficulty, but this is all hearsay because I have never been there myself. After a certain amount of cajoling and persuasion on the part of Herbert, the guide said "Well, I don't want to break my bloody neck and I will not do it for less than £5", and, accordingly, it was agreed on those terms and Levinstein had the pleasure, or otherwise, of climbing Walkers Gulley. He was something of a horseman and frequently fell and finally made a fall more serious than the rest which put him out of this particular kind of action forever. He was very well known in chemical industrial circles and did a great deal for the Society of Chemical Industry and, of course, for the dyestuff industry in Britain. I was extremely fond of him in spite of his exploits of derring-do. His home was at Ford Bank, Didsbury, a very large establishment which we frequently visited.

WAR WORK IN THE LIVERPOOL LABORATORIES

When I arrived in Liverpool from Sydney, I found that Bailey had organised the students' practical work with the idea of making a contribution to the war effort by preparation of certain drugs in quantities sufficient to be of substantial use; similar work was organised in other chemical laboratories throughout the country, and information about improvement in preparations was shared. In Liverpool, for example, we made many kilograms of β-eucaine and novocaine. Acetone was saturated with ammonia, and we found that the process of condensation was very much shortened by the addition of calcium chloride. Another laboratory achieved a similar result by the addition of alcohol. After isolation of diacetonamine hydrogen oxalate, the condensation with acetaldehyde was effected by first converting the latter into the corresponding dibutyl acetal and carrying out the reaction in n-butanol. This gave the erroneously named vinylacetonamine oxalate, and the base was isolated and reduced by sodium and alcohol to the corresponding secondary alcohol. The hydrochloride was then heated with benzoyl chloride without a solvent and the product was β-eucaine hydrochloride, obtained in excellent yield. This protection of a strongly basic secondary amine by conversion to the hydrochloride is effective, and has found many applications. In the case of novocaine we found the known methods satisfactory. The improvisation of suitable apparatus required for this work, and the necessity for careful operation and control, was found to be a good substitute for the conventional courses.

One of the processes used in the manufacture of trinitrotoluene (TNT) involved the washing of the crude product with alcohol. These washings were concentrated at the Silvertown TNT factory — which, incidentally, was eventually destroyed by an explosion and fire — and the resulting sludge of highly dangerous nitro compounds was sent to me. The Rev. F.H. Gornall [114] assisted me in working up this material, which was kept in buckets under the laboratory benches! We found that treatment with concentrated sulphuric acid separated the two main constituents: the solid crytalline β-trinitro-toluene (2,3,4-trinitrotoluene) could be separated, and the solution, on dilution with water, gave 2,4-dinitrotoluene. Gornall proceeded to examine the transformation of β-trinitrotoluene.

Atropine was in short supply during the First World War and the knowledge of this fact led me to recall that I had contemplated in Sydney a synthesis of ψ-pelletierine from glutardialdehyde, methyl-amine and acetone. This idea was a possible extension of pseudo-base condensations and I realised, at Liverpool, that a synthesis of tropinone [37] might be effected in a similar manner, starting with succindial-dehyde, and tropinone could probably be converted to a tropine without difficulty. Accordingly, I tried this synthesis and obtained indications that a very small yield of tropinone had been produced. I then proceeded to activate the acetone and used calcium acetone-dicarboxylate in its stead. After acidification tropinone was pro-duced in 42% yield, estimated by conversion to its dipiperonylidene derivative.

Parenthetically, Willstätter once asked me why I chose this partic-ular derivative, seeing that the dibenzylidene derivative would have been perfectly satisfactory for my purpose. I told him that the sub-stance I chose was a new one, more sparingly soluble than the com-pound that he made, and that it gave a very characteristic colour re-action. Later on, C. Schöpf, using physiological pH, found that the yield of tropinone was considerably increased. I made the necessary succindialdehyde from pyrrole by the known method; later I found that a process starting with the bromination of furan could feasibly be developed into an industrial process, but I do not know whether this route had actually been used. R. Willstätter applied my method to a synthesis of ecgonine and hence of cocaine.

In later years, with R. Menzies, glutardialdehyde was used to synthesise ψ-pelletierine [74], thus confirming the expectation mentioned above. With B.K. Blount [230], a further ring homologue was made starting with adipic dialdehyde. We also prepared thiotropinone, starting with 2,2'-dioxodiethyl sulphide. The derivatives of this substance are worthy of closer study from a pharmacological point of view, since the substance is readily prepared from cheap material.

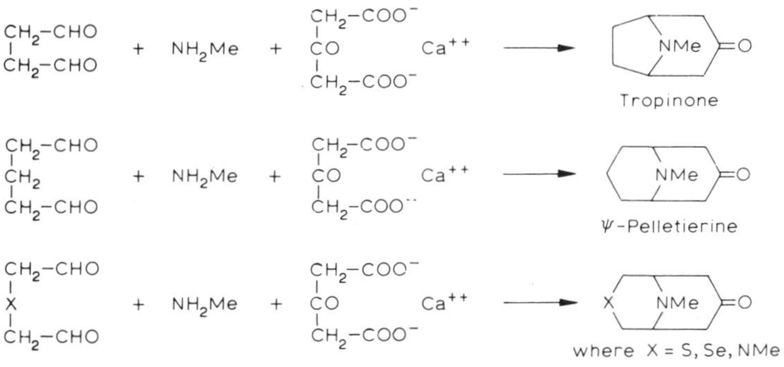

Structural Relations of Plant Products [38]

Shortly after the publication of my first paper on the subject of the biogenesis of alkaloids I abandoned this title and its implications and adopted instead that which stands at the head of this section.

It became clear that many routes were available which would meet the same requirements of structural relations. Earlier work was condensed and collected in lectures delivered at the Weizmann Institute for Science, Rehovot, Israel.

In general, the idea of my work on structural relations was to dissect the molecules so as to show the relation with simpler natural products and, if possible, to use on the dissection the reverse of the reaction which might conceivably occur. As the whole of this work was speculative in nature I can only look back on it with the feeling that it may have given a stimulus to later workers, for at least they had something in black and white which they could disprove, and very often they did just that. However, quite a considerable amount of the original remains, unless one takes the view that the schemes put forward were actual biogenetic syntheses. Although the general idea of the specifications of natural products according to their structural relation is undoubtedly sound, the speculative basis of the operation had to be replaced by experimental methods. This was done with great effect, and among a large number of distinguished investigators in this field I think that Professor A.R. Battersby must be regarded as pre-eminent. In many respects his work has led to most surprising conclusions and thrown a flood of light on the processes of the natural syntheses. Although these remarks come after a discussion of alkaloid chemistry, it must be noted, at this stage, that many others have contributed notably to our knowledge of biosynthesis.

As I have already remarked, my interest in biogenesis of compounds occurring in plants was awakened by a realization of the ease with which the pseudo-bases condense with a large variety of suitably constituted substances. I worked out paper syntheses of a number of alkaloids using carbinol-amines and keto-methylenes. One of these hypothetical schemes concerned the hoped-for synthesis of ψ-pelletierine. This, with a practical modification, was later realised. In Liverpool the analogous synthesis of tropinone was effected and it then seemed worthwhile to see what extensions of the idea could be reasonably made. The results were described in a number of lectures and in greatest detail in the first Weizmann Memorial Lectures (1953), Oxford University Press (1955).

The general theory of such relations was adumbrated in connection with the terpenes and related groups. It was early recognised that the terpenes could all be interpreted as containing structures derived from isoprene (isopentane units). I contributed the observation that the chains contained these units in "head to tail version" (Annual Reports on the Progress of Chemistry, The Chemical Society, 1923). Much later I suggested that squalene (Chem. and Ind., 1934, 53, 1062), when appropriately cyclised, could be the source of cholesterol, a theory which has been experimentally verified. R.B. Woodward and K. Bloch demonstrated the remarkable rearrangement of squalene which led by way of lanosterol to cholesterol (J. Amer. Chem. Soc., 1953, 75, 2023). Further detailed knowledge of the biogenesis of cholesterol has been garnered by G. Popják and J.W. Cornforth, who also proved the occurrence of the molecular transformations of the original iso-pentanoid skeleton. Exceptions to the isoprene rule among the ter-penes and sesquiterpenes are very uncommon and usually the result of molecular rearrangement.

The synthesis of tropinone led to the recognition of the simpler type of alkaloids of the *pyrrolidine group*. One example will suffice, namely that of hygrine, which may result from a pseudo-base conden-sation of an oxidised proline with an acetone equivalent.

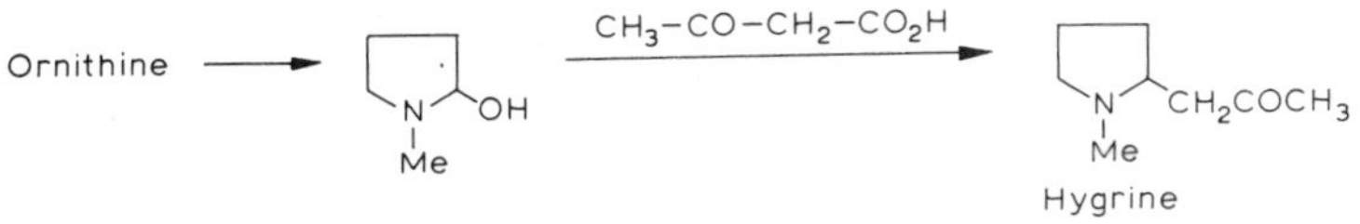

Following the tropinone synthesis [37] it was natural to speculate on the origin of the succindialdehyde moiety and as it was known that aldehydes may be produced by the oxidation of α-amino acids, the most natural hypothesis was that the dialdehyde was derived from α,α-diaminoadipic acid. However, since this is not a common protein amino acid it was thought that ornithine might serve. In the Weizmann Lectures I used this opportunity to emphasise the structure relations aspect and mentioned that even succinic acid might be a source of succinic dialdehyde in a biological system. Nevertheless it seems that the ornithine hypothesis was correct. The assumed extension to hygrine and the pyrollidine part of the nicotine molecule followed naturally.

In the *piperidine group* the ring homologous system was assumed to be derived from lysine and various ketonic components. The syn-thesis of ψ-pelletierine was fully analogous to that of tropinone. In this series the residues of methyl ketones are attached to the 2-po-sition of the piperidine nucleus. However, there are also a number of bases in which groups derived from methyl ketones are attached to the 2- and the 5-positions. The theory of pseudo-base condensation with reactive ketones obviously allows this type of reaction which, in-deed, is also necessary for tropinone and ψ-pelletierine. On the whole these theories have been justified by experiments with radioactive tracers, but the case of coniine is dubious since Leete has shown that glycerol is one of its generators. A particularly interesting case is that of nicotine which both C. Schöpf and I proposed to derive from a tetrahydropyridine and a pyrollidine pseudo-base in the following manner:

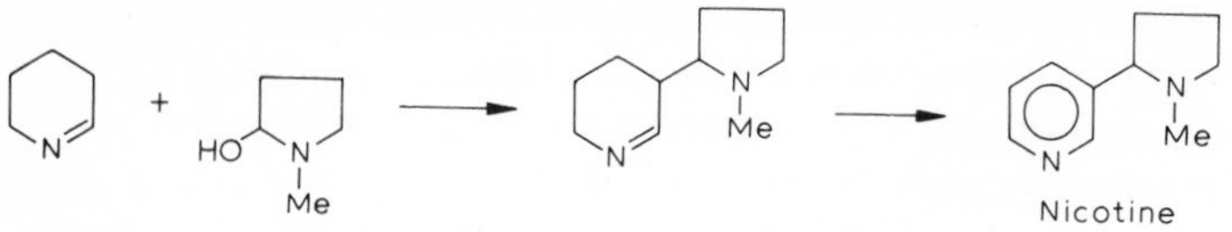

However, it appears from the work of H.L. Dawson that Nature prudently takes the trouble to activate the reactive position in the tetrahydropyridine nucleus as shown in the scheme below.

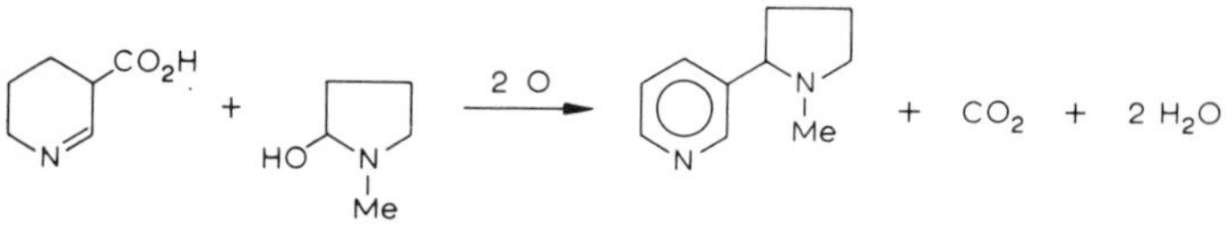

The carboxyl group is eliminated in the final oxidation which yields the alkaloid.

The Isoquinoline Group of Alkaloids

E. Winterstein and G. Trier (*Die Alkaloide*, Borntraeger, Berlin, 1910, p. 307) made the interesting suggestion that the biogenesis of the isoquinoline alkaloids involves the condensation of two units, each derived from substituted phenylalanines. One of the molecules may be supposed to be oxidised to a phenylacetaldehyde and this condenses with the amino acid so as to produce a reduced substituted benzyl-isoquinoline. Other molecular changes follow with a range of alkaloids. The correctness of this theory from the viewpoint of structural re-lations is apparent on inspection and the remaining problems concern subsequent processes which are indeed varied and interesting. It should be noted in the first place that one molecule of the amino acid may be coupled with certain simple aldehydes, themselves possibly derived by oxidation of α-amino acids. As is usually the case, we are concerned chiefly with the carbon-nitrogen skeleton, and can make no assumptions as to the stage at which oxygen or nitrogen becomes methylated. At this point I would like to explain that I have no inten-tion of reproducing here the contents of my Weizmann Lectures or making detailed comment on the subsequent history of the subjects treated. I wish, however, to draw attention to certain suggestions which were novel when made and which appear to be well founded. In the isoquinoline group the appearance of an additional methyl group in the angle position *beta* to the basic nitrogen atom had been noted in members of the indolic subgroup. This was attributed to C-methylation of the enamic system of a substituted indolenine or hydroisoquinoline and the reaction could be brought about in the laboratory using, for example, dihydroberberine. This is entirely analogous to the C-methylation of the middle system which leads to the eserine structure.

The relation of the berberine skeleton to that of laudanosine is apparent on inspection of the formulae. The new bridge must be produced by interaction of a substance containing the benzylisoquinoline skeleton with formaldehyde or one of its many equivalents in this type of reaction. The berberine skeleton gives rise to that of cryptopine and protopine by N-methylation and inner ring fission to a 10-membered ring system. In passing it may be noted that hydrastine and berberine occur together in *Hydrastis canadensis* and this led to a correction of Perkin's first assignment of the position of the methoxyl groups in berberine. A new interpretation of the chemistry of berberal fitted the siting of the two methoxyl groups in the same relative positions as in the congeneric alkaloids. The correctness of this view was demonstrated by a synthesis of berberine by way of oxyberberine, and also by conversion of hydrastine into a substance obtainable from berberine.

Sanguinarine and chelerythrine are evidently derived from a berberine type progenitor by a ring fission which leaves a large part of the molecule free to rotate. This occurs as shown below. A ring closure follows in a new position.

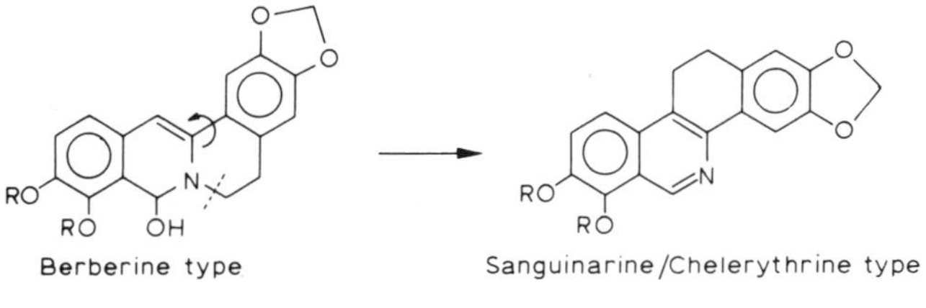

Berberine type   Sanguinarine/Chelerythrine type

One feels confident that this hypothesis must be well founded, and it is only an example of the general statement that coincidents in structural relations are the more convincing the more complex the molecule in which they are noted.

The morphine skeleton could also be related to that of benzylisoquinoline by assuming the formation of a bridge ring in the manner shown below.

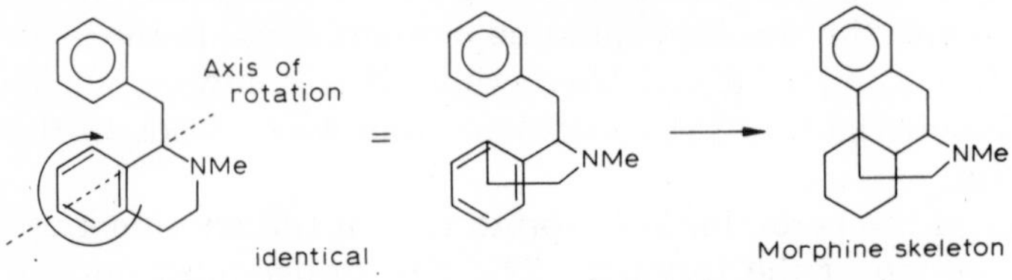

This was one of the suggestions on the structural relations which had an important outcome in the interpretation of the substances concerned. The chemistry of morphine, codeine and thebaine have been intensively studied, especially by Knorr, Pschorr and their collaborators, but the structural formulae deduced did not contain a skeleton that could be brought into line with that of other isoquinoline alkaloids. I made the suggested change and then set to work with my colleagues to find evidence in favour of it. This was soon forthcoming and it was also found possible to explain the remarkable series of the molecular rearrangement discovered by earlier workers in the group. The alkaloid neopine was found to be an isomeride of codeine; it gave dihydrocodeine on catalytic hydrogenation. In fact the whole of the chemistry of morphine, codeine and thebaine was readily interpreted in terms of the new formulae. The confirmation by synthesis followed after some years. The action of phenylmagnesium bromide on thebaine afforded a base termed phenyldihydrothebaine. This was investigated over a number of years by Lyndon Small and his colleagues at Bethesda, and on consideration of their results I propounded a theory on the nature of phenyldihydrothebaine which I thought of sufficient interest to present to the Royal Society as part of my Presidential Address (1947) [467]. The thebaine structure is transformed with formation of a large ring — the relation of the two molecules can be seen from the annexed structural formulae.

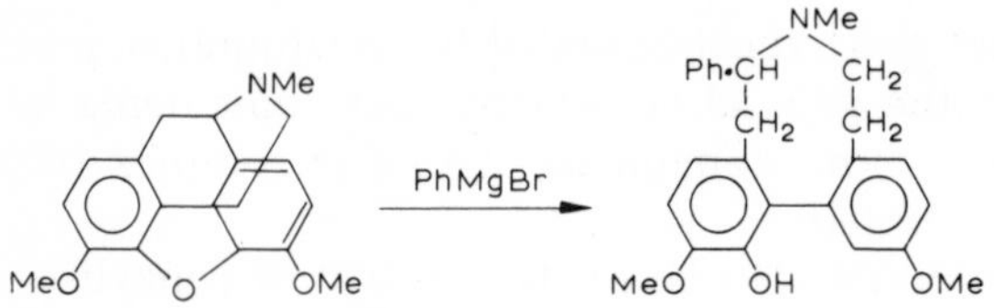

Following this theoretical exposition, experiments designed to confirm it were made in collaboration with K.W. Bentley [515,516]. The results were consistent with the hypothesis advanced.

The details of the biogenetic schemes applicable to the morphine group have been disclosed by experiments with radioactive tracers particularly by A.R. Battersby and D.H.R. Barton and their respective collaborators.

Apart from the alkaloids I had occasion to consider the structural relations of other groups and, because of interest in the flavanoids and anthocyanins, the idea of origin from a C_6—C_3—C_6 was developed, combined with the recognition of the molecular rearrangement which brings an aryl group from position-2 of a chroman ring to position-3, thus including the isoflavones. This scheme appeared to embrace all the known members of the group, i.e. the chalkones, orones, flavones and anthocyanins, as well as the reduced types such as the catechins, protoanthocyanidins, cyanomaclurin, and peltogynidin. There are many natural products based on C_6—C_3 and compounds like eudesmin contain C_6—C_3—C_3—C_6. Several suggestions can be made with regard to the structure of brazilin with the C_6—C_3—C_6 group but this question has not been studied experimentally. The various syntheses of brazilin derivatives do not provide acceptable evidence bearing on this matter. (See, however, page 183.)

Incidentally, an experiment made at Liverpool is perhaps worthy of mention. The joint action of acetic anhydride and potassium cyanide on formaldehyde in the presence of ether and water gives a good yield of acetoxyglycollonitrile, a substance which found many synthetic uses in which I was interested. It occurred to me to apply the benzoylbenzoin type of synthesis so as to obtain acetylglycollaldehyde. Accordingly, the nitrile was carefully treated with sodium ethoxide in alcohol, but the sole product was a good yield of α-acrose (*dl*-fructose). The isolated product was homogeneous and characterised only by conversion to *dl*-glucosazone. A few years ago (I write in 1974) I asked K. Aghoramurthy to repeat this experiment but unfortunately he obtained no satisfactory result. The matter was not pursued but if it were to be taken up again the starting point should be both benzoyl- and acetylglycollonitriles in parallel experiments, with attention to the temperature, concentration of sodium ethoxide, amount of sodium ethoxide, and rate of addition to the mixture.

A novel synthesis [45] of tetraphenylpyrrole was achieved in Liverpool by heating benzyl phenyl ketazine under gaseous hydrogen chloride; the yield was excellent and the process was interpreted as an *o,o*-benzidine type transformation of the related hydrazine derivative obtained by isomeric change. This experiment will be further discussed in Vol. II of these memoirs in connection with a Presidential Address which I delivered to the Chemical Society in 1941 [404].

The Structure of Harmine and Harmaline [48]

These were the first alkaloids to be recognised as members of the indole group. During the Sydney period I made no further progress in the investigation of harmine, but at Liverpool a lucky accident led me directly to the solution of the problem, as often happens. It was hard to believe afterwards that there could be any difficulty in reaching this result. Still it should be remembered that Otto Fischer had carried out a great deal of work on the transformation of harmine without realising what now seems obvious. The accident was that I was interested in a methylnaphthiminazole which has the empirical formula $C_{12}H_{10}N_2$. I looked it up in Richter's Lexicon. At the bottom of the bit on compounds under this heading I read a substance from tryptophan which had m.p. 237°. Otto Fischer's harman had a somewhat lower m.p., 230°, but I thought it worthwhile to follow this up, and found that the author of the paper on tryptophan was F.G.H. Hopkins. I wrote to Professor Hopkins and fortunately he was able to supply a specimen of his base from tryptophan. It was soon found to be identical with harman which I prepared from harmine. He had separated tryptophan from the hydrolysate of casein, and in parenthesis it may be remarked that he claims that the use of mercuric sulphate for the isolation of tryptophan was an inspiration which came he knew not whence, as it had apparently not been employed previously for a similar purpose. The base $C_{12}H_{10}N_2$ was produced by oxidising tryptophan with ferric chloride. The solution was shaken with ether and kept a few hours before it was worked up; undoubtedly the ether contained ethanol which afforded acetaldehyde, which condensed with the tryptophan and was further oxidised.

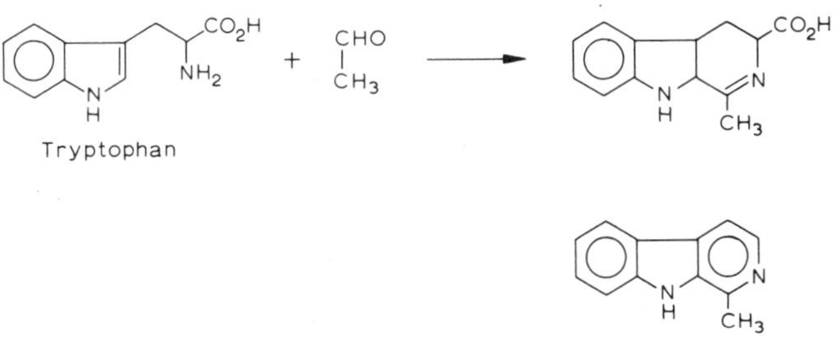

Tryptophan

Harman

This oxidation of tryptophan along with sources of acetaldehyde — for example alanine — is perhaps a model for the biogenesis of aribine, a plant alkaloid identical with harman.

It was thus shown for the first time that tryptophan can be the mother substance of plant alkaloids and the condensation necessary to produce a reduced pyridin ring, using the α-amino acid and the reactive 2-position of the indole nucleus, is closely analogous to the process needed to obtain isoquinoline derivatives from substituted β-phenylethylamines and aldehydes or their equivalent.

It is remarkable, however, that up to the present the analogy with the isoquinoline alkaloids applies only to the simpler second components. The indole alkaloids are now a large and growing group with very varied chemistry, knitted together by a common origin from tryptophan or one of its derivatives.

The synthesis of harmaline was carried out during my second Manchester period which is described on page 154.

Chapter VII

Huddersfield (1920–1921)

We then proceeded with great hopes to Huddersfield, where the chemical laboratories of British Dyes Ltd. were situated. This was an interesting experience and one that I was very glad to have had, but the temperaments of Herbert Levinstein and Sir Joseph Turner, joint Managing Directors of British Dyes Ltd., was so different as to lead to constant friction. They each confided in me their intention to stand on the other's neck. This situation was pretty well known and Sir Henry Birchenough (Chairman of the British Dyestuffs Corporation, a Government nominee) dismissed them both, with three years salary.

My personal assistant/collaborator in the laboratory was Wilfred Lawson, who had graduated at Liverpool. We carried out quite a number of experiments in the azo-dyes series, particularly those based on using creosol and aminocreosol as intermediates, but also worked on a new extension of the Friedländer synthesis (see page 120) and made a rather unconventional synthesis of apoharmine [70] which was published in collaboration with W.H. Perkin. The time spent at Huddersfield was very interesting and, I think, useful because of the insight which it gave me into various aspects of dyestuffs chemistry, but there was in existence a technical chemical laboratory to which the problems were first reported and we got only some crumbs from the diners table. The Director of this laboratory at Huddersfield was Dr. Segaller, who made a number of the known German dyestuffs and acquired considerable kudos thereby.

Then, again, the laboratory at Manchester was under the charge of Professor A.G. Green, F.R.S., and the Huddersfield contact with Manchester was not the closest that could be desired.

We acquired a house called Fairfield in Huddersfield. I mention this merely because when we wished to leave the town, we were visited as if by magic by an American who wanted to know if we would sell him Fairfield. It appeared that he had either been born there or spent very early years in the house and had a sentimental attachment to it. It took approximately two minutes to complete the sales agreement. A similar event occurred when I wished to leave my house in Hendon which was called Bramtoco. This name I had thought was of some American Indian chief, but actually it stands for British American Tobacco Company. When I was ready to leave Oxford, a purchaser for my house, 117 Banbury Road, stepped in — this time it was a Church Society who already occupied the house next door and wished to extend their premises.

The antagonism between Levinstein and Turner, together with some other aspects of a similar nature in the Huddersfield works, and the fact that I did not feel that the research laboratory at Huddersfield was being given a fair chance, led me to try to find a suitable return to university life. The opportunity occurred when James Irvine resigned from his University Chair at St. Andrews, to take up the post of Vice-Chancellor. I knew him very well and wrote to him and asked him whether it might be possible to succeed him at St. Andrews. He replied that this was indeed possible, but that I should need to put in an application in the usual way. This was arranged and done and I was appointed to the Chair of Chemistry in the University of St. Andrews.

It is, perhaps, worth recording that my daughter Marion was born in Huddersfield, and that she later went through a full medical course at Oxford, under the aegis of Lady Margaret Hall, and then took a diploma in tropical medicine at Liverpool, and one in child health at Newcastle. She then came back and told us that she was now ready to do what she wanted to do, which was to go to Africa as a medical missionary. This was hardly our idea of her future, but of course we put the best face on it we could although we were, as a matter of fact, somewhat disappointed. However, she made a very great success of this venture during eight years, and came back to England and married Bishop Mark Way, who was the bishop of the diocese at Masasi, Tanganyika. She continues to acquire fresh medical qualifications and is still practising medicine quite actively, and is now Administrator and Chief Medical Consultant of a hospital near Durham.

SCIENTIFIC WORK AT HUDDERSFIELD

I had a good scientific staff in the Huddersfield laboratory and Wilfred Lawson acted as my private assistant. We worked on the improvement of the preparation of the fundamental intermediates, such as the derivatives of aminoanthraquinone. We also prepared a number of new azo-dyes substantive to cotton, using new third components such as aminoquinol dimethyl ether, amino derivatives of creosol, etc. An interesting double Friedländer synthesis was developed, using diaminoveratrone. This condensed readily with β-diketones and such substances as ethyl acetoacetate, ethyl cyanoacetate and malonate to dibenzopyridopyridines, termed copyrines [70]. The yield was excellent and these substances are the most readily accessible of their type.

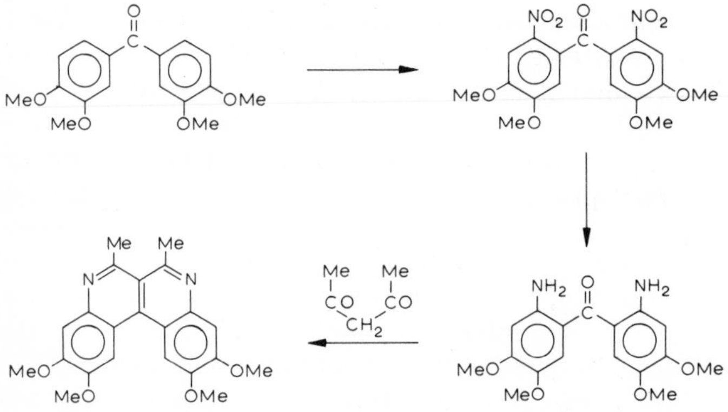

Tetramethoxydimethylcopyrine   Diaminoveratrone

Another tetracyclic base was obtained by condensing diaminoveratrone with bromoacetone in acetic acid solution; it was termed methyldiveratroharmyrine. This base was oxidised with chromic acid to a tetracarboxylic acid which was not isolated but decarboxylated with formation of apoharmine (methylharmyrine).

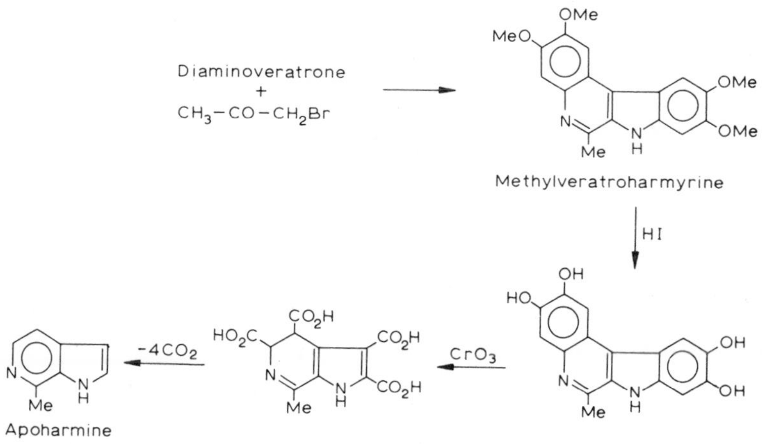

An analogous condensation of diaminoveratrone with ω-bromo-acetophenone proceeded in two stages.

6-Aminoveratrone was prepared at Huddersfield by the action of stannous chloride in concentrated hydrochloric acid on nitroveratrone, and the product had all the expected properties; for example, it could be diazotised and coupled to azo-compounds. A number of dyestuffs made in this way were examined — but none of them appeared worthy of further development.

Unfortunately the melting point of the aminoacetoveratrone was not recorded at Huddersfield, and the published description [70] was devised from further work at St. Andrews, where I prepared a specimen and crystallised it to constant melting point. J.C.E. Simpson pointed out (J. Chem. Soc. 1946, 94) that the product of the reaction as described in ref. 70 is 5,6-dimethoxy-3-methylanthranil and not the aminoketone. At Huddersfield we used considerable excess of stannous chloride and obtained the expected amine as the main product, but at St. Andrews I worked more carefully with something like the required amount of the reducing agent, and the recrystallised product was not the aminoketone but dimethoxyanthranil.

Chapter VIII

St. Andrews (1921–1922)

We found St. Andrews picturesque and fascinating from many points of view. It is an ideal site for a university and, in spite of the occasional biting east winds, we found life there extremely pleasant. Incidentally, it was a good base for exploration of the Highlands and we took full advantage of that fact. The Chemical Laboratory looks down on a tennis court and beyond to the cliffs and the North Sea.

It was during my stay at St. Andrews that I proposed the aromatic sextet of electrons. This was not a theory of bonding. The Kekulé formula was retained as the best representation of the linkage of valency electrons in the nucleus. It was rather a suggestion that 6 electrons form a stable group analogous to a stable group such as the octet. Thus methane has 8 electrons in the chemical bonds but also possesses a stability factor due to the octet. Naphthalene has 10 π-electrons and it is assumed that it contains one electron sextet together with a butadienoid group. However, these functions can be transposed with no change in the total energy of the system. In 1972 E. Clar wrote a monograph on the aromatic sextet in which he shows how the conception can be applied to polycyclic aromatic groups. I had already pointed out that the valency electrons on the pyridine nucleus are adequate for aromaticity without making any calls on the unshared electrons of the nitrogen atom. On the other hand in pyrrole a 6 electron group can only be obtained by using such unshared electrons. Hence pyridine, pyridinium salts, and pyrrole can be aromatic, but not the salts of pyrrole. This conception can obviously be extended to thiophene and furan, and in the former case the iso-electronic character of benzene and thiophene receives a natural explanation. This point has sometimes been overlooked by the critics of the theory.

Kekulé formulae for
benzene and pyridine

Formulae showing the
aromatic sextet

In the case of heterocyclic substances such as harmine or, more simply, iminazole there is scope for tautomerism, although the basic nitrogen can readily be identified in any one given structure. The basic nitrogen can further be identified by the fact that it is the site of alkylation, for example by the action of methyl iodide. When the non-basic nitrogen bears a hydrogen atom decomposition of the alkylated salt yields a base, termed "anhydronium base", in which the originally non-basic nitrogen becomes basic [53,92]. The production of anhydronium bases with transposition of the basic function is very generally applicable to heterocyclic nuclei of simple or quite complex constitution, provided one of the constituent rings is odd-membered.

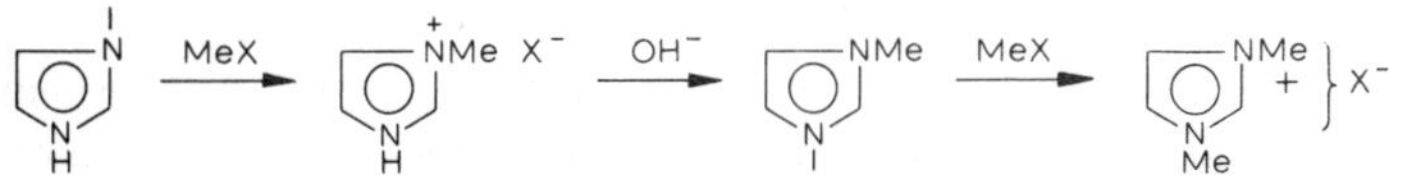

Iminazole   Anhydronium base

With J.M. Gulland [65,90] some experiments were made with the idea of supporting the new structure of the morphine group of alkaloids. It was noticed that according to the Knorr formula generally accepted at that time, one of the positions adjacent to the carbonyl group in dihydrothebainone is attached to the ethanamine side chain, whereas in the new formula this is not the case; hence the ketone mentioned in the new formulation should contain the group $-CH_2 \cdot CO \cdot CO_2-$. This we proved to be indeed the case since it was possible to prepare a dibenzylidene derivative of dihydrothebainone.

Dihydrothebainone

Knorr formula   Revised formula
(Gulland and R.R., loc. cit.)

I had conceived in Manchester a project for the synthesis of 3-

hydroxyflavylium salts, and this was successfully attacked in St. Andrews by Pratt [58,62,63,66,67,79]. The necessary intermediates are acetophenones substituted by MeO—, both in the nucleus and in the methyl group. Various methods were employed to produce these substances and one of these is illustrated below:

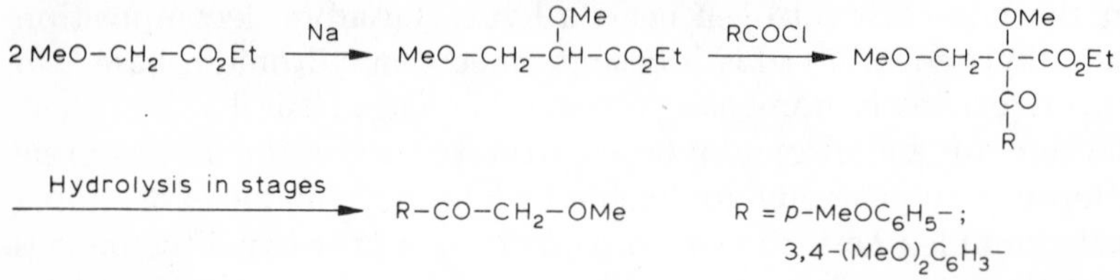

$$2\,MeO-CH_2-CO_2Et \xrightarrow{Na} MeO-CH_2-\overset{\overset{\displaystyle OMe}{|}}{C}H-CO_2Et \xrightarrow{RCOCl} MeO-CH_2-\overset{\overset{\displaystyle OMe}{|}}{\underset{\underset{\displaystyle R}{\underset{|}{CO}}}{C}}-CO_2Et$$

$$\xrightarrow{\text{Hydrolysis in stages}} R-CO-CH_2-OMe \qquad R = p\text{-}MeOC_6H_5-\,;$$
$$3,4\text{-}(MeO)_2C_6H_3-$$

Condensation of the appropriate intermediate with a protected phloroglucinaldehyde, with the help of hydrogen chloride, afforded the desired 3-MeO-substituted flavylium salts which could be demethylated by means of hydriodic acid. In this way the typical anthocyanidins were synthesised. Additionally a variety of other methods were used to produce the necessary intermediates.

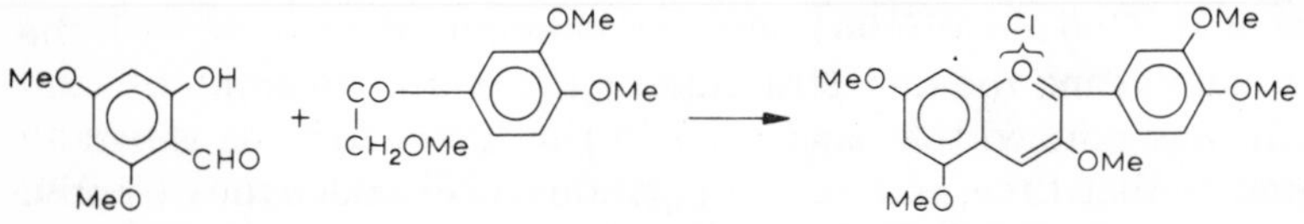

O-Pentamethylcyanidin chloride

By the action of alcoholic sodium ethoxide on benzoylmandelonitrile benzoylbenzoin is produced. Guided by Lapworth's theory of the benzoin synthesis, we wished to use this reaction as a means of preparing mixed benzoins. The experiment proceeded as expected though the yield was only moderate. However, we soon had evidence that the benzoyl group migrated during the process. The paper in which the results were described was the last in which the polarised valencies were used to indicate the course of a reaction — and the migration appears much more natural in the electronic translation which, however, was never published.

SOME NOTES ON THE BRITISH SCHOOL OF CARBOHYDRATE CHEMISTRY

My tangential contacts with prime movers in the British School of Carbohydrate Chemistry began in early days in Manchester with

Walter Norman Haworth who, one recognises now, showed early the qualities that brought him later fame. Then after I left Huddersfield and went to St. Andrews I was in the thick of it. James Irvine was the undisputed leader in the field and carried on the programme first contemplated by his teacher Thomas Purdie.

James Colquhoun Irvine, F.R.S. (1877—1952)

The impetus to a novel mode of investigation of the structure of carbohydrates was first given by Thomas Purdie, who became Professor of Chemistry at the University of St. Andrews in 1884. He discovered that aliphatic hydroxyl groups could be methylated by the joint action of silver oxide and methyl iodide. This mixture became known as the Purdie reagent and has played a most important part in the development of molecular structural studies in the carbohydrates, from the monosides to the complex types of high molecular weight.

Irvine joined Purdie in 1895, having previously worked at the University of Glasgow. Even during his early period at St. Andrews he carried out some work using Purdie's reagent, but he interrupted this first contact with St. Andrews and gained an 1851 Exhibition Scholarship in order to study at the University of Leipzig, where he wrote a thesis on the subject of o-methoxybenzaldehydes (1901). After completing his Ph.D. he returned to St. Andrews to take up a junior lectureship in the department of Purdie. It should be mentioned here that Professor John Read, in his memorial notice of Irvine, attributes the discovery of the Purdie reagent to junior workers. However this may be, I feel that Purdie provided suggestions and encouragement and, moreover, the later development was shared in the first stages by Purdie and Irvine. It is indeed probable that the idea of methylating simple sugar hemi-acetals, such as the methylglucosides, occurred, in the first instance, to Irvine. Professor John Read wrote in his obituary notice (J. Chem. Soc. 1954, 476): "A short note left by Irvine on this matter of considerable historical importance in organic chemistry runs as follows:

'My interest in the sugars was aroused through a special course of lectures given by Professor Hans Stoll, who used in illustration Emil Fischer's original specimens. The idea occurred to me that the constitution of disaccharides and other compound carbohydrates might be solved by methylation, and these suggestions were communicated to

Purdie in written memoranda. His advice was to complete my German degree and then return to St. Andrews (at his own personal cost) to test these ideas. Within a year I had isolated trimethyl- and tetramethyl-glucose — the first methylated sugars — and this was the beginning of a very fruitful line of work which has had a profound effect on our knowledge of carbohydrates. Many collaborators were attracted to take part in this work, among them Professor Sir W.N. Haworth, who for a number of years was a lecturer in my Department, and Professor E.L. Hirst, who was an undergraduate and later a research student in St. Andrews; also Dr. W.S. Denham, the first to methylate cellulose and to describe 2,3,6-trimethylglucose.' "

Purdie recognised at once the great importance of Irvine's suggestion and provided not only all the available manpower, but made arrangements for a new institute for chemical research.

In 1909 Irvine succeeded Purdie as Professor of Chemistry; he was knighted in 1925 and became a K.B.E. in 1948. Amongst the many chemical honours he received were the Longstaff, Davy and Willard Gibbs medals.

Irvine must be recognised as a real pioneer and one of the most important founders of the British School of Carbohydrate Chemistry. He was, however, seriously handicapped by an incorrect idea of the structure of the simple methylmonosides, and he made some mistakes which were later magnified to his disadvantage, so that his original real contribution was unjustly depreciated. The bad relations existing between Irvine and W.N. Haworth became notorious, and I remember very well a dinner at the Athenaeum Club, which was organised by N.V. Sidgwick and other well-wishers of both, with the idea of bringing this distressing state of affairs to an end. After dinner Irvine spoke first. He adopted a most conciliatory tone and acknowledged in gracious terms the very great contribution to sugar chemistry, by W.N. Haworth. Haworth replied with his thumbs in his vest pocket and spoke of a clash of temperaments. He did not really budge an inch. Afterwards, E.F. Armstrong said that he supposed we had temporarily buried the hatchet, but the haft was showing above ground and could be grasped at any convenient moment.

The story of the British School of Carbohydrate Chemistry is continued in sections below, devoted to biographical notes on Sir Edmund Hirst and Sir Walter Haworth.

In 1921 Irvine retired from his Chair of Chemistry to become

Vice-Chancellor of the University of St. Andrews. I was, at that time, Director of Research at the Huddersfield branch of British Dyes Limited, later the British Dyestuffs Corporation, but it was a very uncomfortable position for various reasons already mentioned. As I found myself with so little scope for useful research I decided to return to academic life, and wrote to Irvine and asked him whether I might possibly succeed him at St. Andrews. His reply was very favourable, and I took up the appointment as Professor in the University in October 1921.

I worked in the private laboratory also occupied partly by Dr. Catherine Steele, a colleague of Irvine's who kept alive some of his work on the sugars, but this petered out on account of the onerous duties of the Vice-Chancellor and, above all, because the chase was taken up by W.N. Haworth and E.L. Hirst. During this period there was also the Rectorship of J.M. Barrie, who delivered his famous address on "Courage". He enlivened the occasion by other quips; for example he described a cricket match in which he had taken part, and said that in the first innings, when batting, he had managed to make one run, but in the second innings he was not so fortunate. He told us that he had been invited to speak to 300 odd "bejants" and had not felt himself called upon to make a speech to 300 college girls. However, if it could be arranged he was quite prepared to make 300 separate speeches. There was a real galaxy of stars on the occasion of Barrie's Rectorial Address. The honorary graduands included Ellen Terry, Earl Haig and John Galsworthy, *inter alia.*

There was another matter which fell under my observation and that was that the important change from 5 rings to 6 rings was due, in the first instance, not to Haworth, but to Edmund Hirst. I remember remarking at St. Andrews that it was strange that all the stable sugars were regarded as having 5-rings, and that the 6-ring theory seemed equally applicable, but that was in very early days and I thought no notice was taken of the suggestion. Later I found that Hirst did indeed remember this suggestion (see below). The main point is that Hirst, by applying the Purdie/Irvine method to the aldopentoses, showed that they afforded methyl ethers which can be proved to be 6-ring heterocycles. This is, of course, a simple matter; the fully methylated pentose is oxidised to a trimethoxyglutaric acid from which the 6-ring structure follows immediately. A paper on this question was published and Hirst had already carried out experiments which showed that the theory applied to glucose also. Then he was approached by Haworth who suggested that the work on glucose might be done jointly because he, Haworth, had also evidence of the 6-ring character of the two main glucose isomerides, namely α- and β-methylglucosides. This collaboration became a close one and Hirst went to Birmingham, where he proved the most loyal and effective colleague, carrying out not only work at his own bench, but also supervising that of many others in the laboratory. It was Hirst too, who was responsible for the introduction of physical methods of analysis of the sugar derivatives. All the time Haworth, however, remained in control, had a large school of his own, independent of those who were alloted to Hirst, and carried out very important researches which gradually submerged, by their mass, the earlier work of Irvine and his collaborators.

At this stage I would just like to interpolate that I am speaking of the British School of Carbohydrate Chemistry, and I by no means wish to imply that this was the only place in which advances were made. The American chemist C.S. Hudson also played a great part in the clearing up of the structural system of the carbohydrates.

Edmund Langley Hirst, F.R.S.

E.L. Hirst was born at Preston in 1898; a few years later the family moved to St. Andrews. Edmund entered the University in 1914 and before the end of his first session he volunteered to take part in the work which Professor Irvine was organising in the laboratory to help the war effort. The topics which he attacked, including some work on mustard gas, proved of so much interest that Hirst decided that organic chemistry was the subject he would prefer to follow in the future. After serving with the Royal Engineers in France, he returned to St. Andrews where he joined W.N. Haworth's research group in 1919, and studied the structure of cellobiose. Very soon, however, Haworth took up a post at Newcastle, and Hirst then joined Irvine in the work on 2,3,6-trimethylglucose. At this stage I began to wonder how far I could trust the dogma — for it had become a dogma — that stable sugar rings must be 5-membered, by analogy with lactones which are undoubtedly the most stable of their class. I had asked Sir Edmund whether he recalled that in the course of a conversation I had considered this dubiety and wondered whether the sugars could not also be 6-membered rings. In a letter which Sir Edmund

E.L. Hirst.

Hirst wrote to me in November 1969, he said "I remember very well the conversation you mentioned about ring structures and have referred to it on many occasions, both public and private. It was at that point that I decided to look for a method to decide ring structures which would have the force and validity of proof in the aromatic group, which you held up to me as an example. The method adopted came as the result of a lucky observation. Usually, dilute nitric acid (hot) results in a general decomposition of carbohydrate material, but on one occasion I happened to use strong nitric acid in cleaning a flask containing some methylated sugar residues. To my surprise an easily controllable gentle reaction took place. It seemed possible, therefore, that nitric acid oxidation of a fully methylated hexose or pentose might provide a proof of ring size; for example from tetramethylglucose, production of trimethoxyglutaric acid on oxidation would give unequivocal proof of a 6-membered ring, but isolation of dimethoxysuccinic acid would not rule out a 6-membered ring, because the oxidation could conceivably break the carbon chain on either side, or both, of the unmethylated —CHOH— groups in the aldonic acid first formed. For this reason I chose a methylated pentose to start with, as a simple case for showing that the stable methylhexosides had a 6-membered ring — so far as I know, the first proof of such an occurrence. Other sugars followed, including glucose. Here the oxidation went both ways, as was originally considered likely, and we were faced with the separation of dimethoxysuccinamide and trimethoxyglutaramide (the amides, being crystalline, were convenient substances to work with). I do not know whether you remember a discussion I had with you as to why the solutions of trimethoxyglutaramide in methanol turned violet on standing, whereas the succinamides did not? This could almost be used as a colour test for the presence of the glutaric derivatives. You immediately referred me to a paper of Thorpe's, of several years previously. I have often used this in arguments with the modern teachers who claim to despise facts of memory!"

I certainly do not want to exaggerate the importance of this incident, since my contribution was nothing but an idea, thrown out in conversation. However, I took a great interest in the subsequent developments and I wish to say, here and now, that I am quite sure that Edmund Hirst was the real pioneer whose work led to the establishment of the presently accepted ring structures of the carbohydrates. It is certain that, using the methods which were so convincing in the case of the aldopentoses, he could have covered the whole field of the methylmonosides and, in fact, he was well on the way with the methylglucosides when W.N. Haworth proposed collaboration, as already mentioned. Hirst was well aware of Haworth's great capacity for organisation of research, and he no doubt felt that this drive would be invaluable in the general interest of progress.This action was most unselfish, but it was a sign of strength rather than of weakness in view of the fact that he saw that the ground would be covered more quickly by the collaboration with Haworth, than by his lone efforts. The outcome was that after a year spent as a Lecturer in the University of Manchester, where I was Professor of Organic Chemistry, he joined W.N. Haworth at University College, Newcastle-on-Tyne, and later at Birmingham University. He occupied an independent Chair at Bristol in 1936, and in 1947 he became Professor of Organic Chemistry at Edinburgh. During the greater part of his time at Newcastle and Birmingham, at Haworth's laboratory, I acted as external examiner for many Ph.D. theses and was able to appreciate the large share which Hirst took in the supervision of research. He was instrumental in the introduction of physical methods, such as U.V. spectroscopy and chromatography, and took a major part in the exciting work on the structure and synthesis of ascorbic acid (Vitamin C). When he left for his independent Chair at Bristol, he made a tacit agreement with Haworth that he would be concerned with plant polysaccharides, while the Birmingham group would continue to concentrate on carbohydrates of animal origin, without overlap. In the letter of November 1969, Hirst, with characteristic generosity, pays warm tribute to J.C. Irvine and W.N. Haworth, and says that he always regretted that it did not prove possible to heal the breach between these two men, each of whom made essential contributions to the British School of Carbohydrate Chemistry.

Apart from his purely chemical activities, Hirst's main interests were in agricultural chemistry and technology, and in university organisation. In these connections he served on many public bodies; he was knighted in 1964. He received the Davy Medal and the Royal Medal.

Walter Norman Haworth, F.R.S. (1883—1950)

I was a year senior to Haworth at the Chemical School at the University of Manchester, but on the other hand, he was three years senior to me in age. This was accounted for by the fact that he had some experience in a linoleum factory, of which his father was manager. The decision to attempt the University Entrance Examination

W.N. Howarth.

was his own, and was taken in the face of family disapproval. He overcame this hurdle in 1903 and this was no mean feat, under the circumstances. He was accepted as a research student by W.H. Perkin, jun., and was also given an appointment as private assistant to the Professor. I recall clearly his work on condensation of cyclohexanone and methylcyclohexanone with cyanacetic ester in alcoholic solution containing sodium ethoxide. This was important in connection with the work which Perkin was doing, with W.J. Pope and O. Wallach, on the preparation of substances capable of enantiomorphism, but which do not contain the conventional asymmetric carbon atom. After three years with Perkin he went to work with Wallach at Göttingen, having been awarded an 1851 Fellowship. He gained the doctorate after only one year and returned to Manchester and continued working on problems of the terpene group. In 1911 he received the D.Sc. degree and took up an appointment as Senior Demonstrator under Sir Edward Thorpe at Imperial College. In 1912 he was appointed to a Lectureship (later Readership) at the University of St. Andrews. This was a turning point in his career, since he came into contact with the researches of Purdie and Irvine on carbohydrate chemistry. It was during this period that he introduced the methylation of certain hydroxyl groups in the sugars, by means of methyl sulphate and alkali. From 1914—1919 academic work at St. Andrews was interrupted in favour of fine chemicals, required for the war effort. E.L. Hirst wrote as follows: "Haworth took a notable part in this and by force of personality and skilful distribution of tasks he succeeded in obtaining regular yields of the precious materials from teams of workers, many of whom had never previously seen a test tube. Here, as in later years, Haworth's presence in the laboratory — calm, confident, somewhat austere, outwardly imperturbable as he made a round of visits to the individual workers — unmistakably inspired the feeling that the particular problem in hand not only must, but could and would be solved ."

In 1920 he became Professor of Organic Chemistry at Armstrong College, Newcastle-upon-Tyne, later renamed King's College. This was a constituent college of the University of Durham. Here, with the help of his assistant Stanley Peat, and later with E.L. Hirst, he attacked energetically problems of carbohydrate structure, especially those of the simple glucosides and disaccharides, in the first instance, maltose. After Hirst had shown that the stable methylpentosides are 6-ring compounds, Haworth suggested a joint attack on the structure of glucose. He had already some reason to suppose that the stable glucosides might be 6-ring compounds from considerations based on the physical properties of corresponding lactones, but he had no clear-cut evidence from degradation, such as was already in the possession of Hirst. The proof that the stable monosides are 6-rings was first given by Hirst, but Haworth generalised the conception and suggested the very appropriate pyranose/furanose nomenclature and emphasised more generally the contrast between the lactones and the hemi-acetals. The 5-ring γ-lactones are more resistant to hydrolysis than the isomeric δ-lactones whereas the furanosides are more readily hydrolysed than the pyranosides. Instead of referring to the one process of hydrolysis, one can say generally, more stable and less stable in the respective cases. It should, however, be clearly pointed out that the strong direction in this was provided by Haworth, and all his colleagues acknowledge this, yet the work itself was that of a school, and in the first stages Hirst and Peat were the principal collaborators. Much later a most valuable summary was published by Haworth in the form of a small book called *The Sugars*, in which he sets out very clearly the new system of 6-rings and 5-rings; the former were called pyranoses, and the latter furanoses. I think this is another example of the importance of apt names, since this system of nomenclature caught on and served to emphasise the origin of the new progress that had been made.

In 1925 Haworth became Professor of Chemistry at the University of Birmingham, in succession to Gilbert Morgan. This involved Hirst and Peat, and a strong contingent of research students joined Haworth in Birmingham, and the fundamental work on simple sugars, oligosaccharides, and polysaccharides accelerated. It is not necessary to describe the work in detail, but the claim may be made that the work of the British School of Carbohydrate Chemists systematised molecular structures of the sugars and of their chief derivatives in a manner which has afforded a satisfactory basis for all subsequent work.

Haworth's only outdoor hobby was gardening; he travelled fairly extensively, especially in Europe, Australia and New Zealand. He became F.R.S. in 1928, received the Longstaff Medal of the Chemical Society, jointly with Sir James Irvine, in 1933, the Davy Medal in 1934, and the Royal Medal in 1942. In 1937 he shared the Nobel Prize for Chemistry with P. Karrer, and in 1947 he was made Knight Bachelor. He married Violet, daugther of the late Sir James Dobbie, an eminent physical chemist.

Stanley Peat, F.R.S. (1902—1969)

If, in Colonel Haworth's regiment, Hirst was a captain, Stanley Peat entered and functioned as a subaltern ("I do all the work", said the subaltern). In fact, when he was an undergraduate at Armstrong College, and took his degree with First Class Honours in Chemistry in 1924, almost at once he was appointed assistant to Haworth and worked enthusiastically on various of the early fundamental topics, such as the structure of maltose. It was recorded of him that not infrequently he worked twelve hours a day in the laboratory. After his transfer to Birmingham, he continued to work with Haworth and Hirst, and gradually assumed a more independent role with junior collaborators of his own. He followed G.D. Hughes as Professor of Chemistry at the University of Bangor, Wales in 1948; in that year he also became F.R.S. In 1949 the first paper published with W.J. Whelan appeared, and this was concerned with enzymes of the soya bean — other papers on the enzymes and saccharides, of various kinds (for example laminaria and lichenins), came in a constant stream from the laboratory until 1962. With other collaborators, especially J.R. Turney, he continued to enrich the literature until 1968, only a year before his death. Peat's contribution to carbohydrate chemistry was a varied one. In Newcastle and Birmingham he was closely involved in the work of Haworth and Hirst, and his later independent work as a senior collaborator was largely concerned with the structure of polysaccharides, especially the starches, and with the enzyme chemistry and physical chemistry associated with the problems encountered in their investigation. He certainly made a major contribution to the idea of the full coverage of the field, the fulfilment of which was Haworth's ambition. It may be added here that in 1936 Haworth made Peat responsible for direction of the work on plant polysaccharides and aminosugars. Similarly, Maurice Stacey would direct the work on polysaccharides of micro-organisms and Fred Smith the work on plant gums. This is a paraphrase of a statement made by E.L. Hirst: such an arrangement was not likely to possess good lasting qualities, but it doubtless had its temporary uses.

The premature death of Stanley Peat, from a heart attack, occurred tragically just before two separate arrangements had been made to do him honour. The first was a Volume of Carbohydrate Researches in which he was either the senior collaborator, or the prime mover in bringing about the investigations described. With unusual generosity he withheld his name from at least 50% of the papers and articles based on his original suggestions. Also, the Carbohydrate Discussion Group of the Chemical Society had arranged to hold a meeting of the group in Bangor, in April, in his honour. This again had to become a memorial meeting.

Maurice Stacey, F.R.S. (b.1907)

Maurice Stacey graduated from Birmingham in 1929 and joined the Carbohydrate School when Haworth and Hirst were most active. His first researches were concerned with the synthesis and structure of the higher sugars. He then played a major part in experiments on the synthesis of ascorbic acid and was in fact the senior bench worker engaged on this topic. He carried out much of the analytical work for the structural studies and he executed all the key practical work for the Haworth/Hirst synthesis of ascorbic acid and analogues. He was awarded the Meldola Medal in 1933 for this first synthesis of a vitamin.

Later, he carried out work for I.C.I. on the chemistry of hydrocellulose. From 1929 onwards he had worked for short periods in Raistrick's Laboratory studying the preparation and structure of mould polysaccharides, which were found to be of novel types. After 1933, having been awarded a Beit Fellowship, he continued to work at the London School of Tropical Medicine and turned his attention to bacterial polysaccharides which are important constituents of immunising vaccines in the typhoid series.

In 1936 he took up a lectureship at Birmingham, vacated by Hirst, who had gone to a professorship at Bristol University. Later he succeeded Haworth as Professor of Organic Chemistry in the University of Birmingham. Haworth sent him on a Visiting Fellowship to Michael Heidelberger's Laboratory at Columbia University, New York, where he spent most of 1937 studying the immuno-polysaccharides of the *pneumococcus* and *streptococcus*. On return, he formed a team to work on polysaccharides synthesised by microorganisms.

The Birmingham Carbohydrate School was highly productive until, in 1940, the whole Department was turned over to the study of uranium and its compounds, particularly uranium hexafluoride.

Stacey was able to continue some work on the polyglucose dextran, produced by a *leuconostoc* bacterium. This, with various colleagues and support by the Medical Research Council, he developed as a blood plasma substitute. Parallel work on this was independently carried out by Ingleman and colleagues in Sweden. For this work Stacey was awarded the Grand Award (shared with C.S. Hudson) of the U.S. Academy of Sciences, and later the John Scott Award from the City of Philadelpia.

In 1945 it was possible to resume some carbohydrate studies. In addition to his main work on polysaccharides of micro-organisms Stacey carried out fundamental studies on the chemistry of the surface components of micro-organisms, and this led him to the discovery that the Gram complex in Gram positives is a ribonucleoprotein, and this in turn led to work on the chemistry of deoxysugars and to the chemistry of nucleic acids, on which over one hundred papers have now appeared from his Department. He also embarked on the highly complex field of investigation of nitrogen-containing sugars present as glycoproteins in tissues of all kinds, such as the chondroitins of cartilage, hyaluronic acid of joint fluids, heparin, the blood anticoagulant, blood group factors, and so on.

He made the first synthesis of cellobiose and of D-glucuronic acid and the first constitutional synthesis of chondrosamine (galactosamine). He discovered the sugar L-fucose as a constituent of the blood-group factors and this has revolutionised studies in this complex field. More recently, he has published many papers on the carbohydrate constituents of antibiotics and on fluorine containing sugars.

Alongside his work on sugars he founded a sub-department for studies on fluorocarbon synthesis using gaseous fluorine. Over 2,000 new compounds, straight and branched chain, alicyclic, heterocyclic, aromatic and fused ring systems, have been synthesised and studied and some 200 papers (many with Professor J.C. Tatlow) have been published. He introduced the use of trifluoroacetic anhydride as an acylating and ring closing agent — often described as the Stacey reaction.

Fred Smith (1915—1965)

After graduating at Birmingham University, Smith joined a team working on ascorbic acid and was particularly involved in the extension to analogues. His first major work was on the molecular structure of gum arabic. He had time to extend these studies to other plant gums before he joined in the war work of the department on uranium compounds.

In 1943—1947 he joined the teams at Oak Ridge Atomic Station, U.S.A. After a brief visit to Birmingham, Smith became Professor of Biochemistry in the University of Minnesota, where he worked on plant gums and mucilages to such good effect that a monograph on the subject was published in collaboration with Professor R. Montgomery, also of Birmingham (Rheinhold). Smith thus carried the banner of the British School of Carbohydrate Chemistry into the U.S.A., and it should be added here that many students of Haworth, Hirst and Stacey have occupied Chairs of Chemistry and Biochemistry in different parts of the world. Smith's premature death was a grievous loss to science, as he was undoubtedly one of the most active exponents of the methods contemplated by Purdie and Irvine, and developed by Haworth and Hirst.

C.E.H. Bawn, F.R.S. (b. 1907)

Professor Bawn made contact with the British School of Carbohydrate Chemistry when at Bristol, and at a time when E.L. Hirst became Professor of Organic Chemistry. At the outbreak of war, J.K.N. Jones and G.T. Young and others became members of a team carrying out research on explosives and propellants. One of their first tasks was to investigate the synthesis and nitration of pentaerythritol, and throughout the war they worked together on all kinds of explosives and problems arising in the munitions plants of the South West and South Wales. They also worked on nitrocellulose and cordite and thus the ruling instinct for carbohydrate research found a little scope. Later, this was given full play in the study of relations in the structure of polysaccharides and starch and cellulose, and their physical and chemical properties. A joint paper with Hirst and G.T. Young deals with the problem of the nature of the bonds in starch. Established in his Chair of Physical Chemistry at Liverpool, Bawn became one of the foremost workers in the polymer field in this country, his interest being in the mechanism of the processes involved. I have a lively recollection of a most interesting discussion with him in his laboratory at Liverpool, on the mechanism and the formation of normal hydrocarbon chains by polymerisation of diazomethane with the help of a variety of catalysts such as boron trifluoride. The mechanism proposed bore a striking resemblance to one I myself had proposed in the case of the Ziegler polymerisation [565].

J.K.N. Jones, F.R.S. (b. 1912)

Professor Jones was a member of the team attacking the structure and synthesis of ascorbic acid and its analogues, and had a broad experience of the work at Birmingham. He accompanied Hirst to Bristol and later to Manchester.

In 1952 he was appointed to a Chair at the University of Kingston, Ontario, and devoted his efforts to the study of plant gums, a natural extension of his collaboration with Fred Smith.

E.J. Bourne (1922—1974)

From the time of his entry as an undergraduate in 1939 to his appointment as Professor of Organic Chemistry at the Royal Holloway College in 1956, Bourne worked in the Organic Chemistry Department at the University of Birmingham. His research (D.Sc. 1952) was oriented towards the study of physical aspects of the chemistry of the polysaccharides. The physicochemical methods developed for the study of carbohydrates included infra-red, nuclear magnetic resonance and mass spectrometry. In collaboration with S.G. Peat he studied the fractionation of starches, made structural studies of the fractions and examined their enzymic synthesis and degradation. In these and similar connections he developed the chromatographic processes applicable to the material under examination; he also used electrophoretic techniques. These methods were applied in particular to the structures of dextran and to the study of enzymic synthesis of various polysaccharides. Incidentally, much attention was paid to heterocyclic derivatives of the carbohydrates and related cyclitols. The contributions of Bourne, over a wide field, were highly significant and greatly increased the degree of precision in our knowledge of important regions of biochemistry.

From the original impetus given at St. Andrews, the wave of progress in carbohydrate research expanded in many directions quite unforeseen by the pioneers. They deserved to be honoured for the sound foundation they gave to carbohydrate chemistry in so many regions of biochemistry; certainly not the least important of these is that which includes the nucleic acids.

CHAPTER IX

Manchester – Second Period (1922–1928)

I returned to my first *Alma Mater* in 1922, and here follows a se-lective account of the work undertaken during the period of my tenure of the Chair of Organic Chemistry (1922—1928), together with short notes on some of my collaborators and other scientists, whose names are prominently connected with the fields of inves-tigation studied.

SYNTHESIS OF ANTHOCYANIDINS AND ANTHOCYANINS

Alexander Robertson (1896—1970)

Robertson came to work with me in 1924, having been awarded a Rockefeller International Fellowship (also a Ramsay Memorial Fel-lowship, which he resigned). Apart from a six months period, which he spent at the University of Graz under Professor Pregl, he became a lecturer in the Department of Organic Chemistry in 1926, and re-mained in Manchester until 1928, when he became Reader in Chem-istry at the Queen Mary College at the University of London.

Robertson worked on the bench vacated by Perkin when the latter left Manchester for Oxford. I was in the early days of my second period in Manchester and found the Professor had been promoted to a fine private room in the new Morley Laboratories.

At St. Andrews D.D. Pratt had been my chief collaborator in de-veloping the synthesis of the anthocyanidins. We were now ambitious to improve the methods so that we could extend the synthesis to the glycosides of the anthocyanidins, that is, anthocyanins themselves. It was necessary to do two things — in the first place to find the best kind of protection by acyl groups which would allow the synthesis to proceed, and secondly to find conditions which would allow a satis-factory synthesis with a glycoside component. An early study by Robertson showed that this latter consideration could be satisfied in the case of the synthesis of a flavylium salt — a glycoside not related to the anthocyanins. The first mentioned requirement was met by the use of 2-O-benzoylphloroglucinaldehyde. This highly successful method is further mentioned on p. 142. In all the work on the synthesis of anthocyanins hydroxyl groups either were unprotected or protected by acylation, and subsequently the acylated flavylium glycoside was hydrolysed by alkali, and acidification reconstituted the flavylium salt glycoside free of acyl groups. The problems in particular cases were largely confined to the preparation of the requisite substituted acetophenones, and Robertson completed the synthesis of callistephin and, with K. Murakami [186], that of chrysanthemin. In 1930 he became Reader in Biochemistry at the London School of Hygiene and Tropical Medicine, where he entered into active collaboration with Professor Harold Raistrick when he studied fungal metabolites. Among the subjects which he was able to advance, at that time, was the chemistry of citromycetin. In 1933 he succeeded Heilbron as Heath Harrison Professor of Organic Chemistry at Liverpool. There, he continued to develop his earlier work on natural glycosides, but acquired a new interest in the chemistry of rottlerone and similar substances attractive to the chemist on account of their complex transformation, and to the agricultural technologist by reason of their pronounced insecticidal properties. He was elected F.R.S. in 1941 and awarded the Davy Medal in 1952. The citation in the latter case approved his far-reaching work on the chemistry of natural products, with particular reference to rottlerone and similar substances. Robertson retired from his University Chair in 1957 and devoted the whole of his energies to farming. It was the occupation of his father who had left him some 500 acres in Aberdeenshire. This was expanded into 1,100 acres in Aberdeenshire and Banffshire, but later, when he transferred his interests to Lincolnshire, this became 6,000 acres. He retired to Roxholme Grange and shortly afterwards he suffered a grievous loss in the death of his wife, and more and more he relinquished his agricultural interests to his son. Robertson was a most skilful experimenter and made many important personal contributions to collaborative research. He was an excellent teacher and lecturer. When I first heard that he had retired from his Professorship, I was rather astonished and tried to find some fault in our academic and chemical world, which had led him to this course of action. Later I realised that this was quite unnecessary, but that the farming instinct, passed on to him by his parent, could also be a compulsive factor in his life. He was, in fact, a most enthusiastic chemist, convinced of the rightness of research and the duty to pursue it, taking the greatest pleasure in the chase, but he also felt he had a mission to apply his chemical knowledge to the improvement of farming. As time went on and his record of chemical research had reached a stage at which no really outstanding developments could be expected with any confidence, it was natural that the farmer complex should take control and, looking back, one feels that he did the right thing, in all the circumstances. It was such a pity that his premature decease prevented him from taking full advantage of his wise decision. (Cf. also R.N. Haworth and W.B. Whalley in *Memoirs of Fellows of the Royal Society*, Vol.17, November 1971.)

Discovery of the Value of 2-O-Benzoylphloroglucinaldehyde as a Component in Flavylium Salt Synthesis

The desirability of minimum protection of phloroglucinaldehyde in anthocyanidin synthesis was quite early indicated by the fact that β-resorcylaldehyde could be successfully used as an intermediate, whereas phloroglucinaldehyde could not. The latter substance undergoes self-condensation much too readily under the conditions of the experiment. For some time O-triacetylphloroglucinaldehyde was employed, but the yields were poor. We were led to try the Schotten-Baumann benzoylation of phloroglucinaldehyde even although it seemed unlikely to succeed, seeing that β-resorcylaldehyde is monobenzoylated to the 4-O-benzoyl derivative. To our surprise monobenzoylation of phloroglucinaldehyde attacks the hydroxyl in the 2-position, as proved by the transformations shown below.

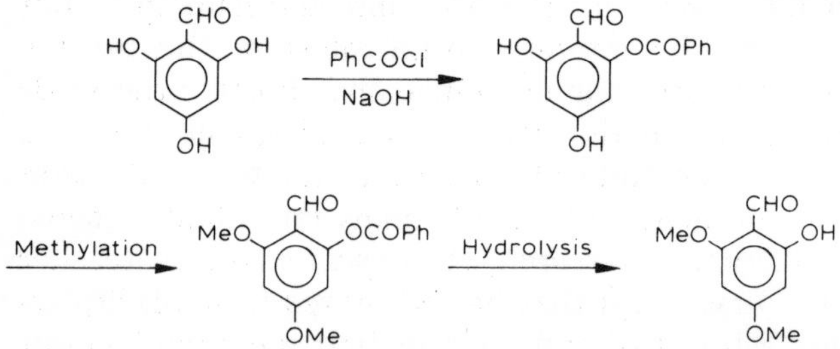

The product is a dimethoxysalicylaldehyde and as such condensed very readily with derivatives of acetophenone and hydrogen chloride to flavylium chloride derivatives. The use of 2-O-benzoylphloroglucinaldehyde in the synthesis of anthocyanidins and anthocyanins is frequently mentioned in the sequel.

The first natural anthocyanin to be synthesized was callistephin (chloride) [159], isolated by Willstätter from a species of aster, and later identified as the anthocyanin of the scarlet carnation [199]. The components for the synthesis were 2-O-benzoylphloroglucinaldehyde (I) and ω-(tetraacetyl-β-glucosidoxy)-4-acetoxyacetophenone (II). The preparation of the latter substance proceeded according to the annexed scheme.

$$\mathrm{HO{-}C_6H_4{-}CO{-}CH_2Cl \xrightarrow{\text{Stages}} AcO{-}C_6H_4{-}CO{-}CH_2OAc \xrightarrow{\text{NaOH}} NaO{-}C_6H_4{-}CO{-}CH_2OH}$$

$$\mathrm{\xrightarrow{Ac_2O} AcO{-}C_6H_4{-}CO{-}CH_2OH \xrightarrow[\text{glucose / Ag}_2\text{O}]{\beta\text{-Bromotetraacetyl-}} AcO{-}C_6H_4{-}CO{-}CH_2OC_6H_7O(OAc)_4}$$

As in all subsequent syntheses the two components were combined by means of hydrogen chloride in a neutral solvent; originally we used ether-chloroform, but later we found that ethyl acetate was a better medium. The solid product was collected and hydrolysed by cold aqueous sodium hydroxide, followed by treatment with hydrochloric acid. The reconstitution of the anthocyanin could be judged by the colour change to red.

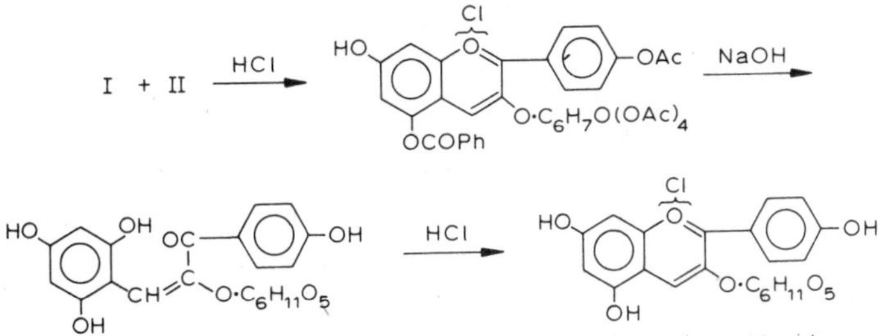

Callistephine chloride

The synthesis of chrysanthemin [186] was effected in an entirely similar fashion, the chief new interest being the preparation of the substituted acetophenone. 4-Chloroacetylcatechol, already known as a product of condensation of catechol with chloroacetic acid by means of phosphoryl chloride, was converted into a triacetoxy derivative by heating with acetic anhydride and sodium acetate. The ω,-3,4,-triacetoxyacetophenone was hydrolysed to the corresponding trihydroxy compound, which was carefully acetylated by acetic anhydride and sodium acetate, applied in the theoretically required quantity for acetylation of two of the three hydroxyl groups. The product was shaken with ether which extracted what was probably a mixture of the di- and triacetyl derivatives, and now comes the point of this otherwise tedious narrative: when the ether was dried with calcium chloride a considerable precipitate appeared; this was collected, and on treatment with water afforded the pure desired intermediate, namely, 3,4-diacetoxy-ω-hydroxyacetophenone. The formation of this calcium chloride compound was another piece of luck, but as Benjamin Franklin declared "Luck is the bonus accruing to industry".

We had certainly worked hard to achieve our objective before we got this unexpected help.

Richard Willstätter (1872—1942)

My scientific work was very much influenced by the pioneering researches of Richard Willstätter on the chemistry of alkaloids such as atropine and cocaine, and on the red, blue and violet pigments of flowers and blossoms termed anthocyanins. I had the greatest admiration for his genius and had the opportunity to give a brief account of his life and work when I wrote a Memorial Lecture for the Chemical Society [528]. I drew attention to the difficulties which he experienced in his early life. It appeared that the first steps towards a chemical career were taken when he attended the Realgymnasium at Nürnberg. At the age of eighteen he entered the school of Adolph von Baeyer, at the University of Munich. In 1902 he became an Extraordinarius Professor and Head of the Department of Organic Chemistry. In 1905 he became Professor at the Zürich Technische Hochschule, and in 1912 he returned to Germany and became Director of the Chemical Research Department of the Kaiser Wilhelm Institut in Berlin—Dahlem. Finally, in 1916 he followed von Baeyer as Head of the Chemistry Department in the University of Munich. He remained at Munich until 1925 when he retired from his Chair while still retaining facilities for work in the Department, but owing to the antisemitism of Hitler's Germany he emigrated to Switzerland. During the following year Willstätter travelled to America and England in order to deliver lectures, take part in discussions and receive distinctions such as medals for research and honorary degrees. On two occasions we were able to extend hospitality to him and I remember very well meeting him at the Grosvenor Hotel, Victoria, and taking him by road to our house in Oxford. In the course of conversation he explained that Einstein was a German Jew, whereas he, Willstätter, was a Jewish German. I tried to commiserate with him on the various troubles that he had recently experienced, but he passed that off lightly by saying "Yes indeed, but nothing so dreadful has happened as when Perkin gave me an ill-fitting dinner jacket at Oxford". "This", he said, "was the most miserable experience of my life". The final blow fell towards the end of 1938, when he was forced by the Gestapo to leave Germany, and lost much valued personal property in the process. He was, however, fortunate to get away at all, and across the frontier his friend and former pupil, Arthur Stoll, an important industrialist (Sandoz), was waiting to insure him the best possible reception in his new home, the Villa Eremitaggio at Muralto-Locarno on Lago Maggiore.

In the early days at Munich, Willstätter established the structure of atropine and cocaine, a classical investigation which ramified along important patterns of chemistry, physiology, and biogenesis. I was able to make a suggestion on the latter aspects and when the synthesis of tropinone was published Willstätter wrote me a most kind letter of congratulation. He followed this up with what is generally called the sincerest form of flattery, by using my method for the synthesis of ecgonine and cocaine.

It is hard to recreate a state of ignorance of earlier times and this is especially true of the chemical ideas (if any) concerning the red, blue and violet colours of flowers, prior to Willstätter's pioneering work. At the present time, it seems almost inconceivable that a suggestion was that they were of the nature of azo-dyestuffs! Willstätter showed that they were glycosides of polyhydroxyflavylium salts that could be isolated as chlorides or picrates, and such salts were termed anthocyanins. They could be hydrolysed to sugar free salts, anthocyanidins. It turned out that there was a limited number of common anthocyanidins, and the structures of these were determined using a sophisticated Grignard synthesis. The anthocyanidins synthesised in this way were pelargonidin and cyanidin (iodides) (see scheme on p. 146).

Meanwhile, the progress of our work on brazilin and haematoxylin had led us to the discovery of a simple synthesis of flavylium salts which could be applied to the synthesis of any desired anthocyanidin (p. 36). Moreover, the work of Willstätter had given no indication of the position of sugar residues in the flavylium molecule. Methods for

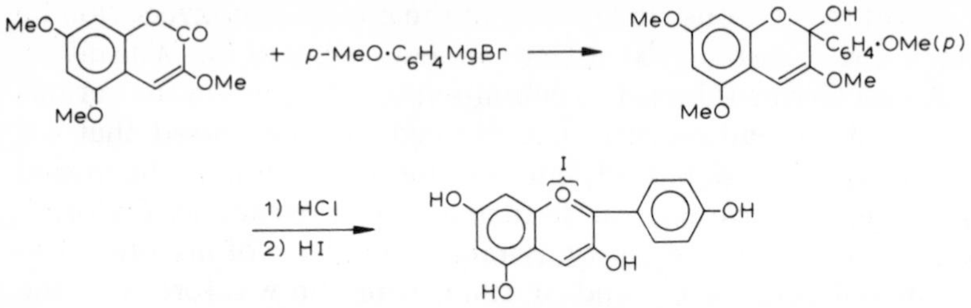

Pelargonidin iodide

filling these gaps were sought and found. Significant were the visible colour changes of solutions at varied pH [150]; furthermore, P. Karrer (Helv. Chim. Acta 1927, *10*, 67, 729, et seq.) supplied some degradative evidence that certain anthocyanins are 3-glycosides. These indications were finally supplemented by the synthesis of anthocyanins which followed.

Early in this development Willstätter, who was much grieved by the forced abandonment of further work on the flower colours, assumed the role of Elijah and selected me as his Elisha. This was done very formally by a passage in the introduction to his *Collected Researches on the Enzymes*. Unfortunately, Willstätter also bequeathed to me a completely wrong idea of the nature of the beet pigment, which he regarded as a flavylium compound with an amino substituent, thus accounting for its bright bluish-red colour. The fog surrounding this work was soon cleared away by the work of Dreiding, who showed that this and similar colouring matters had turned β-cyanins into indole derivatives containing a pyridine nucleus.

In these few notes I have dwelt on matters with which I was later associated, and have made no attempts to describe Willstätter's wonderful achievements in organic chemical research. Just to mention a few headings — we have the study of aniline black and other quinones; improved methods of catalytic hydrogenation; discovery of magnesium in chlorophyll, and other chemistry of chlorophyll; and a long series on the researches of the enzymes and many miscellaneous studies.

Preparation of the Intermediates of the Delphinidin, Petunidin and Hirsutidin Series

The accessible starting materials for the purposes indicated by the above subtitle are gallic acid and certain derivatives, such as syringic acid. We desired to use these substances for another reason also, namely, that orientation of nuclear condensations of the pyrogallol series is ambiguous, the entering group going in position-4 or -5 according to the special circumstances.

The action of diazomethane on acid chlorides has been stated to yield chloromethyl ketones (Nierenstein). Staudinger, however, contributed an interesting example, namely, the action of diazomethane on phosgene: the product was $Cl \cdot CH_2 \cdot CO \cdot CHN_2$. However, this indication of the formation of a diazoketone from an acid chloride was not followed up as a general reaction. We came to the conclusion that the Nierenstein reaction involves, in all probability, the formation of a diazoketone which is decomposed by the hydrogen chloride produced at the same time and not neutralised in any way. Hence, as a test case W. Bradley treated benzoyl chloride with 2 mols. diazomethane and obtained the expected ω-diazoacetophenone, presumably along with methyl chloride. This result was simultaneously obtained by F. Arndt and co-workers and reference to the respective journals shows that our paper [157] was submitted to the Journal of the Chemical Society a fortnight before Arndt's was received by the Berichte. I am not claiming priority on this account; the two investigations were clearly simultaneous, but I mention this circumstance because our contribution has been consistently overlooked. The reaction was basic for the preparation of all the intermediates required for the synthesis of all the anthocyanins in the delphinidin series. For example, oenin [188], the pigment of the skins of black grapes, was synthesised from syringic acid by way of its acetylation, conversion to an acid chloride, and then to the related diazoketone. This could be directly decomposed by careful treatment with very dilute sulphuric acid, and by the action of formic acid it could be converted into a formate which could be hydrolysed by hot water without removal of the acetoxy group.

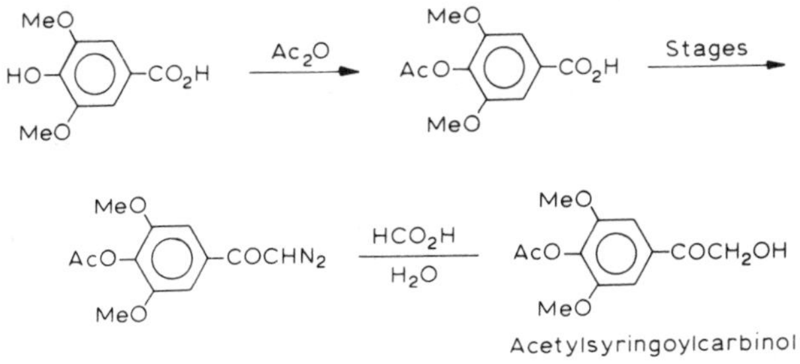

Acetylsyringoylcarbinol

The acetylsyringoylcarbinol was then β-tetraacetylglucosidated with formation of the desired second component for the synthesis which was carried out according to the general method already explained on p. 124.

For the ordinary delphinidin derivatives, i.e. those not complicated by special substitutions, we started from O-triacetylgallic acid. In order to develop the petunidin series we protected adjacent hydroxyl groups by conversion into the diphenylmethylene ether, then methylated the free hydroxyl and prepared the acid chloride, and then the diazoketone. The remaining stages followed the by now well established route.

William Bradley (b. 1903)

William Bradley had a brilliant career as a research student at Manchester University. He was awarded the Dalton Chemical Scholarship in 1925 and the Baeyer Fellowship in 1926, *inter alia*. He graduated Ph.D. and later D.Sc. In addition to his work on diazoketones leading to intermediates for anthocyanin syntheses, he made several studies of theoretical interest. For example, he showed that alkaline hydrolysis of unsymmetrical diaroylmethanes proceeds with the formation of the anion of the stronger of the two acids that might be produced [122].

He found indications that the absorption spectra of tetranitromethane dissolved in phenolic ethers was directly related to the extent of conjugation of the alkyloxy group with the aromatic nucleus. The work was not pursued to the publication stage and the subject is certainly worthy of re-examination. In 1929—1931, he was Research Assistant in the Dyson Perrins Laboratory, Oxford (I believe under I.C.I. auspices). He then became, in succession, Lecturer in Tinctorial Chemistry at the Manchester College of Technology (1931—1942), research worker in the laboratories of British Drug Houses Ltd. (1942—1948), and Professor of Colour Chemistry and Dyeing at the University of Leeds (1948—1963). In this position Bradley exercised considerable influence in research policy in the colour using industries, and in such matters as the operation of the Perkin Centenary Trust. He was very clear headed and had a good grasp of the theory of the course of chemical reactions.

Before leaving the anthocyanidins, an easy preparation of cyanidin [308] should be mentioned. This starts with O-tetramethylcatechin

W. Bradley.

which is brominated in dioxane solution, leading to the formation of a bromotetramethylcyanadin bromide. This reaction only succeeds in dioxane which has been exposed for some time to the air and contains peroxide. The bromo-compound is treated with hydriodic acid which reduces the bromine substituted in the nucleus and affords cyanidine iodide. These reactions provide a preparation of cyanin salts which is probably the best available.

Carajura

Arthur G. Perkin had obtained this material, termed carajura, from a curio dealer in London, and it was in the form of a deep red-brown lump, probably containing some binding material such as starch. This carajura is prepared by the Indians of the Upper Orinoco, and was so much prized by them that it could be used as a form of currency; it undoubtedly had a value as a cosmetic. It is probable that it was obtained from a bush rose, possibly one having violet flowers, and one can imagine that these flowers were stirred up with water, and that a fermentation took place, resulting in the precipitation of this highly valued red-brown powder.

The constitution of carajura was demonstrated, first of all, by showing that it was a dimethyl ether of a colour base, which could be hydrolysed to a 4-methoxyacetophenone. Hydrolysis of carajura by strong hydriodic acid resulted in the formation of carajuretin iodide, convertible easily into carajuretin chloride, which had colour reactions suggestive of its structure. The latter substance was synthesised [149], proving that the surmised structure was correct. The position of the second methoxyl group was indicated by the fact that the salt of carajurin gave a ferric reaction showing that two hydroxyls were in vicinal positions. Accordingly, the colour base has the structure shown and the deductions have been completely confirmed by a synthesis, due to T.R. Seshadri.

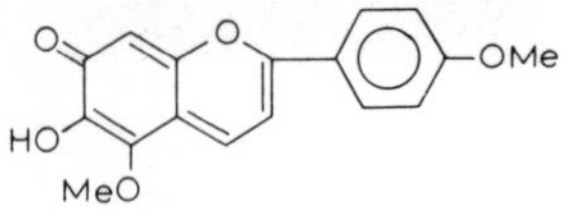

Carajurin

Arthur George Perkin (1861—1937)

A.G. Perkin was only one year junior to William Henry. The brothers grew up in the Perkinian environment and this resulted in the development of many similar interests, especially of course music and organic chemistry. His part in the family orchestra was as flautist and bassoonist. He continued in the latter capacity during the whole of his life, made his own reeds, and was in great demand by Yorkshire orchestras at the time when I knew him best. His chemistry was characteristically original and he is best known for his pioneering work on natural dyestuffs. He followed A.G. Green in 1916 as Professor of Colour Chemistry and Dyeing in the University of Leeds and I was privileged to act as his External Examiner. This was no sinecure as he insisted on reading through the whole of the answers to me. The practical tests in these examinations required the students to show considerable initiative and I found these occasions more stimulating than would normally be expected.

Apart from music and chemistry there was no resemblance between the two brothers at all. A.G. was not at all an ambitious man, he had a rather old fashioned manner at times and I recall the following illustration of this. He owned a motor car which was used for country drives on Sunday, but Mrs. Perkin was the chauffeur. I went with them once, and she said at the beginning of the journey "Arthur, I think you must buy some oil, I don't think we have enough in the sump". So, in due course, we drew up at a garage and Mrs. Perkin issued a reminder "We need some more oil". So Arthur asked the garage attendant to put some oil into the sump. The attendant said "Which oil do you prefer — Castrol or some other?" So Arthur said "I really don't know — automobile oil I suppose".

He had many Japanese and other students from foreign countries, whilst his British students played a great part in establishing the dyestuffs industry in this country. Stages in his work were also milestones in our knowledge of the chemistry of natural products. One need only recall the early work on luteolin, quercetin, and many other flavones and flavonols. He made a considerable survey of naturally occurring colouring matters and wrote a monograph with A.E. Everest (1918) on the subject. My own joint work with A.G. Perkin is described on page 150. It starts with "a brand plucked from the burning" since, if A.G. Perkin had not taken the action he did, there can be little doubt that the whole incident of the cosmetic pigment used by the Indians of the Upper Orinoco would have been lost, at least from the point of view of its chemistry. For further details see Obituary Notice by E.J. Cross and F.M. Rowe, Society of Dyers & Colourists Journal, Sept. 1937, p. 349.

Flavones, Flavonols and Isoflavones

In a reaction discovered by S.T. von Kostanecki, which seemed of great interest because the chromone nucleus was constructed so simply, in a single operation, I wondered whether the same kind of process could be applied to the production of flavones and flavonols, and this has certainly proved to be the case. If one takes a suitably substituted o-hydroxyacetophenone and heats it with the sodium salt of an aromatic acid and the corresponding acid anhydride, a reaction occurs with formation of the flavone, or rather, of various acyl-flavones. By hydrolysis these acyl groups are removed and the flavone can be obtained from solution by acidification, usually in rather good yield. The process works even better for flavonols than for flavones and has been widely applied to the synthesis of both types of substances. The synthesis of galangin [81] by benzoylation of ω-methoxyphloracetophenone may serve as an example.

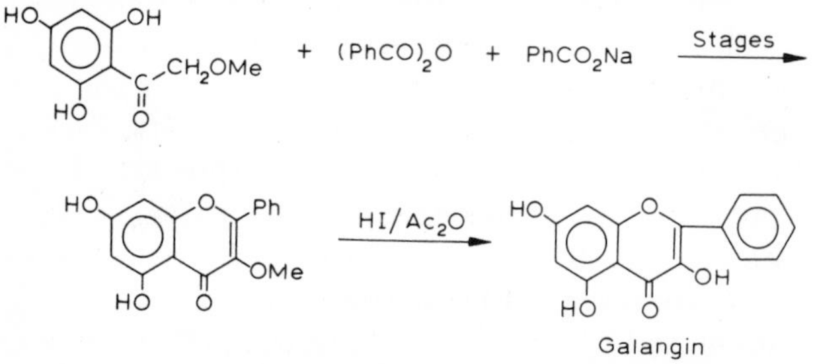

Galangin

We were particularly anxious to show its utility for the preparation of partially methylated flavones and flavonols, and examples of its successful use were the syntheses of isorhamnetin [119] and acacetin [120]. In these and all such cases the phenolic hydroxyls of the acid anhydride component were either acylated or benzylated.

The isoflavones were synthesised by a method essentially analogous to that used for anhydrobrazilic acid (p. 32). The necessary intermediate deoxybenzoins were made by an application of the Hoesch reaction, using polyhydroxyphenols and arylacetonitriles, and were then converted into isoflavones bearing a styryl group, —CH=CHPh, in position-2. This group could be converted into H by oxidation to —COOH and subsequent decarboxylation. The styryl derivatives were obtained either directly, using sodium cinnamate and cinnamic anhydride, or from the 2-methylisoflavones by condensation with benzaldehyde. The method is illustrated by the annexed scheme which depicts the synthesis of daidzein [239].

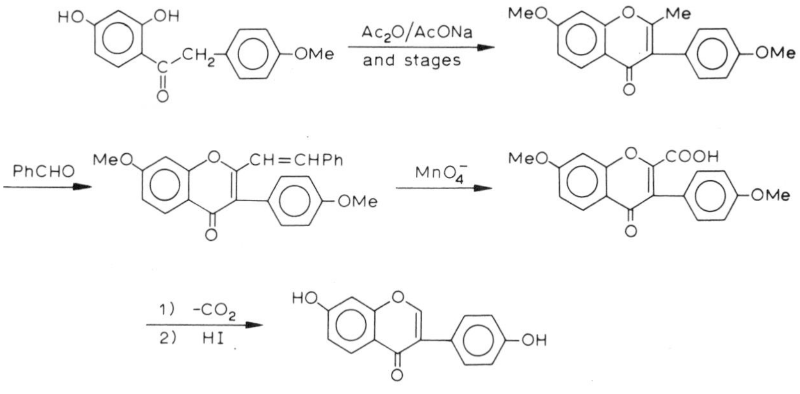

Daidzein

The methods described above have been extended by W. Baker and by K. Venkataraman.

Structural Relation of Catechin to Typical Anthocyanidins

Nierenstein somehow became convinced that the anthocyanidins, in particular cyanidin, are not structurally related to flavylium but rather to 4-phenylchromylium salts and, correspondingly, the aryl group in catechin was, according to him, in position-4 of the pyran ring. This naturally interested K. Freudenberg, who had carried out pioneering work in the catechin series, proving, without doubt, that the pyran ring is in position-2. However, Nierenstein backed up his view of the catechins by an alleged synthesis of a derivative of acacetin, not being deterred by the fact that this had been proved to be a mixture of stereoisomerides (Freudenberg). When tetra-methylcatechin is reduced with sodium and alcohol it affords tri-methoxy-o-hydroxy-1,3-diphenylpropane. This substance was regarded by Nierenstein as a corresponding derivative of 1,1-substituted diarylpropane. He took this compound and oxidised it with permanganate, thus obtaining, as he claimed, a carboxylic acid in which the terminal methyl of the ethyl group had been converted into carboxyl. On this dubious foundation he claimed a synthesis of acacetin could be erected. T. Malkin, a former collaborator with me, supported Nierenstein's view of the structure of catechin and cyanidin, and hence it seemed to Freudenberg and myself that the matter should be settled by fresh studies made by an entirely independent investigator. T. Wagner-Jauregg made an extremely careful comparison of 2,4,6,3',4'-pentamethoxy-1,3-diphenylpropane prepared from catechin, and also by independent synthesis, the result of which showed that the two were unquestionably identical.

MISCELLANEOUS PROJECTS

A Synthesis of Harmaline

Most of the syntheses of 4-carboline derivatives related to harmine involved either a Bischler-Napieralski type of condensation using acyltryptamines, or variations, as the original method of oxidation of tryptophan in the presence of an aldehyde or a source of an aldehyde. Shortly after I had taken charge in the Manchester Laboratories, I occupied the Professor's private laboratory, a step across a corridor to the Schunck research laboratory. R.H.F. Manske had a bench in the Schunck and carried out with skill a new type of synthesis in this group which I had devised. I mention this propinquity because the success of this study was for a time one of my main interests, and discussions of progress were quite frequent. The idea was to prepare the appropriate methoxyphenylhydrazone of an α-diketone, namely 6-phthalimidohexane-2,3-dione, and submit this to the Fischer indole synthesis. This scheme was very successfully implemented [126] and if harmaline were ever required for medical purposes there is no doubt that the method is far superior technically to the alternative starting with a methoxytryptamine. Although the latter gives a satisfactory ring closure in the final stage, the production of the tryptamine itself is not at all easily accomplished. I mention this point because the simplicity of the final stage in the tryptamine route has been used to depreciate the method now being described. Overall our method is doubtless the better one. The various stages of the synthesis are illustrated below.

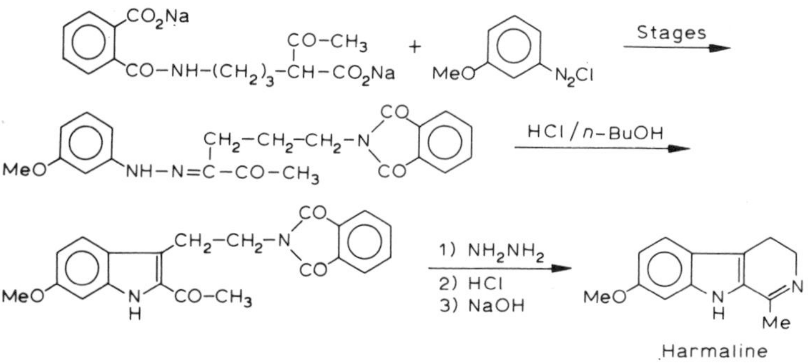

.Harmaline

It should be noted this was the first occasion on which the phthalimido group, used for purpose of protection, was removed by the smooth process employing treatment with hydrazine and, eventually, the formation of the free amine and phthalhydrazide.

Another occupier of the laboratory was H.R. Ing. As I was so impressed by the smoother operation of the hydrazine method for the hydrolysis of the N-substituted phthalimides I asked Ing and Manske to join together and make a few further applications of the method in order to prove its generality. They did this with considerable enthusiasm and unfortunately published a paper on the subject before the synthesis of harmaline by the above method could be submitted to the Chemical Society. In consequence this rather bright idea of mine is now known as the Ing and Manske method!

Manske carried out other synthetical schemes, of which the most interesting involved the formation of β-3-indolylpropionic azide and its decomposition to the 3-oxo-3,4,5,6,-tetrahydro-4-carboline, with evolution of nitrogen. The reaction sequence is shown below, together with the synthesis of rutaecarpine.

Synthesis of Rutaecarpine [129]

Professor Y. Asahina isolated the alkaloid and in the course of its study found that it could be split into norharman and anthranilic acid. While he was on a visit to England he came to Manchester and we determined the melting point of a mixture of a synthetic harman (4-carboline) and the base derived from rutaecarpin; no depression of the m.p. was found. We decided to carry out the synthesis of rutaecarpine jointly, chiefly I think, because we had in Manchester intermediates which could be useful in the project. Actually the synthesis was very easily accomplished: after an experiment with a model, we obtained rutaecarpine by condensation of the above mentioned 3-oxotetrahydro-4-carboline (Manske and R.R. [127]) with methyl anthranilate in the presence of phorphorous trichloride.

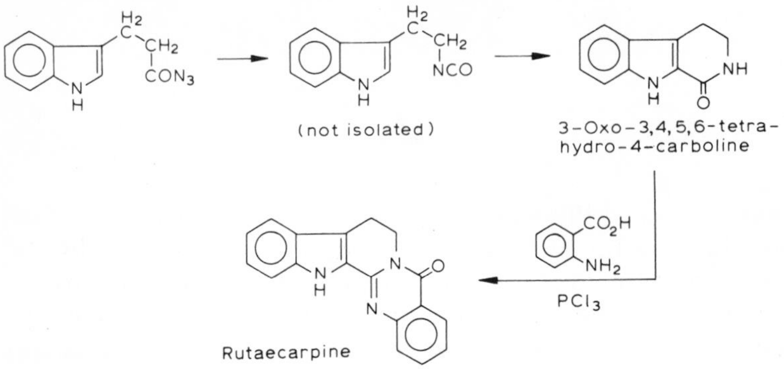

(not isolated)

3-Oxo-3,4,5,6-tetra-hydro-4-carboline

PCl$_3$

Rutaecarpine

Finally may be mentioned that 3-carboline [70] and 5-carboline [75] were prepared in this series of studies by decomposition of the appropriate triazoles. In the case of 5-carboline the interesting observation was made that the decomposition with loss of nitrogen proceeded well on heating the triazole with syrupy phosphoric acid; the following scheme illustrates the reaction sequence.

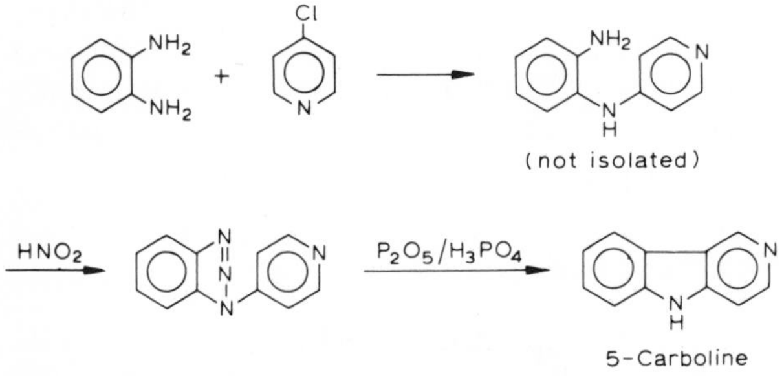

(not isolated)

HNO$_2$

P$_2$O$_5$/H$_3$PO$_4$

5-Carboline

I do not know whether 6-carboline has been synthesised, but certainly we made no attempt to do this.

Anthocyanin Synthesis

In this domain extension to peonidin, petunidin, hirsutidin, and delphinidin were included. Some variation of the sugars in the pyrylium nucleus, for example pentosides, were prepared and of these it was cyanidin-3-xyloside that was thought to occur naturally in the primrose. Cyanidin-3-galactoside was synthesised [190] and found to be identical with Willstätter's idaein. Four 3-biosides of cyanidin were made, namely the cellobioside, lactoside, maltoside and gentiobioside. For comparison the distribution ratios between *n*-butyl and amyl alcohol and 0.5% aqueous hydrochloric acid were examined. The colour reactions of all four were identical, a violet colour in aqueous sodium carbonate which becomes blue on addition of sodium hydroxide. The time of fading of the blue solution was also noted. As a result of these admittedly insecure comparisons there was no doubt that natural glucocyanin and the synthetical 3-gentiobioside were closely similar up to this point. It has, however, been proved by chromatographic and analytical methods that the biose that can be liberated by hydrolysis of mecocyanin is not gentiobiose but an isomeride. I never felt really convinced about this and made preparations to study the possibility of the synthesis of the 2-β-glucosylglucose from the gentiobiose chain alone or *in situ* in the anthocyanin by rearrangement. Unfortunately the onset of blindness due to severe glaucoma prevented me from pursuing this project. However, it is freely admitted that the comparisons we made were not sufficient to establish firmly the true nature of mecocyanin.

A synthesis of keracyanin was carried through, using acetobromo-glucose and acetylated rhamnose. The final product was a rhamno-glucoside, and so far as could be ascertained from tests, not including those based on chromatography, it was identical with Willstätter's kerocyanin. Unfortunately the whole of the material was lost some-where in the transfer from University College, London to Oxford.

In 1925 my wife and I published the first of a new series of syntheses of higher aliphatic compounds which included oxoderivatives of the fatty acids. The methods employed for this purpose have already been briefly indicated before (cf. chapter III, p. 55); a more detailed account of work in this field follows now.

Synthesis of Oleic Acid [80]

10-Ketostearic acid was already known as a product of hydration of stearolic acid. It has also been reduced to a hydroxy-acid and con-verted to a corresponding iodostearic acid, and the latter changed by loss of hydrogen iodide into a mixture containing oleic and elaidic acid. These two isomeric acids can be converted into stearolic acid. We completed the first true formal synthesis of oleic acid by synthesising 10-ketostearic acid (which had the melting point 83°, ascribed by earlier workers to a hydration product of stearolic acid), and by reducing stearolic acid to pure oleic acid. The reducing agent was zinc dust in aqueous acetic acid containing titanous chloride; concentrated hydrochloric acid was very slowly added to the boiling solution. The freezing point of the oleic acid produced was 13°, not depressed by the addition of oleic acid prepared from olive oil and rigorously purified. This synthesis has been described above as formal, and certainly the stages from 10-ketostearic acid are unsatisfactory in that they are ambiguous in regard to the position of the acetylenic bond in stearolic acid. We intended an independent synthesis of this acid but never attempted it as there is in any case plenty of evidence bearing on the structures of oleic and stearolic acids. We probably thought that it would be a case of flogging a dead horse.

$$\overset{18}{CH_3}-(CH_2)_7-\overset{10}{CH}=\overset{9}{CH}-(CH_2)_7-\overset{1}{CO_2H}$$

Oleic acid

$$CH_3-(CH_2)_7-C\equiv C-(CH_2)_7-CO_2H$$

Stearolic acid

Experiments on the hydration of stearolic acid were made after 11-ketostearic acid had also been synthesised [117]. The products obtained were submitted to further analysis, using a mixture of the 10- and 11-keto-acids to construct the mixed melting point thermal diagram. We thought we had detected a small electric effect of the carboxyl group but this was apparently due to an error in the diagram on the side of the 10-oxo acid. Actually the carboxyl group is so remote from the triple bond that no field effect can be observed and the hydration of stearolic acid by means of mercury salts and concentrated sulphuric acid goes 50% in each of the two possible directions. I am grateful to Dr. J.C. Smith for drawing my attention to this error and for locating the cause of the trouble. It seems possible that the use of ethanol for crystallisation of the acid gave rise to a small quantity of ester which remained in the product even if it were later crystallised from other solvents.

The methods in this series of researches were much varied in later work and the yields improved. The fundamental idea remained the same, it was simply interpreted in new procedures. For example, 4-ketomyristic acid was prepared starting with ethyl 2-acetosuccinate and undecoyl chloride; 5-, 7- and 8-ketopalmitic acids were prepared, the latter two in connection with the study of palmitoleic acid. As an example, the 8-ketopalmitic acid was obtained from 7-carbethoxy-heptoyl chloride and ethyl 2-acetononoate.

A substance of great value for extension to the chain of the n-carboxylic acids was found to be ethyl ω-bromoundecoate [176]. This was introduced in the normal manner into ethyl acetoacetate, and the sodio derivative condensed in ethereal solution with the acid chloride of a carboxylic acid of the normal series. After hydrolysis in stages a keto-acid is obtained which can be reduced by the Clemmensen method to a saturated carboxylic acid. The normal chain is thus extended by 12 carbon atoms and this process can be repeated; thus, using ethyl ω-bromoundecoate and stearoyl chloride, triacontanoic acid (C_{30}) was synthesised and from this a keto-acid containing 42 carbon atoms. In part IV [283A] of this series by G.M. Robinson the keto-acid ($C_{42}H_{82}O_3$) is described and reference was made to X-ray crystallographic examination of the keto-acid by D.S.H. Piper. I have a clear recollection of the reduction of this substance to the fatty acid ($C_{42}H_{84}O_2$), but I can find no reference to the publication of this work and the experiment should be repeated for the record, and also in order to examine the metabolism of this acid in an animal.

Further Work in the Group of Alkaloids

The synthesis of α-gnoscopine (*dl*-narcotine) [12] was greatly improved by the use of halogenated meconin, which condensed with pseudo-bases, for example cotarnine, with formation of the halogeno-α-*dl*-bases of the phthalide type. Reduction of the halogen was effected by aluminium amalgam [27]. Although this work was published in 1914, its description was deferred until now because of its relevance to the partial racemisation of the phthalide alkaloids, and also to the synthesis of bicuculline.

The synthesis of *d*-bicuculline [327] was carried out by condensation of cotarnine with bromomethylenedioxyphthalide. The latter was prepared from meconin by bromination, demethylation, and methylenation using methylene sulphate and aqueous sodium hydroxide (cf. W. Baker, J. Chem. Soc. 1931, 1965). The yield was 45%, adequate for our purpose, but it could probably be improved by the use of J.W. Cornforth's modification — the use of methylene chloride. After condensation, bromobicuculline was dehalogenated by hydrogen in the presence of palladium on strontium carbonate. *dl*-Bicuculline was resolved by crystallisation of its *d*-tartrate. In view of the difficulty experienced in the case of most phthalide-isoquinoline alkaloids, it is remarkable that *d*-bicuculline-*d*-tartrate separated in an almost pure condition in the first crystallisation. The base was isolated therefrom and proved to be identical with the alkaloid from natural sources.

Partial Racemisation of Narcotine and Hydrastine

Marshall, Pyman and R.R. [277] found that treatment with hot dilute caustic alkali slowly racemised the asymmetric centre in the phtalide group "and the corresponding salt of the hydroxy acid was obtained on opening of the lactone ring". After acidification of the solution the phtalide group is reconstituted and the base can then be isolated in the usual manner. Narcotine, in this way, yields a base, β-*l*-narcotine.

The enantiomorph, β-*d*-narcotine, was made by partial racemisation of *d*-narcotine, made by the resolution of α-gnoscopine. On mixing the β-*l*-narcotine with the β-*d*-narcotine we obtained β-gnoscopine. This substance was already well known since the condensation of cotarnine with nitromeconin gave a nearly theoretical yield of nitro-β-gnoscopine. Removal of the nitro group, for example by successive conversion into the corresponding primary amine, hydrazino derivative, and oxidation thereof, furnished β-gnoscopine.

In order to throw light on the stereochemistry of the α- and β-gnoscopines we proposed to use the principle of optical superposition. Our polarimetric observations were all made with the use of sodium light and this led us astray, since a comparison of quotations appeared to show clearly that natural narcotine and hydrastine were in different series. Unfortunately the relatives we noted appeared to hold only for the *D* line, and A. Battersby has shown, by a study of the rotatory powers over a range of wave lengths, that the two alkaloids are in fact in the same stereochemical group.

Frank Lee Pyman (1882—1944)

Pyman was a year senior to me in the School of Chemistry, and after taking his degree with First Class Honours at the head of the list of candidates, he went to Zürich to work with Bamberger at the Eidgenössische Technische Hochschule. He returned to England in

F.L. Pyman.

1905 and, after a period in the Government Laboratory, he was appointed in 1906 to the staff of the Wellcome Chemical Works at Dartford. In 1914 he became Director of the Wellcome Chemical Research Laboratory in London. He then followed Sir William Pope as Head of the Department of Applied Chemistry in the Manchester College of Technology. In 1922 he became F.R.S.

My contact with Pyman and his work was, in the first place, partly in connection with problems of the isoquinoline group of alkaloids, and partly arose from his appointment in 1927 as Director of the Research Department of Boots Pure Drug Co. Ltd., and continued when some years later he acted as a consultant to that firm. He had already, whilst at Dartford, studied the alkaloids of ipecacuanha and, in collaboration with Francis H. Carr, had elucidated the constitution of emetine with exception of one detail, which was left open (see Vol. II). Later, his reduction of hydrocotarnine to hydrohydrastinine by means of sodium and amyl alchohol was both of technological and scientific interest. By the reduction of papaverine, using tin and hydrochloric acid, he obtained an isomeride of dihydropapaverine which he called pavine. The remarkable mechanism of the formation of this substance was cleared up by A. Battersby, many years later. The very pardonable error made by Pyman, in the interpretation of this reaction, was the only one that he ever made in the course of a long record of research. As a student of Perkin and Bamberger he seemed to combine the better qualities of both, adding a certain meticulosity, which was entirely his own contribution. A joint publication with Pyman concerned racemisation of narcotine and hydrastine leading to the isolation of a new isomeride of each of the bases, as has just been mentioned.

Earlier, Pyman had rebuffed an attack made on me by A. Pictet (see p. 74). At the Boots Laboratory we worked together on several problems, for example, the preparation of antimalarials containing a harmine moiety. A rather amusing result was obtained. It was found that if the methoxy group of harmine was replaced by a longer alkoxyl chain considerable antimalarial activity resulted, but the substances were far too toxic for use. (It should be said, in parenthesis, that the use of harmine was first suggested by J.A. Gunn, Professor of Pharmacology at Oxford University.) In order to reduce the toxicity an amino group was introduced at the end of the long chain, but this also reduced the antimalarial activity, so the amino group was again alkylated and there was recovery of antimalarial activity and toxicity, and finally, another amino group was introduced at the end of the chain, and this seemed to give reasonably satisfactory results on all grounds. The antimalarial activity was not, however, of the most striking order and, having introduced such a bulky substituent, it occurred to Pyman to try the substituent alone, without the harmine part, and that, indeed, gave an active substance.

Another and more successful investigation was designed to find an improved phenol of a type of thymol, with the idea of replacing the latter in various medicaments. A synthesis was devised which yielded n-alkyl-m-cresols, and a study of their bactericidal power showed that n-amyl-m-cresol (AMC) was far more effective than the next lower and the next higher homologue. As the bactericidal power of this substance is approximately a hundredfold that of phenol, and as it proved to be as good as non-toxic, it was selected for manufacture and recommended, in diluted form, as a gargle and mouth wash. Its properties suggest, however, that in a more concentrated form, it could have a wider use.

However busy my day at the Boots Laboratories might be, there was always time for a game of billiards or snooker, after lunch at the County Club. Pyman was quite a good performer, and I held my own pretty well at billiards, but was quite outclassed at snooker.

Pyman is probably best known for his work in the iminazole series, especially the brilliant synthesis of histidine. In this he used an intermediate which contained, at the same time, a chloromethyl group and a basic group protected from alkylation in the form of hydrochloride. His studies naturally included work on the physiological base, histamine, which is decarboxyhistidine, which Barger and Dale had isolated from ergot, a fungus growing on rye.

Another study of a glyoxaline derivative to which Pyman made a contribution was that of the alkaloid pilocarpine. The earlier work of Jowett and of Pinner laid the foundations, but some difficult questions connected with the tautomerism remained and the whole subject was cleared up by Pyman in a most elegant manner. His contribution to the chemistry of natural products containing the iminazole nucleus certainly interested him more than any other part of his work and turned out to be of considerable biochemical importance. His work was recognised by the award of the Hanbury Medal of the Pharmaceutical Society in 1936. I find it strange, however, that his merit was not fully understood in his own country, either by the Royal Society or the Chemical Society. His unassuming manner and complete lack of self-advertisement may possibly account for this unfortunate oversight.

Some years ago, in Zagreb, we happened to meet his son, Lancelot Frank Lee Pyman, C.M.G., who at that time was H.M. Consul General there. It is perhaps of some interest that his son is carrying on the chemical tradition in the family.

NOTES ON MISCELLANEOUS STUDIES IN THE SECOND MANCHESTER PERIOD

Synthesis of Tertiary Bases [61]

Alkoxy-amines of the form $RR'N-CH_2OR''$ react with Grignard agents, $R'''MgX$, to give $RR'N-CH_2R'''$. The method works smoothly and in most cases the yields are good.

A Direct Synthesis of Certain Xanthylium Derivatives [62]

β-Resorcylaldehyde or phloroglucinaldehyde may be condensed with resorcinol or phloroglucinol with the aid of hydrogen chloride. A highly reactive phenol, such as phloroglucinol, may be condensed with formic ester using gaseous HCl.

The Fischer Indole Synthesis [72]

1. The method was applied to certain syntheses of pyrindoles.
2. The mechanism for synthesis was suggested which started with tautomerism to a hydrazine, followed by rearrangement of a double o-benzidine type, followed by elimination of ammonia.
3. A new synthesis of tetraphenylpyrrole: the azine of deoxybenzoin yields tetraphenylpyrrole when heated under hydrogen chloride. This reaction affords support for the mechanism of the Fischer indole synthesis previously advanced. It may be assumed that the azine is converted into a hydrazino-bis-stilbene which undergoes an o-benzidine rearrangement — an analogous reaction is the conversion of di-β-naphthylhydrazine into o-dibenzcarbazole in which the naphthalene rings are linked through their 1-positions.

An Accessible Derivative of Chromonol [76]

A New Route to the 3-Hydroxybenzopyrylium Salts [77]

Phenyl Benzyl Diketone and some Derivatives [82]

Synthesis of Oxyberberin. Part I [83]

3-Chlorobenzopyrylium Derivatives [84]

A Qualitative Test for Weak Bases [85]

This depends on the formation of salts of $HFeCl_4$ and affords a good experiment for demonstration purposes. For example, one may mix in a stoppered glass cylinder a strong solution of ferric chloride in concentrated hydrochloric acid with equal volumes of light petroleum and ether; on shaking the mixture it will separate into three layers. The originally opaque ferric chloride solution becomes pale yellow, the middle ethereal layer is green and contains the $HFeCl_4$, and the upper colourless layer is the light petroleum. Doubtless the ether combines with the acid and we are probably justified in our supposition that an oxonium salt is formed.

Synthetical Experiments in the Naphthyridine Group [91]

We were attracted to this subject by noting the remarkable ease of condensation of ethylamino-β-crotonate with ethyl oxalacetate; the yield of substituted pyridine on admixture in cold ether is almost quantitative. 2,6-Lutidine-3,4-dicarboxylic acid is readily available by this route and we converted its imide to a related 3-amino-4-carboxylic acid by the action of potassium hypobromite. The acid is easily decarboxylated and the resulting aminolutidine may prove to be a useful intermediate. Good yields were also obtained in the oxidation of the methyl groups in the first product and selective decarboxylation of the pyridinetetracarboxylic acid.

The facile synthesis of copyrine mentioned on p. 120 had up to this time been confined to substances made from diaminoveratrone. In this paper we describe another *o,o'*-diaminobenzophenone, namely 2,4,2',4'-tetraaminobenzophenone. This was converted by the double Friedländer synthesis into a number of copyrine derivatives by condensation with 1,3-diketones, β-keto-esters, and analogous substances. The biological properties of the substances were not examined and this is certainly something which should be carried out in the future.

Polynuclear Heterocyclic Aromatic Types. Part II [92]

In this paper, the conception of the anhydronium base was greatly extended and a number of new types were synthesised. In some of these the conjugated system included double bonds in 5-rings, and long conjugated chains in such anhydronium bases gave rise to visible colour. The theory predicted the course of alkylation in heterocyclic series containing two or more nitrogen atoms, and in analogous systems. The genesis of the idea of the aromatic sextet (see page 122) was in part due to a consideration of the formation, reactions and properties of anhydronium salts.

The Synthesis of Certain 2-Styrylchromonol Derivatives [97]

Synthetical Experiments in the Isoflavone Group. Part I [98]

The Morphine Group. Part IV. A New Oxidation Product of Codeine [105]

My collaborator in this work was R.S. Cahn who later became editor of the Journal of the Chemical Society and is an influential member of the I.U.P.A.C. committee on nomenclature. Oxidation of codeine with very dilute permanganate was shown to yield dihydroxydihydrocodeine by attack of the double bond.

2,3,4-Trinitrotoluene [114]

Publication of this work, carried on in Liverpool (see page 108) was delayed until 1926.

Synthetical Experiments in the Phenanthrene Group of the Alkaloids. Part I [116]

This paper, which describes a series of ups and downs in the development of the route to apoporphines, is based on work started in Sydney, but not published. It is mentioned that a specimen of the methosulphate of isoapomorphine dimethyl ether had survived the disastrous fire at Sydney University. This was further examined by J. Shinoda in Manchester and the original work was naturally much elaborated. The route to aporphines starts with condensation between pseudo-bases of the isoquinoline series and substituted *o*-nitrotoluene. The fact that Gadamer and collaborators had taken over this method of synthesis of aporphines with interesting results is also mentioned. This paper contains some further interesting work for which the original must be consulted.

Years later I met Dr. Shinoda again during the course of a visit to Japan and learnt that he had become the director of the research laboratory of an important firm manufacturing pharmaceuticals.

The Fission of Some Methoxylated Benzophenones [121]

Synthetical Experiments in the Isoflavone Group. Part II. A Synthesis of Methylgenistein (Methylprunetol) Dimethyl Ether and the Constitution of Prunetol (Genistein) [123]

This paper described an extension of the method of the synthesis of isoflavones to some relatively simple members of the group found as natural products.

Polynuclear Heterocyclic Aromatic Types. Part III. Pyrroloquinoline Derivatives [137]

The Fischer Indole synthesis is only with difficulty extended to the preparation of pyrrolopyridines. However, as the experiments here described show, the reaction can be realised in some cases.

3-Hydroxycyclohexylacetolactone [141]

m-Hydroxyphenylacetic acid was reduced, albeit in poor yield, to a secondary alcohol which readily lactonised. This substance has a similar ring structure to that occurring in morphine and it was hoped to extend the work in ramifying directions. However, A. Zaki, my collaborator, had to return to Egypt where he had a distinguished career.

Facile Ring-closure to a Derivative of Dihydroisoquinoline contrasted with the Difficulty of Analogous Formation of a Derivative of Isoindole [145]

The substance chosen could theoretically cyclise so as to form either a 5- or a 6-ring. The product was exclusively the latter.

Attempts to find New Antimalarials. Parts I to IV [173]

Extensive work organised by the Chemotherapy Committee of the Medical Research Council was co-ordinated with similar studies in U.S.A. and was undertaken in the hope of finding more effective drugs than plasmochin and atebrin which, along with quinine, were at that time the best known antimalarials. Our own contribution covered at first a moderately wide field. The reputed action of harmine as an antimalarial was soon discounted but led to the production of pyrolloquinolines; no significant activity was displayed by any of the substances tested. We turned our attention to a narrower field and studied substances made from 6-methoxy-8-aminoquinoline, especially the secondary amines derived therefrom. For example, the methoxyaminquinoline reacted with a bromoalkylphthalimide to give a secondary base which was hydrolysed by successive treatment with hydrazine and aqueous hydrochloric acid. The aminopropyl-aminomethoxyquinoline was approximately equal in activity to plasmochin; by repeating this process so as to obtain aminopropyl-aminopropylamino as a side chain we obtained a still more active substance. The tests were made at Cambridge on canaries infected with plasmodia and were obtained in two separate sets of trials. However, they were not confirmed by another worker in an industrial group. Later, in Oxford, we also found that 6-methoxy-8-allylamino-quinoline was an active substance approximately equivalent to plasmochin. None of the substances prepared during those few years, either here or in U.S.A., was ever brought into medical practice. A few years later the discovery of paludrine by chemists of Imperial Chemical Industries provided a really effective remedy for the disease and has revolutionised its treatment world wide. The substance is an aryldiguanine and thus could not have been encountered by following any of the earlier leads. According to reports some strains of plasmodia have accustomed themselves to the drug; consequently paludrine may have received a set-back in some areas. Metabolism of paludrine in the animal organism furnishes by one route a substance in which a new ring has been closed between the diguanidine chain and the aromatic nucleus. The resulting substance was stated to be one hundred times as active an antimalarial as paludrine. So far as I know this highly active substance has not been employed as an antimalarial. What may be called the classical programme has resulted in the discovery of another good antimalarial, namely chloroquine.

Anthoxanthins. Part XII. Transition from a Flavylium Salt to a Flavone, Illustrated by a New Synthesis of Scutellarein Tetramethyl Ether [179]

The method developed in this paper is certainly an interesting one but the actual process employed was far too complex to be of general use. In the final stage a flavone-imine was hydrolysed by alkali with formation of a flavone. Going back another stage, a 4-amino-flavylium chloride could be formally regarded as the salt of the imine and was itself produced from the amide of a 4-carboxyflavylium chloride by the Hofmann reaction. If I were to take this matter up again I would look for a simple synthesis of the 4-amino compounds. It is unlikely that this would be found in the action of ammonia on the flavylium salt because the tendency to obtain the two amino derivatives would probably divert the reaction into undesired channels. The original of this paper should be consulted.

Chapter X

Brazilin

CONTINUATION OF THE STUDY OF BRAZILIN AND HAEMOTOXYLIN
AND THEIR DERIVATIVES

Although the determination of the structure of brazilinic acid
(see page 33) was decisive evidence against the molecular structure
of brazilin suggested by Perkin, various substances related to the latter were prepared before we knew that the brazilin was constructed
on different lines. This was extremely fortunate as it was this work
which led to the discovery of the pyrylium salt synthesis by the
condensation of derivatives of salicylaldehyde. with ketones of the
type $R-CO-CH_2-OMe$ (see p. 124). After the early synthesis had
led us to a recognition of the correct structures of brazilin and
haematoxylin, there remained two major problems concerning the
chemistry of the derivatives of these substances which called urgent-
ly for further study. These were the chemistry of brazilein and that
of trimethylbrazilone. Naturally, the corresponding haematoxylin
derivatives are also concerned, but this is the last mention that will
be made of this fact, unless some specific point of difference emer-
ges later in this narrative. Perkin wished to study the brazilein derivatives himself and asked me to take charge of those of trimethylbrazilone. This division of labour was not strictly observed and I carried out all the work that became necessary on brazylium salts obtained from methylated brazilein. The oxidation of O-trimethylbrazilein by chromic anhydride in acetic acid solution was apparently
first carried out by von Kostanecki in 1902 (Bolina, von Kostanecki
and Tambor, Ber. 1902, *35*, 1675). It was also investigated by
Herzig in 1904 (Ber. 1904, *37*, 631) who prepared anhydrotrimethylbrazilone and some of its derivatives. However, up to this stage
no reasonable suggestion was made as to the constitution of trimethylbrazilone, and it was not until 1909 (W.H.P. and R.R. [6])
that the course of the reaction was elucidated. Meanwhile Perkin and

Gilbody (A.W. Gilbody and W.H.P., J. Chem. Soc. 1902, *81*, 1048) extended the work and added the interesting reactions with concentrated nitric acid and with phenylhydrazine. In the former case the elements of nitric acid are added to a carbon of the inner ring system and to the catechol ether group; the product was accordingly named nitrohydroxydihydrotrimethylbrazilone. The latter reaction removed two oxygen atoms from the trimethylbrazilone molecule and the product was termed deoxytrimethylbrazilone (Gilbody and Perkin, loc. cit.). This substance occupied a prominent position in our thoughts in planning the synthesis of brazilin derivatives. It was obvious from the early Manchester days, that if water could be added to this compound, trimethylbrazilin might result. All our efforts in this direction failed but, parenthetically, it may be noted that the reaction has recently been accomplished by hydroboration (B.S. Kirkiacharian, Compt. rend. 1972, *274C*, 2096). Deoxtrimethylbrazilone can also be called O-trimethylanhydrobrazilin. In later years the required dehydration of brazilin derivatives has indeed been effected in various ways (cf. J.N. Chatterjea, R.R. and M.L. Tomlinson [630]). The formation of trimethylbrazilone was early thought to depend on oxidation of the carbon atoms in positions-3 and -4 of the pyran ring to carbonyl groups, but to accommodate the ready formation of anhydrotrimethylbrazilone, internal condensation to a β-hydroxyketone was assumed [6]. Later, we found that this was incorrect and trimethylbrazilone contains two carbonyl groups in a nine membered ring. The I.R. absorption spectrum includes two carbonyl bands which are almost exactly reproduced in simpler models (K.W. Bentley, R.H. Jaeger and R.R., unpublished). Trimethylbrazilone undergoes remarkable molecular transformations.

α-Anhydrotrimethylbrazilone

The salts of this substance are produced by the action of bases on trimethylbrazilone or its acyl derivatives. By reaction with acid anhydrides it was found that acyl derivatives of the α-anhydro compound are obtained. α-Anhydrotrimethylbrazilone is a β-naphthol derivative; this was indicated by colour reactions such as formation of azo-compounds on coupling with aryldiazonium salts, and specific tests such as that with chloroform and alcoholic potassium hydroxide which gives a bluish-green colouration. The derivatives of α-anhydrotrimethylbrazilone are readily nitrated in position-1 of the naphthol nucleus and, after reduction of the nitro-naphthol, can be oxidised to a β-naphthaquinone derivative (trimethylbrazanquinone) which condenses with aromatic *ortho*-diamines with formation of highly characteristic phenazine derivatives. Direct oxidation of the α-anhydrotrimethylbrazilone with ferric chloride couples two molecules at the 1-position to give a product which can be dehydrated to a substituted bis-naphthalene oxide.

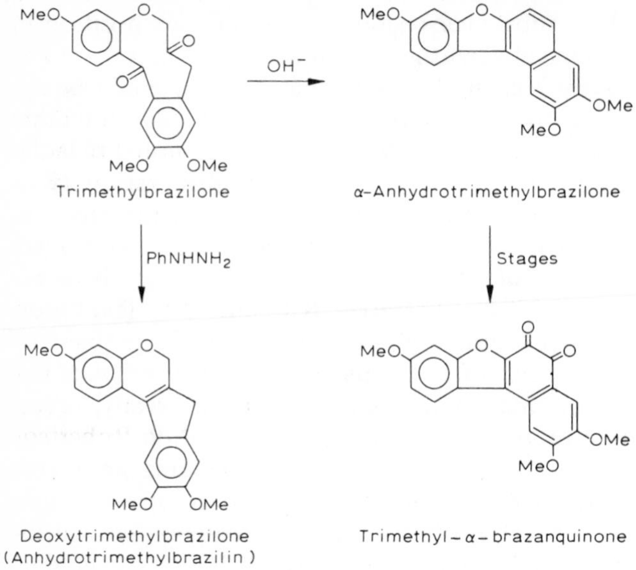

Trimethylbrazilone   α–Anhydrotrimethylbrazilone

Deoxytrimethylbrazilone   Trimethyl–α–brazanquinone
(Anhydrotrimethylbrazilin)

ψ-Trimethylbrazilone

The action of sulphuric acid on trimethylbrazilone had been examined by von Kostanecki (Ber. 1902, *35*, 1675), Herzig (Ber. 1904, *37*, 631), and their collaborators. The product is an acid, termed ψ-trimethylbrazilone, isomeric with the starting material. It is produced as the result of an interesting molecular rearrangement which takes us far from the original brazilin skeleton. It should be realised that neither von Kostanecki nor Herzig had a glimmering of an idea as to the nature of that skeleton and an unfortunate result was that a name based on brazan was given to a substance which is very far from being justly regarded as a brazilin derivative. Hence we cannot use the term brazan in any satisfactory manner in a system of nomenclature in the group and to circumvent this difficulty we have recently suggested that the basic brazilin skeleton may be termed brazilane. In the following procedure the trouble was that trimethylbrazilone was first changed to ψ-trimethylbrazilone and this was also demethylated and dehydrated, thereby forming an α-naphthol derivative. The latter was the first isolated product in this series and when it was distilled over zinc dust a benzphenylene oxide (termed brazan) was produced.

In considering the possible course of reactions leading to the formation of ψ-trimethylbrazilone it seemed clear that one of the carbonyl groups had become carboxyl and consequently the other carbonyl group must have lost its oxygen. We found that oxidation of ψ-trimethylbrazilone with permanganate gave 4,5-dimethoxyhomophthalic acid; hence the methylene groups of this substance had not taken part in the isomerisation process which must be assumed. A plausible mechanism [6] for the latter is illustrated in the scheme below. The α-naphthol ring can be closed in various ways as, for example, by heating ψ-trimethylbrazilone with acetic anhydride. This procedure affords the acetate of β-anhydrotrimethylbrazilone. This substance was synthesised by K.W. Bentley and R.R. [493] whilst α-anhydrotrimethylbrazilone has been synthesised by A.R. Robertson (P.C. Johnson, A.R. Robertson, J. Chem. Soc. 1950, 2391). It is rather unfortunate that an α-anhydrotrimethylbrazilone is a β-naphthol and that a β-anhydrotrimethylbrazilone is an α-naphthol. Hence we have recently suggested that the Greek letters hitherto used may be dispensed with altogether especially since the substance previously called β-anhydrotrimethylbrazilone is a result of a complex rearrangement. An interesting degradation series [6] was realised in a study of the action of hypobromite on ψ-trimethylbrazilone. The reaction afforded a chalky white precipitate which could not be recrystallised but which, after careful drying, was found to have the composition $C_{18}H_{15}O_6Br$ (loss of one C from the precursor). When the dry substance was boiled with chloroform, hydrogen bromide was evolved and a pale yellow crystalline compound ($C_{18}H_{14}O_6$) was obtainable from the solution. We consider this substance to be trimethoxycoumarano-isocoumarin and the original chalky substance was its hydrobromide. When the latter was hydrolysed with alkali it afforded a phenolic lactone which gave a violet colouration with ferric chloride. After methylation and oxidation with permanganate,

2,4-dimethoxybenzoic acid and metahemipinic acid were obtained.

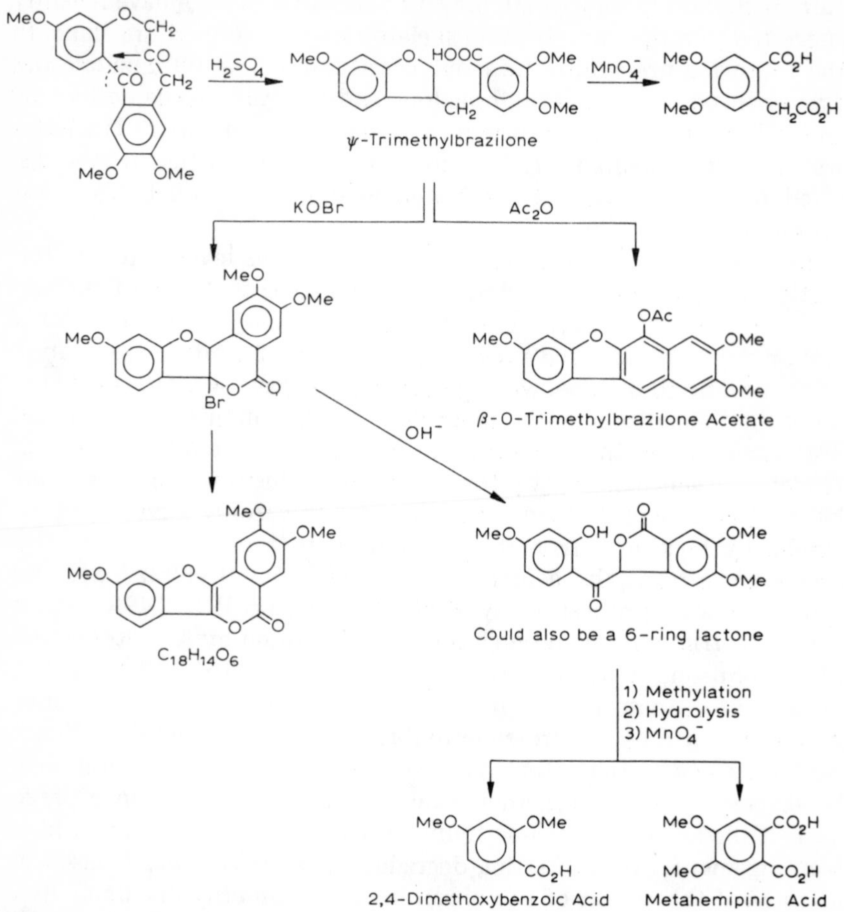

ψ-Trimethylbrazilone

β-O-Trimethylbrazilone Acetate

$C_{18}H_{14}O_6$

Could also be a 6-ring lactone

1) Methylation
2) Hydrolysis
3) MnO_4^-

2,4-Dimethoxybenzoic Acid

Metahemipinic Acid

The reaction whereby trimethyl brazilone is converted by treatment with phenylhydrazine into trimethyldeoxybrazilone was discovered as a result of Perkin's uncanny gift for a choice of a suitable reagent and, following that, his capacity for keen observation. K.W. Bentley (private communication, later *The Chemistry of Natural Products*, Vol. IV, Interscience, New York, 1966, p. 82) has suggested that this reduction is a reaction involving the monophenylhydrazone as an intermediate; he thought it probable that the phenylhydrazine was oxidised to benzenediazonium salt.

Brazylium Salts and Their Synthesis

J.J. Hummel and A.G. Perkin (J. Chem. Soc. 1882, *41*, 367) found that strong mineral acids, for example concentrated sulphuric acid, converted brazilein into red salt-like substances termed iso-brazilein salts. Nothing much could be done with these substances which were early recognised as oxonium salts. The methylated brazil-eins obtained by P. Engles, W.H.P. and R.R. [5] could also be con-verted in strong acid into methylated isobrazilein salts which were at first described as anhydropyranol salts and then as pyrylium salts — the particular class as brazylium salts. A very characteristic member of this group was obtained from trimethylbrazilein, first by treatment with hot dilute alkali which adds water to a quino-noid group, and then by methylation of the new phenolic function. This O-tetramethyldihydrobrazileinol is converted by treatment with acid into O-trimethylbrazylium salts. These are highly characteris-tic substances fluorescing bright green at high dilution in weakly acid-ic aqueous solution. The ferrichloride crystallises from acetic acid as coppery leaflets having a rather sharp melting point. Its formation from trimethylbrazilein involves the following stages.

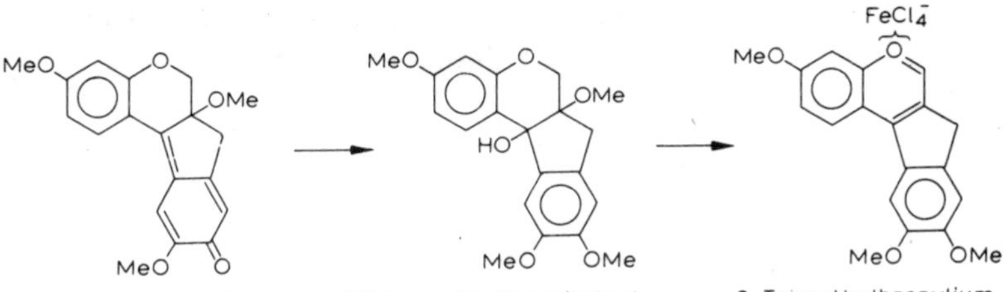

O-Trimethylbrazilein   O-Tetramethylbrazileinol   O-Trimethylbrazylium ferrichloride

This substance was synthesised by Crabtree and R.R. [47, 56] dur-ing my period at Liverpool. The paper describing it included a note on a different subject, namely a possibility that brazilin derivatives could be synthesised from a substituted coumarin made by conden-sing resorcinol with suitably substituted indan-1-onecarboxylic acid (or ester). The simplest possible example of such a coumarin deriva-tive was mentioned in the Crabtree, R.R. papers (with J.A. Prescott).

The completion of this work so as to obtain a brazilin derivative was effected in 1947 but for various reasons disclosure was delayed and the communication on this subject has only recently been pub-lished [630].

Formation of brazylium salt from deoxytrimethylbrazilone (anhydrotrimethylbrazilin) takes place very easily in the presence of acid under a variety of conditions but the best method is to react the substance with bromine in acetone. On the addition to a solution of ferric chloride in hydrochloric acid the O-trimethylbrazylium ferrichloride is precipitated in almost quantitative yield. The synthesis of deoxytrimethylbrazilone is mentioned below (p. 177).

Constitution of Brazilein

It is obvious that brazilein is a quinonoid substance involving a keto group derivable from one of the hydroxyls of the resorcinol nucleus or the appropriate hydroxyl of the catechol nucleus. If, instead of methylating O-trimethyldihydrobrazileinol, we prepare an ethyl ether, the resulting ethoxyl group will mark the position of the quinonoid oxygen in the O-trimethylbrazilein. Hence we synthesised the two isomeric O-ethyl-O-dimethylbrazylium ferrichlorides having the constitution thus indicated. The Crabtree/R.R. synthesis was used for the preparation of the ethyldimethylbrazylium salt having the ethoxyl group in the resorcinol, whereas the synthesis via a deoxyethyldimethylbrazilone followed closely the synthesis of trimethylbrazilone itself (M.V. Mičovič and R.R. [341]). Of the former, only the last stages are depicted below.

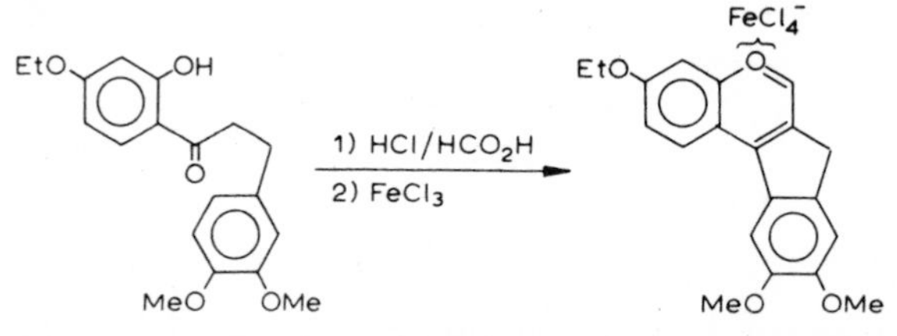

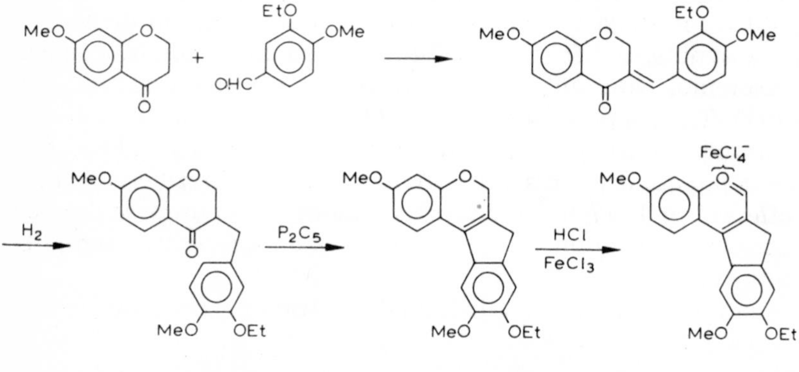

The two isomeric brazylium ferrichlorides had sufficiently different melting points and showed a depressed melting point on admixture. The result was a demonstration that trimethylbrazilein is quinonoid in the catechol nucleus. This does not carry with it a determination of the constitution of brazilein itself but it can at least be said that the methylation of brazilein does not afford isomeric trimethyl ethers.

Synthesis of Trimethylbrazilone and Deoxytrimethylbrazilone

The method foreshadowed for these syntheses was indicated as early as 1912 in a paper (W.H.P. and R.R., Proc. Chem. Soc. 1912, 28) on the synthesis of 3-veratrylidene-7-methoxychromanone. It was clearly understood at that time that this substance was to be reduced to a dihydro-derivative and then cyclodehydrated to deoxytrimethylbrazilone. As a result of our preoccupation with other topics a preliminary statement of our intention was not followed for some years by further work. By curious coincidence, when we did take it up, P. Pfeiffer and his collaborators had also decided to follow up this particular line of research (cf. P. Pfeiffer, O. Angern, E. Haack and J. Willems, Ber. 1928, *61B*, 839 and 1923). For an explanation of the complex situation that followed I must ask the reader to refer to W.H.P., J.N. Rây and R.R., parts II [138] and III [161], dealing with attempts to synthesise brazilin and its derivatives. A salient point was the finding of a good method of catalytic hydrogenation of the starting material to its dihydro-derivative. This proved more difficult than might have been expected and we overcame the obstacles by the use of protocatechualdehyde instead of veratraldehyde in the original condensation. Eventually the synthesis of deoxytrimethylbrazilone was completed by both groups of workers but at that time no success followed the attempts to hydrate this substance to give trimethylbrazilin. It was reduced to a dihydro-derivative and this was oxidised to trimethylbrazilone.

In the haematoxylin series Pfeiffer and colleagues synthesised the tetramethyl derivatives, whereas we made the bis-ethylene ether. In one of the later papers of the series (W.H.P., J.N. Rây and R.R.) a method for the synthesis of brazilin and haematoxylin themselves was indicated [161].

Synthesis of Brazilin and Haematoxylin

I have thought it desirable to include the later work on brazilin and haematoxylin for the sake of continuity of treatment, in spite of the fact that it lies beyond the scope of Vol. I of these memoirs. The idea was a simple one, namely to prepare an acylated brazilone, to reduce this to a pinacol and remove the acyl groups by hydrolysis. We anticipated that this might yield *dl*-brazilein. The stages are illustrated by the part formulae below. The problem of the synthesis of brazilin required for its solution also a satisfactory method of reduction of brazilein to brazilin and, later, for the optical resolution of *dl*-brazilin. The work was carried out in the Dyson Perrins Laboratory in 1955, but only published in 1970 [623]. O-Triacetylbrazilone is most easily obtained by the oxidation of triacetylbrazilin with chromic anhydride under the usual conditions for this type of reaction. However, for the sake of total synthesis, deoxytrimethylbrazilone was catalytically reduced to a dihydro-derivative which was successively demethylated and acetylated to O-triacetylbrazilane. This could be oxidised in the usual way to triacetylbrazilone identical with the substance obtained by oxidation of triacetylbrazilin. On reduction with zinc dust and acetic acid the pinacol was produced as anticipated, and when this was hydrolysed with alkali *dl*-brazilein was the product. It was found that this compound could be reduced by means of potassium borohydride to give the hitherto undescribed *dl*-brazilin. The optical resolution was effected by crystallisation of its tetra-*l*-menthoxyacetates. We were very much assisted at this stage by the excellent experimental work carried out by Dr. L.J. Goldsworthy. The tetramenthoxyacetyl derivatives of the *d*-brazilin could be purified by crystallisation. On hydrolysis it afforded *d*-brazilin identical with the natural product. The synthesis of *d*-haematoxylin was carried out in an analogous manner. The U.V. absorptions of the natural and synthetic materials were identical as far as the various bands were concerned, but the ε values of the synthetic materials were usually smaller than the corresponding natural products. This was certainly due to the fact that after a long series of operations the material available was relatively small and the minute amount of yellow colouring matter, the formation of which could not be avoided, had a relatively large blanketing effect on the absorption. In contrast, a large sample of brazilin could be crystallised until it was free from coloured oxidation products and the U.V. absorption bands were then found to be more intense.

The formulae illustrating this synthesis are written according to the I.U.P.A.C. convention, which we also used in later publications.

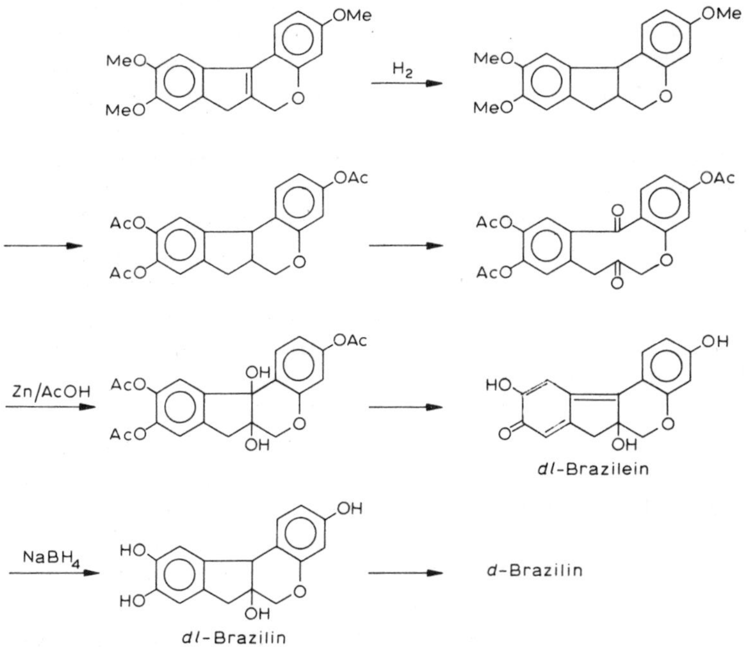

d*l*-Brazilein

d*l*-Brazilin

d-Brazilin

Another paper, based on work carried out in 1947, has recently been re-examined and — as has already been mentioned — was published in 1974 (Chatterjea, R.R. and Tomlinson, loc.cit.). This had a chequered career even in 1972 and 1973. The subject matter included the dehydration of trimethylbrazilin, some new derivatives of haematoxylin and, perhaps mainly, the completion of the synthesis of brazilin derivatives by way of the coumarins as briefly outlined above. Unfortunately the results were interpreted as proof of the formation of a *trans*-brazilin structure but we were never quite satisfied with this idea and eventually it proved to be erroneous. The paper was accordingly withdrawn and all mention of *trans*-brazilin excised from it.

Reductive Dimerisation of Brazilein

Herzig and Pollak and other collaborators (J. Herzig et al., Monatsh. 1901, 22, 211 et seq.) reduced brazilein with zinc dust, acetic acid and acetic anhydride under several sets of conditions, and obtained a series of products of which one was recognised in our group to be O-triacetylanhydrobrazilin, but perhaps the most interesting product obtained by Herzig and his colleagues was a high melting substance regarded as a tetraacetate. This has been carefully examined by Dr. R.H. Jaeger and Dr. P.M. Lewis with the result that they have demonstrated the true nature of the substance, primarily as the result of NMR studies [631]. In the reductive acetylation two molecules of brazilein are joined at the 4-positions of each by reductive dimerization and the hydroxyls are acetylated. Professor D. Crowfoot-Hodgkin has undertaken the X-Ray crystallographic study of this substance as it will be interesting to determine its stereochemistry and perhaps to note any abnormality in the 4,4'-bond. Professor W.D. Ollis has informed me in a personal communication that one of his collaborators at Bristol, J.R. Herbert (1960—1963) examined the reduction of 7-hydroxy-2-methylisoflavylium chloride, using zinc dust and acetic anhydride at room temperature, as a model for the synthesis of the rotenoid munduserone. This reaction yields two diasteroisomeric dimeric products which have been shown by R. Somanathan at Sheffield University to contain two isoflavan residues linked through their 4-positions. ·

The possibility that stereoisomerides are obtained by reductive acetylation of brazilein exists, but the substance isolated by crystallisation appears to be homogeneous [631].

Mechanism of Reductive Dimerisation of Brazilein

The first process in the reductive dimerisation of brazilein with zinc and acetic acid cannot be the reduction of the quinone nucleus because the product would be brazilin, and we have found in independent trials that brazilin is unchanged by zinc and acetic acid under the conditions employed. Hence, stage I should be a reaction involving the removal of the hydroxyl in position-3. Under the acid conditions an allylic change is feasible, and this would produce a substance containing the group:

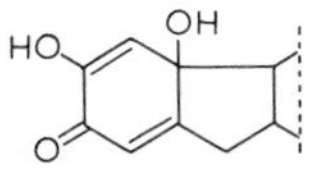

Stage II is the reduction of the quinone alkide to a phenol, a facile transformation for which many analogies are available (cf. Bamberger's work on the "Chinole").

Stage III is the tautomerism of the alkylidenediarylmethane derivative which affords deoxybrazilein.

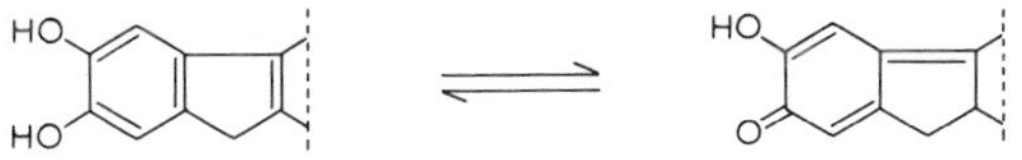

Stage IV: Finally, the reductive dimerisation of deoxybrazilein clearly involves coupling the radicals, the lone electrons being on positions-4 in two molecules.

These radicals are produced by a one electron reduction of the quinone-methide, followed by attachment of a proton to the oxygen atom. This stage has occasionally been attributed to the formation of a radical ion, but the term has little meaning when the ion is phenoxide or alkoxide, and the medium is strongly acidic. Indeed, the exact sequence of processes is unknown. It may be that the carbonyl combines with a hydrogen atom, which is split so that a proton is attached to oxygen, and an electron to carbon. In this case the oxygen octet can be preserved as shown below, but the configuration associated with carbon is one electron short until dimerisation makes up for the deficiency.

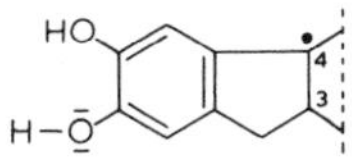

The suggested mechanism does not exclude the formation of other reduction products under the conditions of the experiment, and some of these have in fact been isolated [631].

Using borohydride, Morsingh and R.R. obtained brazilin as a chief product [623].

Stages I and II may be combined, in that the rate determining process may well be the allylic transformation. When the hydroxyl reaches the benzene nucleus, reduction should follow very rapidly.

182

A similar situation may arise in the case of stages III and IV, though both the transformations assumed should be facile. Doubtless the second aryl group (resorcinol type) makes a contribution to the appearance of the free radical on position-4. This is commonly understood in a general fashion, as a result of comparison of reactions in the substituted toluene, diarylmethane, and triarylmethane series, but it is difficult to express this in terms of a qualitative electronic theory. Doubtless the wave mechanical methods could throw light on this aspect.

TWO RECENT DEVELOPMENTS 1972/74

The Optical Activity of Brazilic Acid

There is no reason why the permanganate oxidation of O-trimethylbrazilin should cause the racemisation of the asymmetric carbon at position-3 in the chroman nucleus. Hence brazilic acid should be optically active but W.H.P. did not examine it in this respect.

Professor W.D. Ollis and Dr. M.M. Mahandru at Sheffield University implemented a scheme based on a device formerly used for a preparation of petunidin with the object of improving the yield of brazilic acid which was quite small (0.7%) in the original work. The idea was to burn away an unprotected catechol nucleus in 7-O-methylbrazilin. This compound was prepared by diphenylmethylenation of brazilin, followed by methylation of the free phenolic hydroxyl group and hydrolysis of the diphenylmethylene ether. The 7-O-methylbrazilin was oxidised by permanganate and afforded brazilic acid which was found to be optically active ($[\alpha]_D^{CHCl_3}$ = +26.4°).

Professor Ollis has informed me that a new synthesis of dl-brazilic acid has now been carried out by Dr. Mahandru and that the product is a well crystallised material, in marked contrast with the description given by Pfeiffer et al. of a synthetic product alleged to be dl-brazilic acid.

The Synthesis of Brazilane Derivatives by way of Substituted Indeno-coumarins.

Previous references to this project made it clear that we expected to be able to reduce the pyran nucleus with formation of brazilane and anhydrobrazilin methyl ethers, and this has now been accomplished [630].

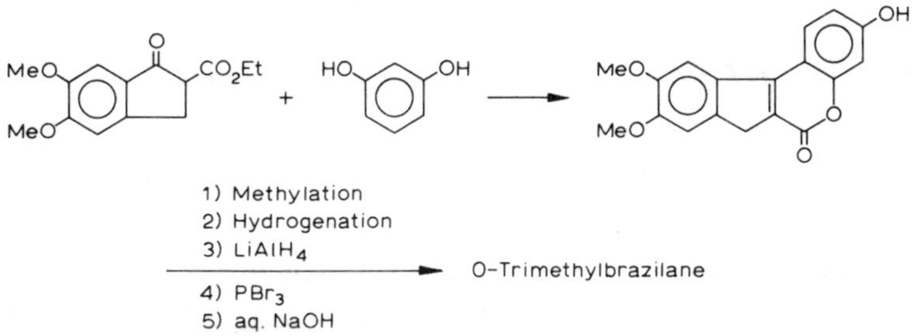

The route joins that of Morsingh and R.R. when the brazilane derivative is oxidised to trimethylbrazilone.

Biosynthesis of Brazilin

Professor Holger Erdtman has very kindly drawn my attention to the existence of a natural product which he suggests may give a clue to the biogenesis of brazilin. The substance is scillascillin which occurs in *Scilla scilloidis*. The very unusual feature of the molecular make-up of this compound is that it has a 4-ring, as shown in the annexed formula (I. Kuono, T. Komori and T. Kawasaki, Tetrahedron Letters 1973, 4569).

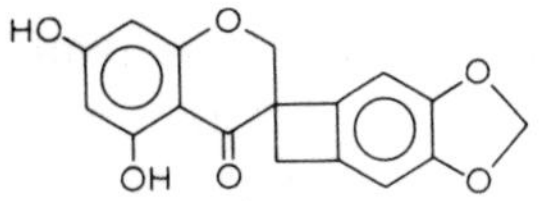

Following known analogies, the secondary alcohol corresponding to this ketone can undergo a molecular rearrangement, giving the brazilin skeleton with hydroxyl in position-3.

Chapter XI

Development of an Electronic Theory

The development of these ideas constituted, in the writer's opinion, his most important contribution to knowledge. The starting point was the theory of partial valency which differed from the well known views of J. Thiele in an important respect. Thiele suggested that an unsaturated atom possesses a partial or residual valency in addition to those normally represented by ordinary bonds. My idea was that of bonds themselves being split and thus providing partial valencies. The difference between the two conceptions may appear exiguous but turned out to be important in that the theory of divisable valency could be used to illustrate reaction mechanistic theories which were capable of direct translation on the basis of electronic theory of valency. The theory of divisable valency was occasionally used by authors who imagined that they were explaining Thiele's hypothesis; for example, a small text book written by de Barry Barnett includes a figure which employs divisable valency to provide an explanation of 1,4-addition to butadiene.

However, no further comment for the adoption of this scheme was made. A second stage of the development in my own theoretical ideas was the recognition that when a bond is divided it will *ipso facto* be polarised. At first two dotted lines marked + and − were used, but later the dotted line marked + was not included because it represented a quantity in defect. At this stage the electronic theory of valency was already recognised as the basis of a complete theory but the full change from partial valency to polarised covalent bonds was only published in 1922, although it was used in lectures during the preceding six years. In 1916 I wrote as follows [35]:

" In general agreement with the theory of chemical reactivity advocated by Baly (*J. Amer. Chem. Soc.*, 1915, **37**, 981—982), it seems probable that such movements are the characteristic feature of all chemical reactions resulting in formation of stable additive products, or which are formally represented as substitutions or decompositions. It will be necessary to assume the disruption of partial valencies connecting two atoms as well as the possibility of combination by residual affinity. The following examples of the representation of reactions on these lines may be appended :

Kekulé's theory of the chlorination of methane :

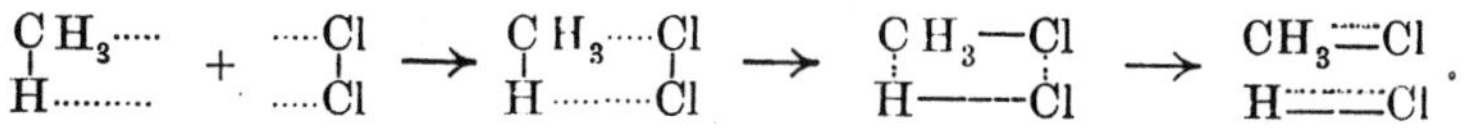

$$\begin{matrix} C\,H_3\text{\ldots} \\ H\text{\ldots} \end{matrix} + \begin{matrix} \text{\ldots}Cl \\ \text{\ldots}Cl \end{matrix} \rightarrow \begin{matrix} C\,H_3\text{\ldots}Cl \\ H\text{\ldots}Cl \end{matrix} \rightarrow \begin{matrix} C\,H_3\text{—}Cl \\ H\text{———}Cl \end{matrix} \rightarrow \begin{matrix} CH_3\text{==}Cl \\ H\text{==}Cl \end{matrix} .$$

Stewart's explanation of the transmutation of ethylene isomerides (P., 1905, 21, 73) :

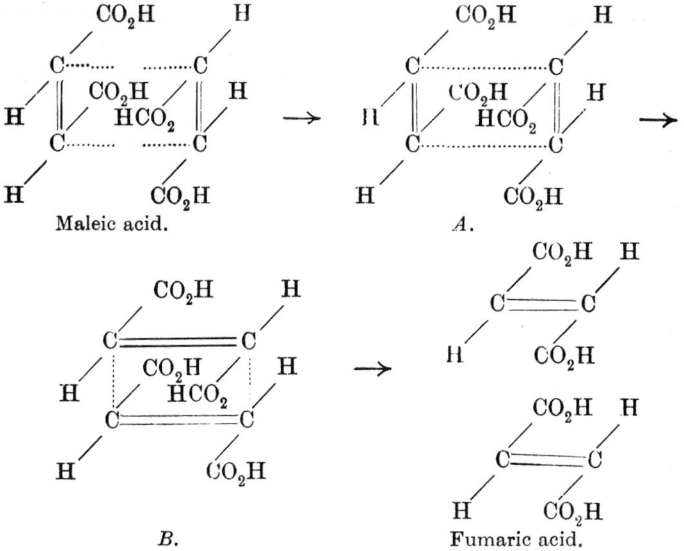

Maleic acid. $A.$

$B.$ Fumaric acid.

In this case the change from A to B, which involves the alteration in position of electrons, need not pass through the stage of *cyclo*butane-tetracarboxylic acid.

It is in connexion with molecular rearrangement and migration that the advantage of the expression of all the partial valencies, or what may be called the unsaturation of the single bond, becomes most apparent, since the authors have become convinced tnat the majority, if not all, such changes are best explained by the assumption of preliminary ring-formation with the aid of partial valency. The pinacone-pinacolin change may be cited as an example. Accepting the theory that the pinacone first loses water with the formation of an oxide, the latter substance will be represented as :

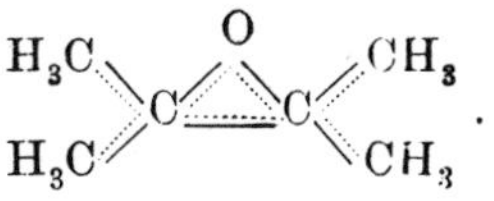

$$\begin{matrix} H_3C \\ H_3C \end{matrix} \!\!\diagdown\!\! C \overset{O}{\underset{\text{==}}{\diagup\diagdown}} C \!\!\diagup\!\! \begin{matrix} CH_3 \\ CH_3 \end{matrix} .$$

Conjugation of the partial valencies then results in the stages

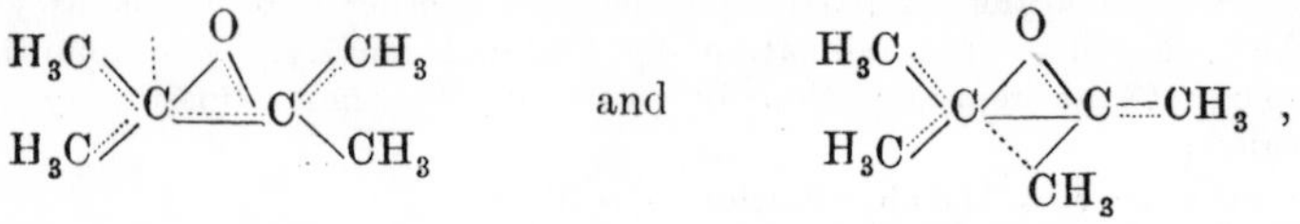

and the same condition may obviously be reached by three other similar routes. The last stage already has the same atomic arrangement as pinacolin, which is reached by a movement of electrons.

A modified view of the mechanism of the pinacol-pinacolin (also Wagner-Meerwein) rearrangement was adopted later, following a suggestion by Lapworth. In this a hydroxyl group of the pinacol accepts a proton and a molecule of water is extruded. The cation so obtained loses a proton and the rearrangement occurs as formerly contemplated. This view was first advanced during a lecture which I gave to the Chemical and Physical Society of Cambridge University.

The following exerpts from publications will show how the theory of polarised partial valencies was developed.

RESEARCHES ON PSEUDO-BASES. PART II [44].
THE MECHANISM OF PSEUDO-BASE CONDENSATION.

A representation of the mechanism of the Knoevenagel reaction, based on the assumption of a reaction between ions, was suggested by Lapworth (Hope and Robinson, *loc. cit.*, 2117), and was a great advance on the ideas existing at that time, especially as it facilitated the collation of data derived from such separate investigations as those of Knoevenagel on the use of amines, particularly secondary amines, as catalysts in condensations, of Dobbie, Lauder, and Tinkler on the spectrochemistry of pseudo-bases, and of numerous workers on the chemistry of these substances. These advantages are secured by the recognition that the reactive form of a carbinol-amine (II) is the unsaturated ammonium hydroxide (III), but instead of representing the further stages as due to ionisation, combination of the ion with a negative residue, and, finally, migration, the present authors prefer to regard the condensations as due to a simple addition of the components as illustrated in the scheme:

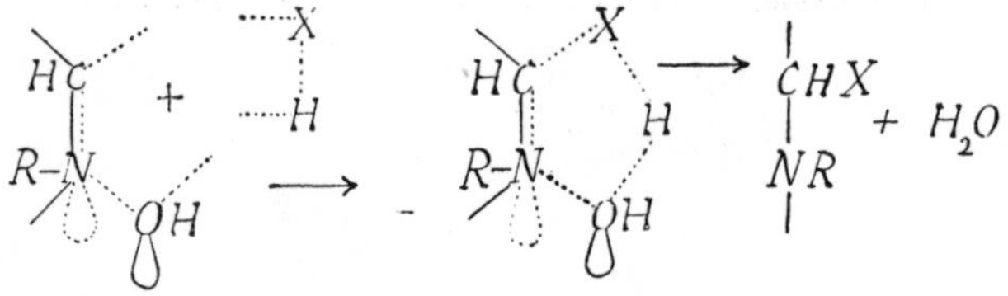

In the case of a condensation between a pseudo-base and pseudo-acid, the theory of the reaction between ions demands two intra-molecular changes, but on the hypothesis now advanced the carbon to carbon synthesis occurs in the first stage of the process and migrations are not required. This is illustrated in the case of anhydrocotarninenitromethane, and it will be seen that the *aci*-modification of nitromethane and the ammonium hydroxide form of cotarnine yield a complex (IV) in which there may be a change in affinity distribution which results in the separation of water and the production of anhydrocotarninenitromethane.

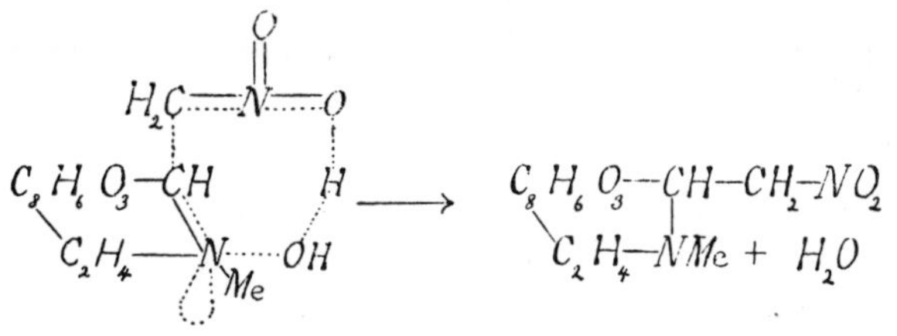

(IV.)

The essential feature of these representations is the postulation of conjugated partial dissociation as a preliminary stage of the reactions, and this is a particular case of the process described by Baly as "opening up the molecular force fields." The mode of expression is, however, slightly different from that employed in a former communication (T., 1916, **109**, 1031 * et seq., 1042).

Taking methyl iodide as an example, then, in reactions in which the iodine becomes separated from the methyl group, it is assumed that there is a partial dissociation and that the reactive molecule should be represented as ...CH_3I.... The present suggestion is merely that the partial valency so expressed shall be considered

* In this paper, the residual affinity was regarded as additional to the normal valency, not as a part of the latter. The theory of the reactions is not fundamentally altered, and in accordance with the suggested method of expression the addition of an alkyl haloid to an unsaturated base would be represented by the scheme:

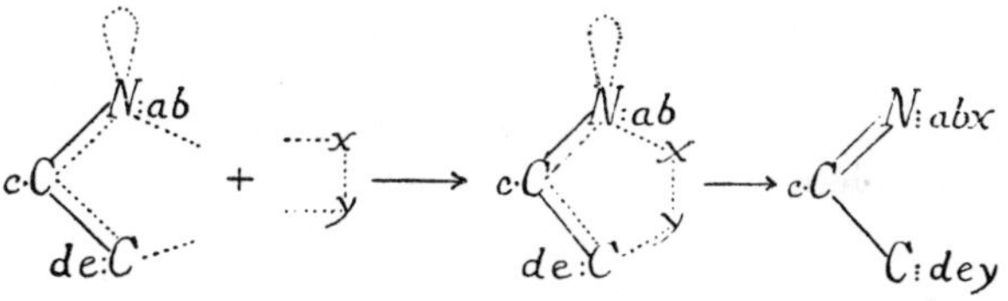

to be derived from the normal valencies and that the dissociation necessarily weakens the bond between the carbon and iodine atoms, so that the complete symbol is ...CH_3...I.... . Where a partial dissociation can be followed by complete electrolytic dissociation, there is a clue to the polarity of the partial valencies, since it may reasonably be assumed that the partial dissociation is a stage in the complete process. Further, it is clear that the partial dissociation of latent valencies must be assumed in some cases, as, for example, in the combination of ammonia with hydrochloric acid:

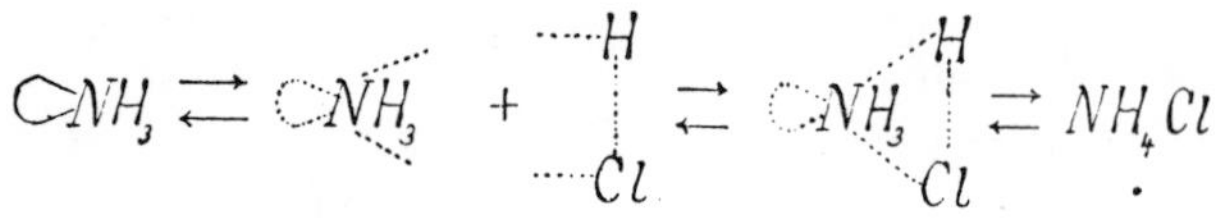

$$C{\cdot}NH_3 \rightleftarrows C{\cdot}N\ddot{H_3} + \begin{matrix} \cdots H \\ \vdots \\ \cdots Cl \end{matrix} \rightleftarrows C{\cdot}NH_3 \begin{matrix} H \\ \vdots \\ Cl \end{matrix} \rightleftarrows NH_4Cl .$$

The conjugated partial dissociation of such an ammonium hydroxide as cotarninium hydroxide is a more complex example of the same kind:

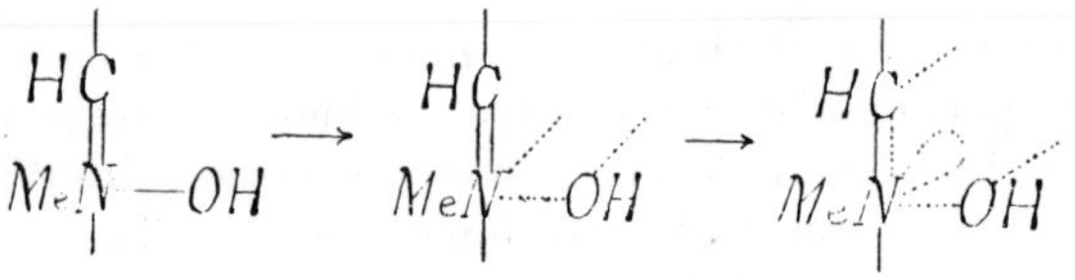

$$\begin{matrix} H\overset{|}{C} \\ \| \\ Me{\cdot}N{-}OH \\ | \end{matrix} \rightarrow \begin{matrix} H\overset{|}{C} \\ | \\ Me{\cdot}N{\cdots}OH \\ | \end{matrix} \rightarrow \begin{matrix} H\overset{|}{C} \\ | \\ Me{\cdot}N{\cdots}OH \\ | \end{matrix}$$

In partial dissociation of latent valencies, two partial valencies of opposite sign become available, and these emanate from the same atom, whereas when a normal valency is divided, the two parts will be of the same sign, so that the ring in **IV** in regard to the polarity of the partial valencies should be expressed as shown below:

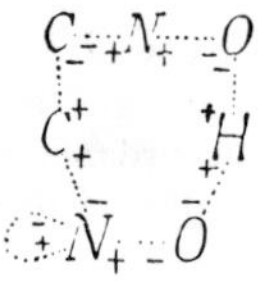

$$\begin{matrix} \overset{-}{C}{\cdot}_+\overset{}{N}{\cdots}_-O \\ \overset{+}{C}_+ \quad \overset{+}{_+}H \\ {\cdot}\overset{-}{N}_+ {\cdot}_-\overset{-}{O} \end{matrix}$$

The logical application of schemes of partial dissociation, simple and conjugated, of addition and decomposition by making and breaking of partial valencies, and of redistribution of affinity, demands the consideration of these questions of polarity and leads to a system of mechanism of reactions which appears to be capable of including the representation of chemical changes of the most varied type, and the present authors are not acquainted with any examples of reactions the course of which cannot be illustrated in the manner implied. It is true that the subdivision of units invariably supplies greater facilities for explanations, but in the present instance there is the important restriction on the elasticity of the theory which is imposed by the necessity of providing the reactive complexes with two free partial valencies of opposite sign, and this has introduced no difficulty in any case examined. In order to avoid possible misapprehension, it should be stated that reactions between ions are not excluded, but regarded as the limiting case, and, further, that it is recognised that the symbols which are used to express the activated condition of molecules can represent only a first approximation to the actual distribution of affinity.

We cannot deal with every instance in which it is imagined that the method of representation advocated has clear advantages in the summarisation of the experimental data, and we therefore confine ourselves to two reactions which have been the subject of comparatively recent controversy.

The Bromination of Ketones.

Lapworth's theory of the mechanism of the bromination of acetone and other ketones (T., 1904, **85**, 30) has received much support from subsequent experimental work, and it may be said to be universally accepted that the essential reaction is the addition of bromine to the enolic form of the ketone. Leuchs (*Ber.*, 1913, **46**, 2435), however, brominated optically active *o*-carboxy-2-benzyl-1-hydrindone and obtained 5—10 per cent. of an optically active bromo-derivative, and since the enolic form of this ketone contains no asymmetric carbon atom, it was claimed that the bromination was in part a direct substitution. In accordance with the theory of partial conjugated dissociation of an enol, however, the actual reactive conditions is not

and this reactive form is seen to be intermediate as regards its distribution of affinity between the ketone and its enolic modification. Consequently, the catalytic action of hydrobromic acid on the ketone in producing the enol will involve the reactive form of the latter as an intermediate stage. In this molecule, the partial valency preserves the asymmetric environment of the carbon atom, and the formation of an optically active bromo-derivative is therefore possible. The whole process may be represented in the following manner:

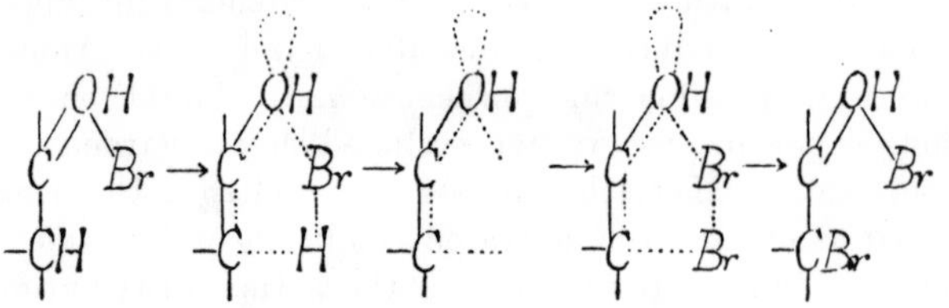

Mechanism of Diazo-coupling.

K. H. Meyer (compare "Annual Reports," 1914, **11**, 100; 1915, **12**, 115) and his co-workers hold the view that diazo-coupling is due to an addition of the diazonium salt to a double bond or conjugated double bond in the second component. Other authors, as Auwers and Michaelis, and Karrer (*loc. cit.*), are of the opinion that the reaction is in the first place one of addition to the oxygen or nitrogen atom of the phenol or amine, and that this is followed by migration. Both these views are experimentally founded and at present regarded as contradictory. The application of the theory of addition of partly dissociated complexes leads to a representation which in the present authors' opinion explains the whole of the facts, including those relating to the chemistry of the diazonium salts themselves. It has already been suggested (T., 1916, **109**, 1042) that the characteristic reactions of aromatic amines and phenols must be ascribed to additions to a conjugated unsaturated system which includes the nitrogen or oxygen atoms. The neutral and reactive phases of a phenol, such as *m*-cresol, will therefore be the following:

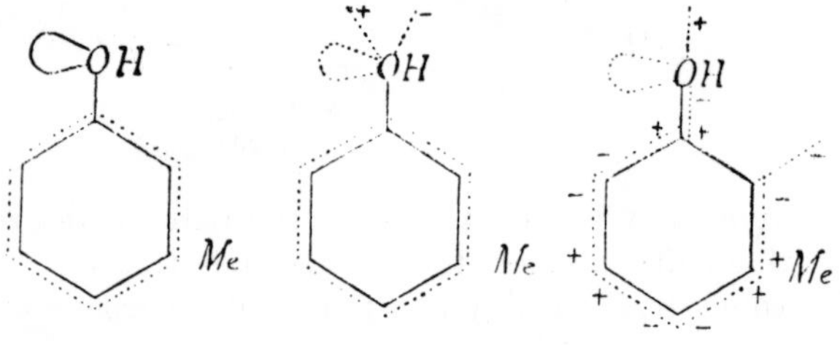

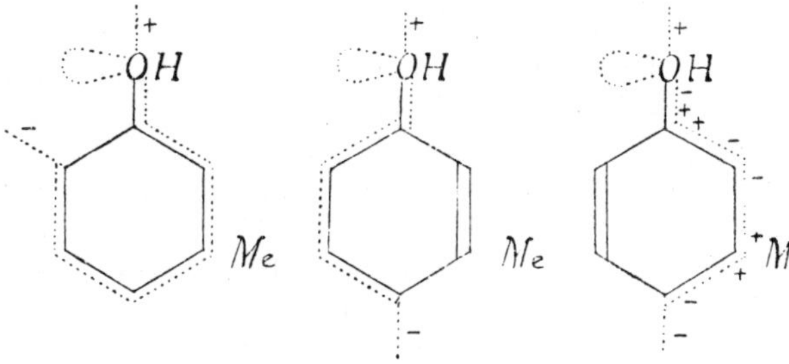

An examination of the polar properties of the partial valencies shows that the orientation rules are a direct consequence of the opposite sign of the latent valencies of elements, such as oxygen and nitrogen, but it must be remembered that in dealing with amines and phenols the effects observed are considerable and well defined, and that in connexion with the general problem of orientation in the benzene ring it may be necessary to take cognisance of even more delicate influences than the conjugation of partial valencies. The reactive phases of an aromatic amine will correspond with those figured above in the case of *m*-cresol. Addition to the unconjugated reactive modifications will involve the attachment of a group to the oxygen or nitrogen atoms, whereas addition to the molecule in its conjugated dissociated condition will involve nuclear substitution. If the former reaction is reversible, and this is usually the case, there may ensue an apparent transference of a group from oxygen or nitrogen to the nucleus, and the transformation of diazoamino-compounds into true azo-derivatives is not improbably a reaction of this type. The phenomenon is analogous to that involved in the production of mesidine from phenyltrimethylammonium chloride, and as this is a simpler case, the first stage of the process may be illustrated:

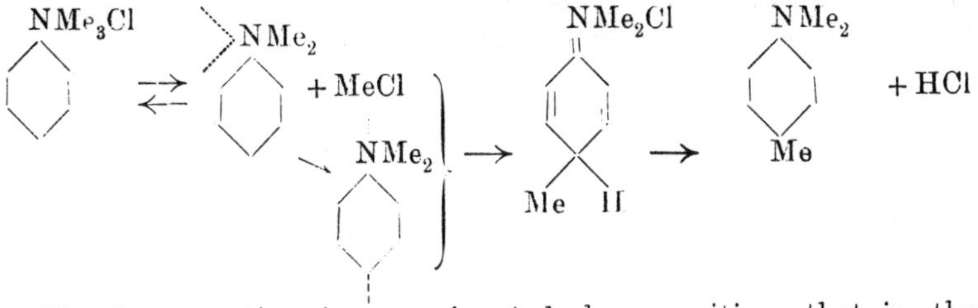

The last reaction is a conjugated decomposition, that is, the reverse of addition to a conjugated system. Such reactions are of great importance in the aromatic series, and there appears to be no valid reason why the decomposition should have a more complex mechanism than the formation of the additive product.

Turning to the diazonium compounds, it must be noted that these substances (for example, hydroxides) are in constitution and properties strikingly analogous to such substances as cotarninium hydroxide and owe their reactivity to a similar partial decomposition, which is expressed in V. Addition between the reactive phases of a phenol and of a diazonium hydroxide will result in VI, and possibly VII may then be obtained by a redistribution of affinity.

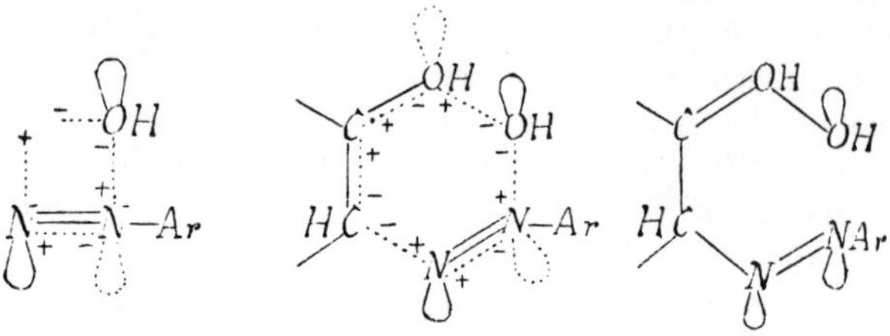

(V.)   (VI.)   (VII.)

VII is clearly the oxonium hydrate of the keto-form of an azo-phenol, but it is also the hydrate by conjugated addition of the enolic modification, and the latter may be obtained by conjugated decomposition as shown above for the precisely similar conversion of a ketone into an enol with the aid of hydrobromic acid. It should be pointed out, however, that it is unnecessary to go so far as VII in rearranging the affinity of VI. If, for example, the partial valency connecting the nitrogen atoms is broken, the natural result of the activity of the free partial valencies is indicated in VIII, IX, and X.

The above will apply to a phenol, such as β-naphthol, which couples in the ortho-position. Para-substitution will involve the inclusion of an additional double bond in the conjugated system, and it is clear that the scheme is applicable to amines as well as to phenols.

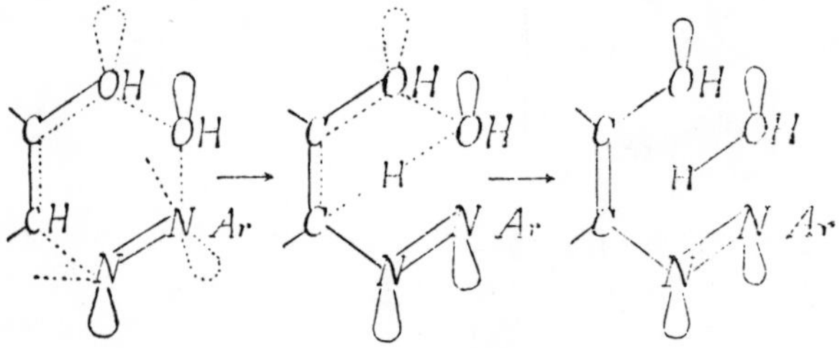

(VIII.)   (IX.)   (X.)

In 1920 I published the paper [51] which is reproduced *in extenso* below as being the summary of my views on the presentation of reactions by the use of partial valencies.

The Conjugation of Partial Valencies

DURING the past five years the author has made use of a hypothesis which has appeared to simplify the representation of the possible mechanism of reactions in certain isolated cases, and the object of the present communication is to indicate some of the lines along which the theory may receive more general application. The necessary condition precedent to chemical change is assumed to be the " activation " of one or more of the molecules taking part in the reaction; this is followed by cohesion and rearrangement of valencies, most probably synonymous with changes in position of electrons. The result is either molecular rearrangement, the formation of an additive product or of new substances by fission of the complex. The activated molecules are further assumed to be polarised and to contain partially dissociated valencies. Thus H – Cl is supposed to be chemically inert, the molecule absorbs energy and becomes . . . . H . . . Cl . . . which is the reactive form termed partially dissociated because it is a stage towards complete ionisation. In thus splitting a valency it is always understood that the two or more dotted lines, though not necessarily themselves of equal value, are quantitatively equivalent in the sum to the normal unit valency from which they have been derived and the polar character of all these fractional valencies is identical. It is possible to allocate definite signs to the partial valencies in most cases as the result of a consideration of the relative polarities of atoms evinced for example in the limiting case of true electrolytic dissociation. A significant exception to the rule that partial valencies of similar sign emanate from the same atom at the same time exists in the case of those elements which exhibit latent valancies such as trivalent nitrogen. A neutral nitrogen

atom is represented thus :— $\overset{\diagdown}{\underset{\diagup}{-}} \text{N} \bigcirc$

and the loop, it is supposed, can be opened up in stages with the result that two partial valencies of opposite sign are produced. This condition of affairs may be expressed by the symbol :—

The chlorination of methane may be given as a simple illustration of the representation of a reaction in accordance with the above postulates :—

(A). *Reaction between two activated molecules.*

$$\text{CH}_3 \quad \text{Cl} \qquad \text{CH}_3 \quad \text{Cl} \qquad \text{CH}_3 \quad \text{Cl} \qquad \text{CH}_3\!\!-\!\!\text{Cl}$$
$$| \;+\; | \;\rightarrow\; \vdots \;+\; \vdots \;\rightarrow\; \vdots \qquad \vdots \;\rightarrow\; \div$$
$$\text{H} \quad \text{Cl} \qquad \text{H} \cdots\cdots \text{Cl} \qquad \text{H} \cdots\cdots\text{Cl} \qquad \text{H}\_\_\_\text{Cl}$$

(B). *Reaction between an activated molecule and a neutral molecule.*

$$\text{CH}_3 \;\overset{+}{\cdots}\text{Cl} \qquad \overset{\cdots}{\text{CH}_3} \;\overset{-}{\cdots} \;\overset{:+}{\text{Cl}} \qquad \text{CH}_3\cdots\cdots\text{Cl} \qquad \text{CH}_3\!\!-\!\!\text{Cl}$$
$$| \;+\; | \;\rightarrow\; \vdots \;+\; \cdots \;\rightarrow\; \vdots \qquad \vdots \;\rightarrow\; \div$$
$$\text{H} \quad ..\text{Cl} \qquad \text{H}\cdots\cdots\text{Cl} \qquad \text{H}\cdots \;\;\cdots\text{Cl} \qquad \text{H}\_\_\_\_\text{Cl}$$

In passing it may be remarked that the rôle of a catalyst must very often be to produce activated molecules by the formation and subsequent decomposition of additive complexes. Thus in catalytic hydrogenation the hydrogen may be able to form a loose addition compound with nickel or palladium by the aid of a degree of dissociation so small that reaction with a substance containing an ethylene linkage cannot be effected. This compound on decomposition, however, may be assumed to liberate a strongly polarised hydrogen molecule, which is highly reactive and is capable of direct union with unsaturated substances.

$$\text{H}\!:\!:\!:\!:\!\text{H} \qquad \text{H}\!:\!:\!:\!:\!:\!\text{H} \qquad \text{H}\cdots\cdots\text{H} \qquad \text{H}\cdots\cdots\text{H}$$

(Catalyst
surface)

The representation of the phenomena of conjugation and addition to conjugated systems is much simplified by the use of the theory of divisible and polar valency and the definition of a conjugated system may be widely extended when the matter is considered from this point of view. Conjugation is the transfer of a free partial valency to an adjacent atom or to the end of a chain of atoms—it is the explanation of action at a distance in a molecule. The most elementary case may be exemplified by the scheme B above where the disturbance of the valency of a hydrogen atom of methane, due to the proximity of the reactive chlorine, involves the carrying through of this effect to the carbon atom and the appearance thereon of a negative free partial valency. There is clearly no definite limit to this process, but it is certain that the larger the number of saturated atoms in a chain the weaker will be the effect which can be carried through. The facts in relation to the azo-dyes which are substantive to cotton suggest the existence of very long conjugated chains in which all the atoms are unsaturated. A conjugated polarised complex capable of taking part in reactions must clearly have free partial valencies of opposite sign and the chain must accordingly comprise an even number of atoms, the exception being those systems which contain a nitrogen, oxygen or sulphur atom in which part use is made of the latent valencies. The even and the odd membered conjugations are shown below, the examples chosen being butadiene and ethyl β-amino-crotonate.

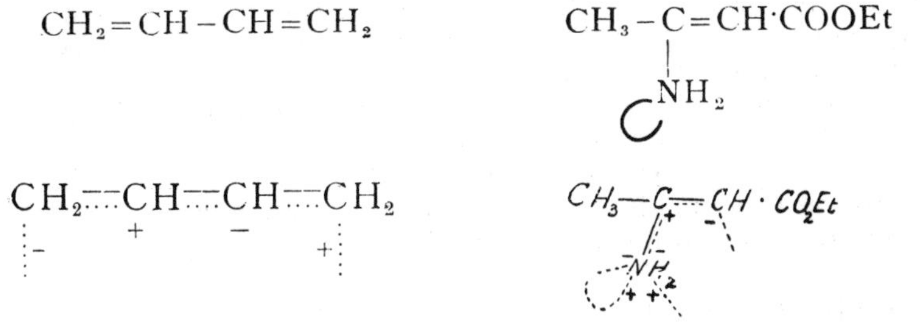

$$CH_2 = CH - CH = CH_2 \qquad CH_3 - C = CH \cdot COOEt$$

It is convenient to classify as " primary " those conjugated systems or partially dissociated complexes which take part in reactions characterised by addition at the ends of the chain. Thus, in reacting with bromine, butadiene undergoes a primary conjugation of its partial valencies, and the same is true of ethyl-β-aminocrotonate in reacting with methyl iodide.*

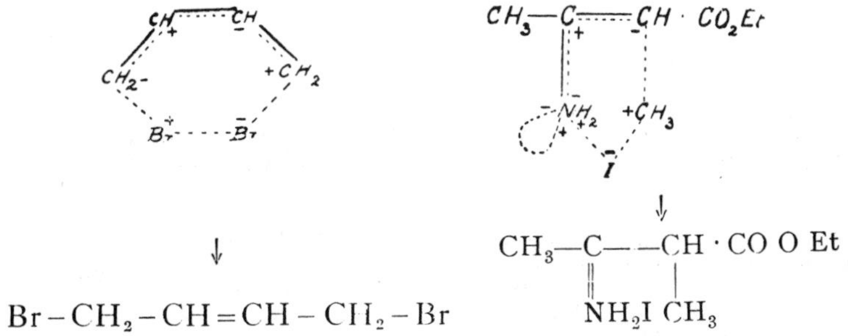

$$Br - CH_2 - CH = CH - CH_2 - Br \qquad CH_3 - C - -CH \cdot CO\ O\ Et$$

$$NH_2I\ CH_3$$

* See footnote on p. 196.

It is important to notice that in the series :—initial compounds, intermediate additive complex, final products, all the alterations of valency are progressive. Take, for instance, the bond connecting the two central carbon atoms of butadiene. In the additive complex this becomes a sesqui-valency and a double bond in the product, and a similar gradual change will be found to be true of all the valency rearrangements whether involving making or breaking of unions or the transformation of single into double bonds and *vice versa*. Therefore, by assuming the possibility of great subdivision of valency, all these reactions could be represented as being almost continuous and with many intermediate phases.

The recognition of primary conjugation is rendered difficult when fission follows addition although analogies are usually available to assist in the determination. Thus there can be little doubt, in the author's view, that the facile reactions of aromatic phenols and amines are due to primary conjugations involving the latent valencies of the oxygen or nitrogen in association with the unsaturated carbon atoms of the nucleus. (Cf. G. M. Robinson and R. Robinson, *Trans. Chem. Soc.*, 1917, **111**, 964.)

In " secondary " conjugation addition does not wholly occur to the ends of the system and the existence of the condition is usually recognised by an orienting effect. This will perhaps best be made clear by means of an example, the addition of hydrobromic acid to allyl bromide. $(- = \ldots)$.

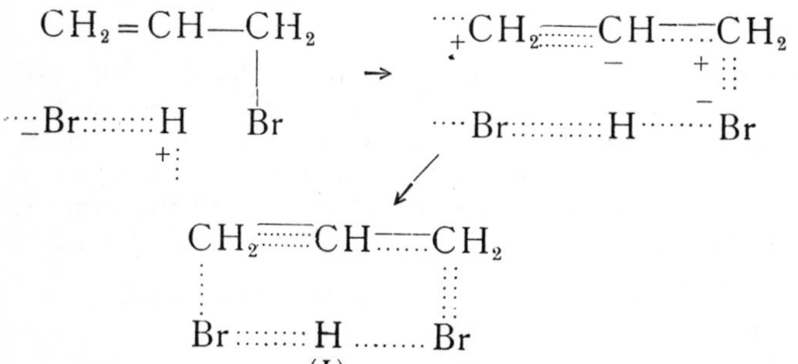

$$CH_2 = CH—CH_2 \qquad \overset{..}{+}CH_2 \overset{.}{=} CH \overset{.}{=} CH_2$$

$$\overset{..}{=}Br \ldots H \quad Br \qquad \cdots Br \ldots H \cdots Br$$

$$CH_2 \overset{.}{=} CH \overset{.}{=} CH_2$$

$$Br \ldots H \ldots Br$$

$$(I)$$

In the above scheme, the attack of the free partial valency of the hydrogen of hydrobromic acid on the bromine of allyl

---

* This is an unpublished observation made in collaboration with P. W. Denny and for further examples of this type of addition to a conjugated system Cf.—Decker. *Ber.*, 1905, **38**, 2893 ; Hamilton and Robinson, *Trans. Chem. Soc.*, 1916, **109**, 1029 ; Robinson, *ibid.*, 1039 ; G. M. Robinson and R. Robinson, *ibid.*, 1917, **111**, 958.

bromide induces a conjugation resulting in the appearance of a positive partial valency at the other end of the chain. Ring formation follows and the orienting effect is secured since the bromine is already partly attached to the position which it ultimately retains in trimethylene bromide. The further rearrangements may be conceived in the following manner :—

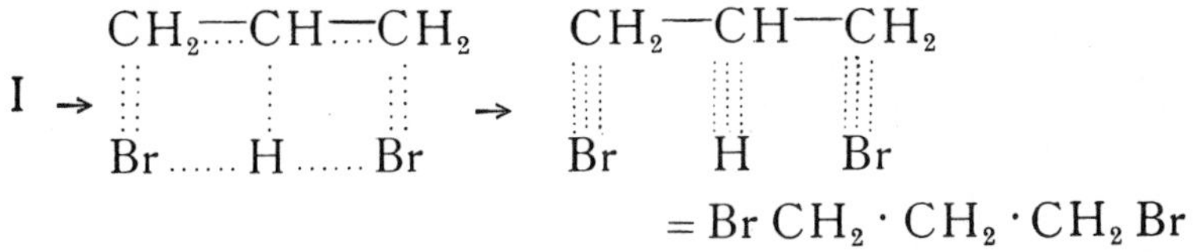

$$\mathrm{CH_2\!\cdots\!CH\!\cdots\!CH_2} \qquad \mathrm{CH_2\!-\!CH\!-\!CH_2}$$

$$\mathrm{I} \rightarrow \quad \mathrm{Br\cdots H\cdots Br} \rightarrow \quad \mathrm{Br \quad H \quad Br}$$

$$= \mathrm{Br\,CH_2\cdot CH_2\cdot CH_2\,Br}$$

On the other hand one of the hydrogen atoms of allyl bromide might be attacked by the bromine of hydrobromic acid and this leads to a different result as shown below :—

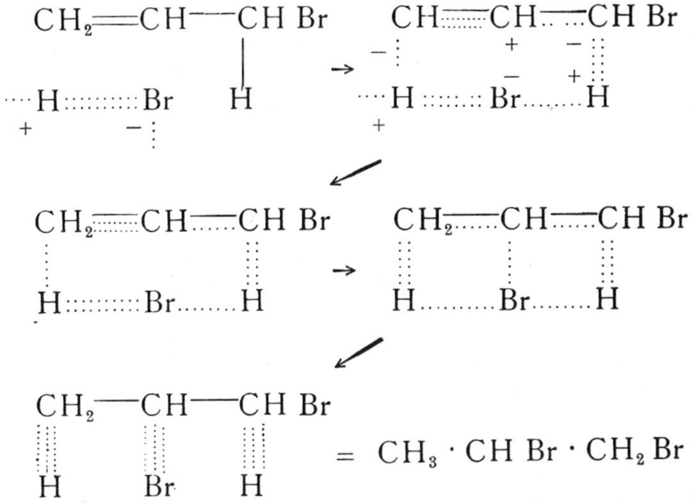

$$\mathrm{CH_2\!=\!CH\!-\!CH\,Br} \qquad \mathrm{CH\!=\!CH\!\cdots\!CH\,Br}$$

$$\cdots H\cdots Br \quad H \qquad \cdots H\cdots Br\cdots H$$

$$\mathrm{CH_2\!=\!CH\!\cdots\!CH\,Br} \qquad \mathrm{CH_2\!\cdots\!CH\!\cdots\!CH\,Br}$$

$$H\cdots Br\cdots H \rightarrow \quad H\cdots Br\cdots H$$

$$\mathrm{CH_2\!-\!CH\!-\!CH\,Br}$$

$$H \quad Br \quad H \qquad = \mathrm{CH_3\cdot CH\,Br\cdot CH_2\,Br}$$

A. F. Hollemann and B. F. H. J. Matthes (*Proc. K. Akad. Wetensch.*, Amsterdam, 1918, **21**, 90) have shown that in bright light allyl bromide absorbs hydrobromic acid with production of trimethylene dibromide, but that in the dark, although the latter remains the main product, considerable amounts of propylene dibromide are also formed. The present writer, in view of the simplification in expression, proposes to adopt the alternate labelling with + and − signs to denote the existence of secondary conjugation, and in accordance with Professor Lapworth's suggestion (this vol., Memoir No. 3, p. 5) the " key " atom may be indicated by an additional dot. Thus to follow out the examples already given, the secondary conjugations involved in the production of trimethylene bromide and propylenedibromide from allyl bromide are : —

$$\overset{+}{C}H_2 = \overset{-}{C}H \cdot \overset{+}{C}H_2 - \overset{-}{B}r \quad \text{and} \quad \overset{-}{C}H_2 = \overset{+}{C}H \cdot \overset{-}{C}HBr - \overset{+}{H}$$

respectively. Secondary conjugation is no doubt a widespread phenomenon. It is concerned in meta substitution in aromatic compounds and very frequently also reinforces the effect of a primary conjugation.

e.g.

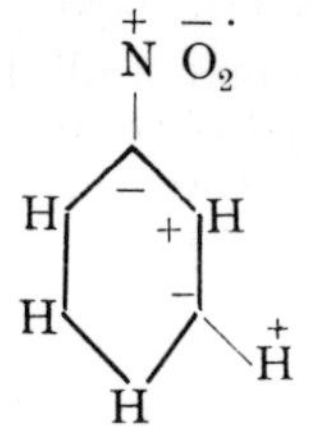

and

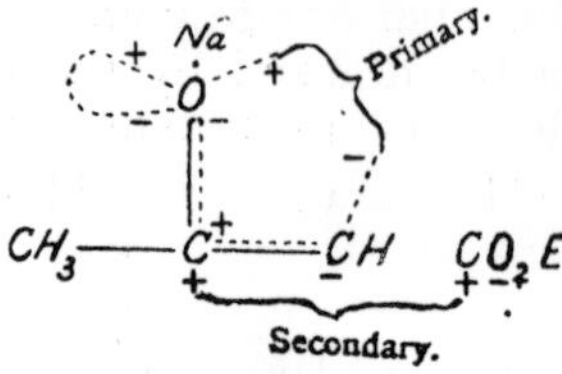

Examples of primary and secondary conjugations could be indefinitely extended, but it is not the present purpose to survey the field of organic chemistry from this point of view, but rather to indicate the general principles applicable to the symbolisation of the mechanism of reactions. There is, however, one group of reactions which occupies a somewhat special position, namely, those which involve molecular rearrangement. A theory of partial valency obviously offers scope for the explanation of such changes, which, it may plausibly be assumed, are in all cases due to an initial ring formation by the aid of fractional valencies. A generalisation of the transformation, of which the change of hydrazobenzene into benzidine is an example, has been discussed elsewhere (G. M. Robinson and R. Robinson, *Trans. Chem. Soc.*, 1918, **113**, 639), and it is of interest to note that the benzidine-type change in the glyoxaline series discovered by R. G. Fargher and F. L. Pyman (*Trans. Chem. Soc.*, 1919, **115**, 217, 1015) is covered by the general statement and could perhaps have been predicted with its aid. All true intramolecular changes can be similarly generalised and the number of distinct types may be comparatively small. Reference may be made here to the dehydration of pinacone to pinacoline and that of borneol to camphene, two apparently dissimilar reactions which may nevertheless be brought under the same heading. In the expression

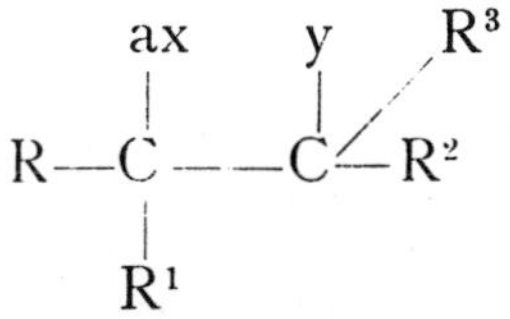

$$\begin{array}{ccc} ax & y & R^3 \\ | & | & \diagup \\ R\!-\!C\!-\!-\!-\!C\!\!\diagup\!\!-R^2 \\ | \\ R^1 \end{array}$$

R, R^1, R^2, R^3 are neutral groups, *e.g.*, alkyl or aryl groups, a is a divalent atom or group and x, y, are monovalent atoms or groups of such a character that there is a strong tendency to form the compound xy. For purposes of convenience (and because it usually is so) x will be assumed to have electropositive character and y is electronegative. If x and y become attached by a partial valency then conjugation occurs and we have at once the conditions :—

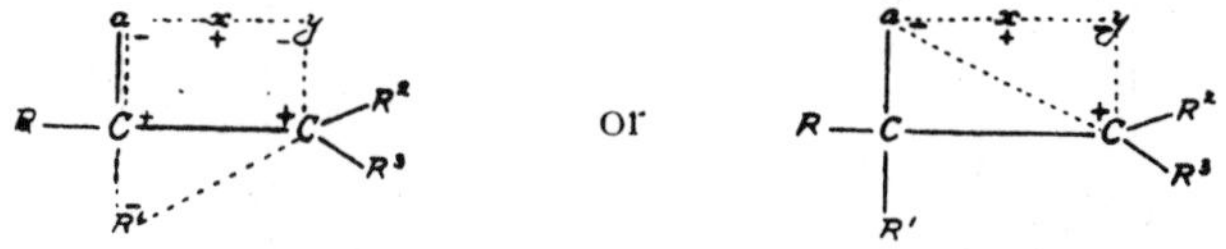

(A)   or   (B)

since ring formation of the partial valencies is clearly impossible unless there are an even number of atoms in the ring. If now the process is continued in the same direction and the compound xy is separated, the result will be in case B that a three-membered ring will be formed :

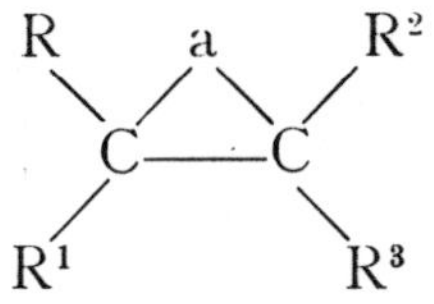

$$\begin{array}{ccc} R & a & R^2 \\ \diagdown & \diagup\diagdown & \diagup \\ & C\!-\!-\!-\!C \\ \diagup & & \diagdown \\ R^1 & & R^3 \end{array}$$

This occasionally happens, but in most cases the structure is unstable and undergoes ring scission under appropriate conditions reverting to the original substance or another compound resembling it in essential respects. Separation of xy from the complex A, however, involves the following result :

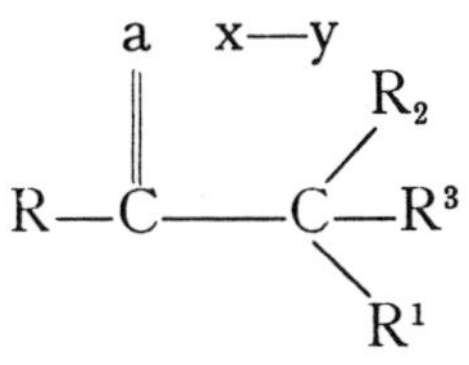

$$\begin{array}{ccc} a & x\!-\!y \\ \| & & R_2 \\ \| & & \diagup \\ R\!-\!C\!-\!-\!-\!C\!-\!R^3 \\ & & \diagdown \\ & & R^1 \end{array}$$

that is, the group R^1 is transferred to the adjacent carbon atom. In the pinacone-pinacoline reaction, a is oxygen, x is hydrogen and y is hydroxyl. In the borneol-camphene or Wagner rearrangement a is $-CH^2-$, x is hydrogen, and y is hydroxyl or a halogen atom. It will be found on inspection that a very large number of molecular changes, particularly in the terpene series, can be brought under the above generalisation. In view of the complexity of the formulæ the following examples may be quoted :—

Borneol-Camphene.

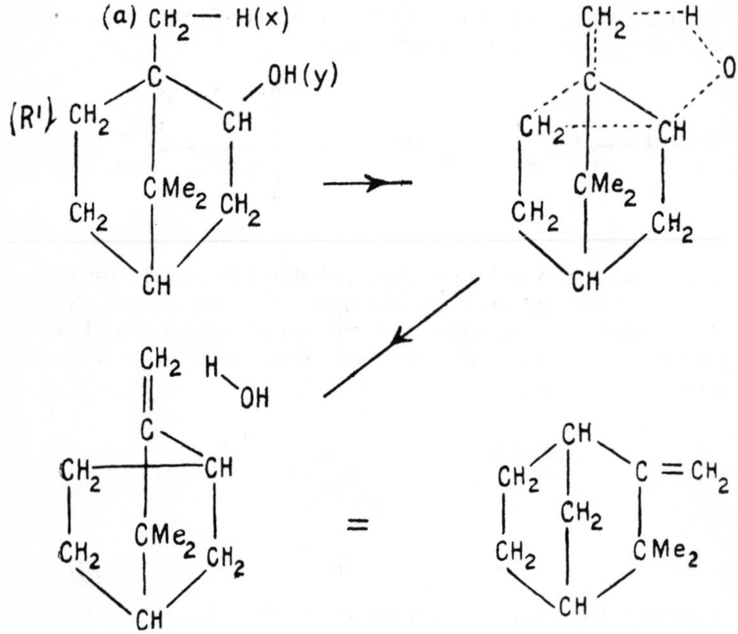

(a) CH_2— $H(x)$
$OH(y)$
(R^1) CH_2 C CH
CH_2 CMe_2 CH_2
CH

CH_2----H
C OH
CH_2---- CH
CH_2 CMe_2 CH_2
CH

$\longrightarrow$

CH_2 H OH
C
CH_2 CH
CH_2 CMe_2 CH_2
CH

$=$

CH
CH_2 $C=CH_2$
CH_2
CH_2 CMe_2
CH

Fenchyl Alcohol-Fenchene.

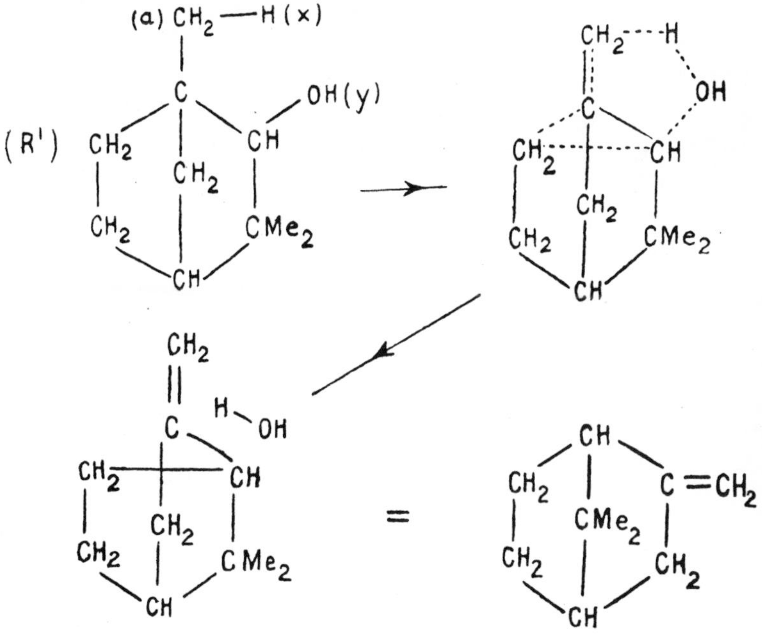

α-*Campholytic acid* → β-*Campholytic acid (isolauronolic acid)*.

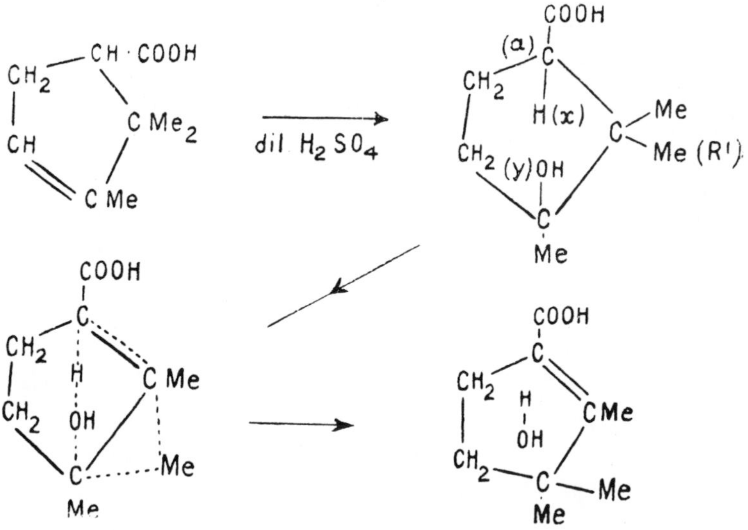

1-Methyl-1-α-hydroxyethyl*cyclo*pentane → 1.2-Dimethyl-Δ^1 *cyclo*hexene. (H. Meerwein, *Annalen*, 1918, **417**, 255.)

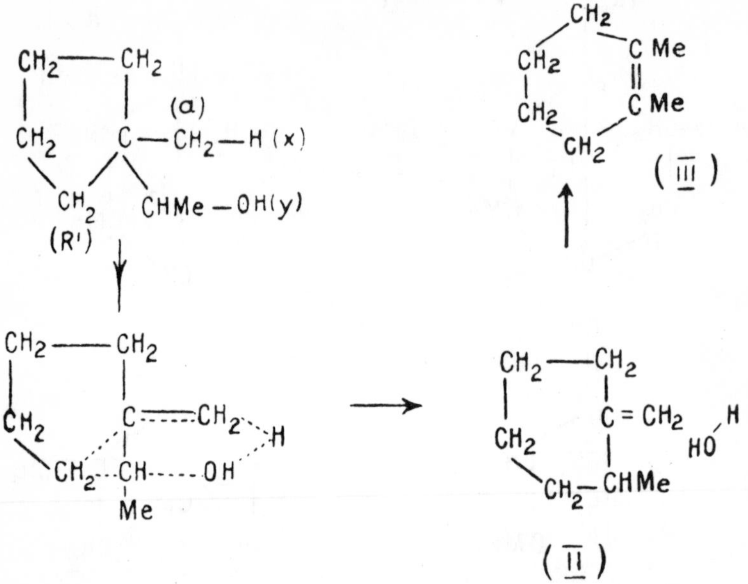

The product should therefore be the exocyclic hydrocarbon (II), whilst Meerwein actually isolates Δ^1-dimethyl*cyclo*hexene (III). Under the conditions of the transformation the change of position of the ethylene linkage would, however, be anticipated.

Before leaving the subject of molecular rearrangement, an interesting recent observation of J. Meisenheimer (*Ber.*, 1919, **52**, (B), 1667) may be noted. Methylallylaniline N-oxide (IV) on distillation with a solution of sodium hydroxide in a current of steam is converted into the allyl ether of phenyl-methylhydroxylamine (V). This reaction is interesting from the present point of view because, however regarded, it involves the formation of an odd-membered ring. This, as shown below, is rendered possible by the circumstance that a pentavalent nitrogen atom becomes trivalent in the course of the process.

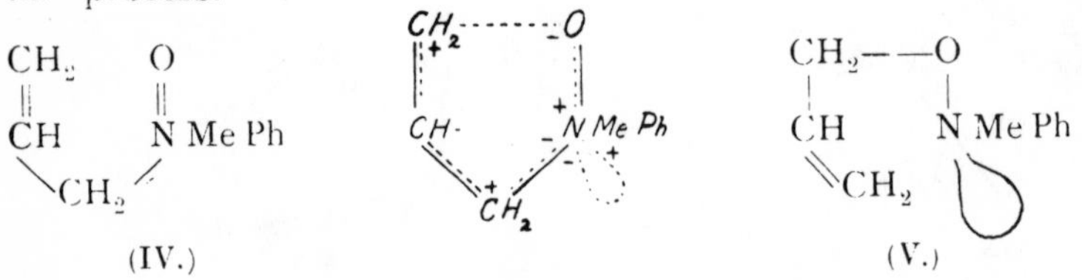

An almost inexhaustible subject for speculation is concerned with the existence of partial valencies and cyclic conjugation of partial valencies in normal molecules as distinct from those which are considered only at the moment of reaction. It has already been pointed out (G. M. Robinson and R. Robinson, *Trans. Chem. Soc.*, 1917, **111**, 964; *ibid.*, 1918, **113**, 640; Perkin and Robinson, *ibid.*, 1919, **115**, 943) that the theory of cyclic conjugation of benzene originated by Thiele, combined with a consideration of the part use of latent valencies of nitrogen, affords an explanation of the aromatic character and degree of basicity of pyrrole, glyoxaline, harmine and other heterocyclic types. The extension of such views to even more complex compounds is well illustrated by the case of indigotin, the usual formula of which is of course

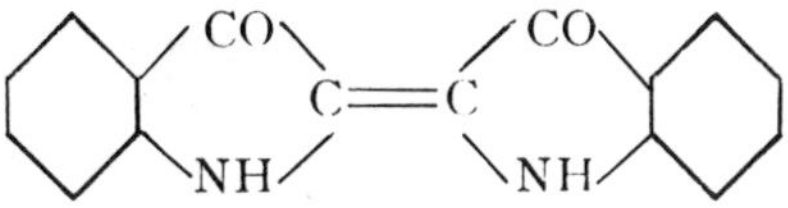

This expression as a vehicle for the explanation of the behaviour of the compound has grave defects, and, since the interpretation of the properties of the carbonyl group is very much a matter of opinion and relations of colour to structure still more so, the criticism of the formula may be confined to its failure to indicate the non-basic character of indigotin and the anomaly of the non-existence of cis-trans modifications. There seems to be no reason why the isomeride,

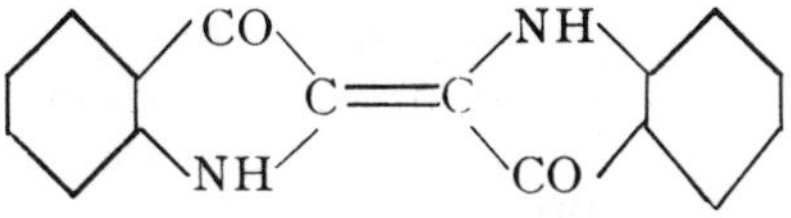

has never been isolated. All these and other objections are completely met by regarding indigotin as a true indole derivative. The series of formulæ now suggested are :—

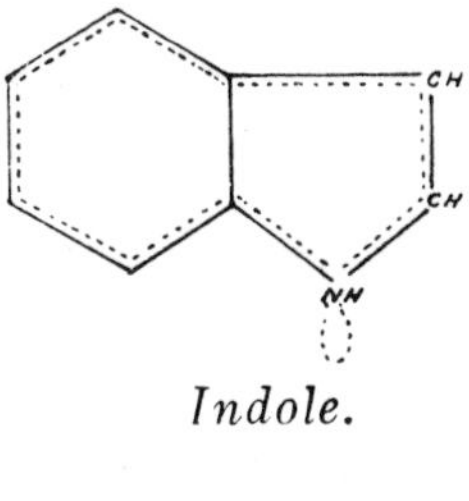

Indole.

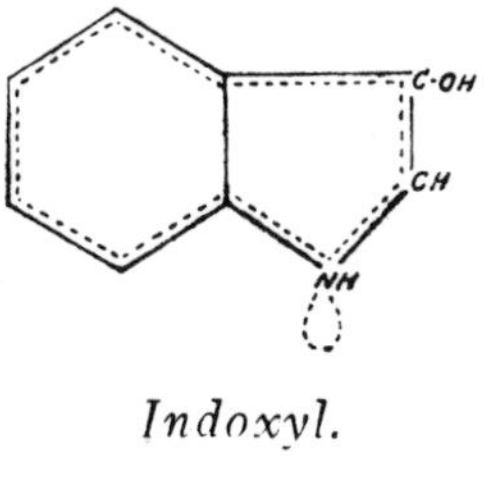

Indoxyl.

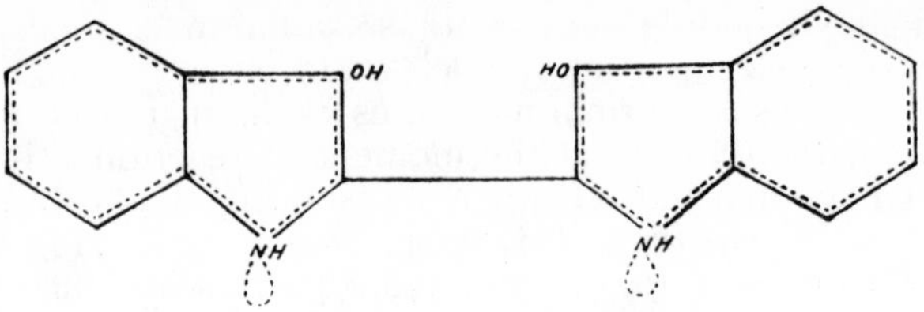

Indigo White.

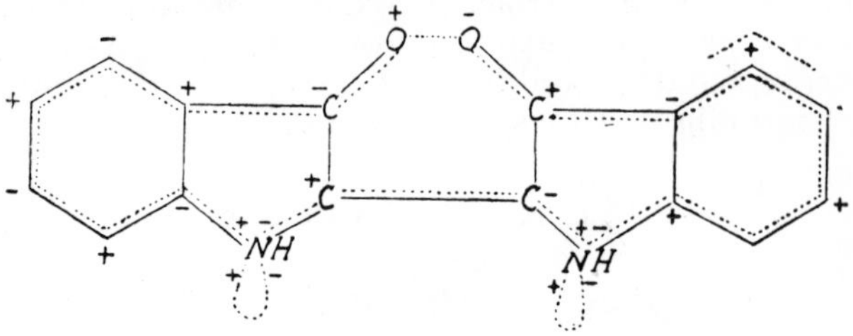

Indigotin.

On this view the oxidation of indoxyl with formation of indigo white resembles the oxidation of β-naphthol to dinaphthol, and the extremely ready reduction of indigotin is well explained by the peroxidic character of the substance. At the same time the nitrogen atoms are not capable of forming stable additive compounds and the possibility of cis-trans isomerism is not indicated. The aromatic cyclic conjugation embraces the whole molecule, the weakest link in the chain being the partial bond connecting the oxygen atoms.

Of other partial valency formulæ the following may be put forward without further comment beyond the statement that the majority represent efforts to indicate the absence of basic properties in nitrogen compounds and that the formula for triphenylmethyl represents the third valency of the central carbon atom as taken up equally by the three nuclei each of which becomes partially quinonoid. Similar formulæ are possible for the rosaniline salts.

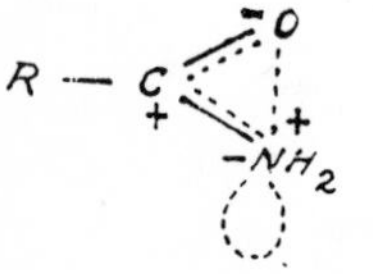

for acid amides and similar expressions for the carboxyl group and derivatives.

for isonitriles and nitriles respectively.

for carbon monoxide, nitrogen & the azo-compounds

for triphenyl methyl.

The explanation of the nature of loose additive compounds, such as the picrates of aromatic hydrocarbons, on the basis of the theory of divisible valency is so obvious as not to require further elaboration. Water of crystallisation and the ammonia of the metal-ammines no doubt involve the bipolar partially dissociated forms

and

*The decomposition, on heating, of ethyl oxalacetate into carbon monoxide and ethyl malonate provides an analogy to the separation of nitrogen from so many azo-derivatives.

with the aid of which it is possible to construct formulæ for
hydrated salts and the most complex of the compounds now
represented in accordance with Werner's co-ordination theory.
The author gratefully acknowledges the influence of the
writings of Werner, Thiele, Flürscheim, Decker, Kauffmann
and particularly Lapworth, with whom he has had the great
advantage of frequently discussing these and similar problems.

It can be seen that the theory of partial valencies, as employed
by me for more than five years prior to this publication, included a
clear recognition of molecules containing hybridised valencies, i.e.
molecules which were neither electrically neutral nor fully polarised,
but in some intermediate condition. The structure given for indigotin, for example, represented a polarisation and regrouping of the
partial valencies in the normal valencies and this conception was
justified by the reference to the properties of the substances. Similarly, in the case of the carboxylic acids and their derivatives, the
hybridisation of the partial valencies seemed to give an excellent
explanation of carboxylic acids, their esters and amides. However,
no quantitative treatment of this earliest from of the resonance theory was ever attempted.

I now turn to the second epoch of my theoretical development,
in which the partial valency theories were translated into electronic
terms in accordance with the system of C.N. Lewis.

It is true that Stark in his *Atom Dynamik* and J.J. Thomson in
his Silliman Lectures had already developed the idea that the chemical bond is essentially electronic, holding together two positively
charged atoms, and many explanations of reactions and properties were advanced which are in approximate agreement with modern conceptions. But Lewis gave us more precise ideas, especially the octet and the clear distinction between covalency and elec-
trovalency. He delved more deeply into the detail of chemical
structure and reactions, and presented a theory which was obviously
much more satisfactory than its somewhat illdefined predecessors.
My own concern was with conjugation and the mechanism of reactions of conjugated systems. This flowed naturally from my work
on the alkylations of enamines and the recognition of the similar
conjugations responsible for the reactions of the phenols, aromatic
amines, and pyrroles.

Major contributions to chemical theory were made by Flürscheim
whose conception of alternatively strengthened and diminished

bonds in a chain was in many respects similar to that of polarised conjugation. It worked well, for example, in its application to hetero enoid systems, but failed completely when an attempt was made to use it to illustrate the behaviour of unsaturated ketones, nitro-arenes, etc.

I employed Flürscheim's theory to explain the hydrolysis of nitro-veratrole [33]. The methoxyl *para* to nitroxyl is hydrolysed by alkalis, whereas strong acids attack the methoxyl in the *m*-position. Later it was realised that the hydrolysis in the *p*-position is due to crotonoid conjugation and the hydrolysis in the *m*-position results from the fact that the *m*-nitromethoxyl is a stronger base than that in the *p*-position. Flürscheim was a pioneer also in his recognition of the importance of stereochemical and electrical effects. These he illustrated pertinently in their applications to the strength of acids and bases. Unfortunately he obstinately refused to give up the idea of a special chemical affinity and wrote a series of highly controversial letters opposing the theories of Lapworth and myself based on the electronic theory of valency. Both Lapworth and I were much concerned with the classification of reagents as having activity comparable with that of anions, or with that of cations, termed anionoid and cationoid respectively. We also recognised that radicals and atoms with an incomplete complement can be both anionoid and cationoid.

A series of analogies demonstrated the anionoid character of ethylene and benzene. In the case of ethylene the facile reactions with acids, halogens and other well recognised acceptors of electrons left little room for doubt, but many years later the Ziegler polymerisation of ethylene was regarded by some chemists as a process in which the hydrocarbon accepted electrons in the first phase. However, I drew attention to a mechanism (see Vol. II) which depends on ethylene acting as a donor of electrons in the first instance [565].

The nitration of catechol and quinol ethers of the form $(MeO)-C_6H_4-(OR)$ was studied in order to determine the effect of changes in the group R on the orienting power of the group RO. The assumption, made on the initiation of the research, that the hetero-enoid systems including MeO and RO functioned independently was justified in the course of the work. I had previously considered the case of the polarisation of nitrosobenzene and drawn attention to the fact that the molecules of this substance react in two different ways according to the type of reagent presented. Hence we have a normal state of valency distribution which can develop two types of reactive polarised conjugation. Analogously, the dihydric phenol ethers, though probably polarised to a small extent in the normal state, can develop stronger effects on the approach of a reagent. Replacement of H by CH_3 is known to involve repulsion of electrons from the affected point. Thus propionic acid is weaker than acetic acid and *p*-toluic acid is weaker than benzoic acid; furthermore the dipole moment of *p*-nitrotoluene is greater than that of nitrobenzene and these are only examples of a relation observed generally. Considering a hetero-enoid system $R'—CH_2OC_6H_5$ therefore, we anticipate that the R', if it is an alkyl group, will push the electrons of the bond towards O relatively to the situation in the group CH_3O.

Reference has been made above to the hydrolysis of nitroveratrole under two sets of conditions leading to isomeric nitroguaiacols which were converted into their R-ethers from which mixed melting point curves were constructed. The nitration of veratrole in cold acetic acid gives 4-nitroveratrole in virtually quantitative yield; no trace of product in which the nitro group is *ortho* to methoxyl has ever been isolated.

The orienting powers of groups RO were compared with MeO, which was taken to be 100, and in the catechol series [99] we found EtO, 135, but *n*-BuO, 123. Several other mixed catechol ethers were nitrated, but the results were surprising since we certainly expected the butoxy group to have a higher orienting power than the ethoxy group. It became evident that the longer alkyl chain was stimulating the conjugating system starting with O of the methoxy group. This result might have been anticipated had we realised that the additional alkyl groups could exert a general electrical effect through space as a neighbouring group. Such a phenomenon could not occur in the corresponding quinol ether series and in fact the values found were EtO, 164 and *n*-BuO, 186. Other results were in full accord with the theory; for example, if the chain was branched, the orienting power was greater than in the case of the isomeric normal chain: PrO, 180; *iso*PrO, 229; *tert*-BuO, 328 (L.J. Goldsworthy, J. Chem. Soc. 1936, 1148). Later these and other cases were reinvestigated by Korte and his colleagues using spectrometric methods for the estimation of the relative isomerides produced (Tetrahedron 1972, *28*, 4871, and references therein).

Another paper is in preparation for the press in which R.R. (who is one of the authors) along with F. Korte and his collaborators describe still further extension and a method of estimation of the proportion of the isomerides dependent on quantitative photometry. An interesting point in this communication is that cyclopropylmethoxy has a higher orienting power than isopropylmethoxy. Removal of two hydrogen atoms evidently increases the electronic concentration in the group.

The various parts of my theoretical system had already been mentioned in short communications and, more widely, in the course of lectures in many centres, but it was thought desirable to put together the chief items applicable to a discussion of the nitration phenomena examined. The outcome was a paper [102] in which the elctronic theory developed in the earlier years of the third decade were seen to constitute a set of postulates covering the field of organic chemistry and not merely that of the particular matter of aromatic substitution. A reprint of this follows below.

LII.—*The Relative Directive Powers of Groups of the Forms* RO *and* RR′N *in Aromatic Substitution. Part IV. A Discussion of the Observations Recorded in Parts I, II, and III.*

By JAMES ALLAN, ALBERT EDWARD OXFORD, ROBERT ROBINSON, and JOHN CHARLES SMITH.

IN order to avoid misconception as to the point of view adopted as a working hypothesis in this series of memoirs, a brief discussion of the fundamental principles is necessary.

It is recognised that certain ions, for example, those from sodium chloride, exhibit a high affinity for their charge and are relatively inert in the matter of co-valency formation, whereas other ions, for example, those from hydrogen cyanide or benzenediazonium hydroxide, have an intrinsic lower affinity for their charge and are active in the production of new bindings by co-valency. In effect, the former class are chemically inactive, the latter class active and, following Abegg and Bodländer, Kauffmann and Briggs, we can recognise in the two types diffuse and intense valency fields respectively. Lapworth has recently contributed a valuable classification of reagents as *anionoid* or *kationoid* according as they behave in the same way as active negative or positive ions (Paper read at the Manchester Literary and Philosophical Society on March 3, 1925;

see abstract, *Nature*, **115**, 625). Ethylene, butadiene and benzene are anionoid, their *active* free valency has a negative polar character, and it is obvious that the ethers and amines are even more definitely anionoid. The systems which one of us has called *crotenoid* (Robinson, *J. Soc. Chem. Ind.*, 1925, **44**, 456) are strongly anionoid, the natural character of the unsaturated carbon being reinforced by direct union with an *onium* element. Lapworth points out that, when ethylene polarises, the implication is that the unsaturated carbon with a positive charge is in the more natural or stable condition and is surrounded by a diffuse field. The active unsaturated carbon with a negative charge is in a less natural condition, and this is justly held to be related to the observation that, except C_2H,* no hydrocarbon radicals have been observed to occur with a negative charge in Thomson's vacuum tube experiments. Independent of these acute comparisons, the development of the theory of crotenoid systems (Decker, *Ber.*, 1905, **38**, 2893; Hamilton and Robinson, *J.*, 1916, **109**, 1029; Robinson, *ibid.*, p. 1038; *Mem. Manchester Phil. Soc.*, 1920, **64**, 4; Robinson and Robinson, *J.*, 1917, **111**, 958; 1918, **113**, 640; Kermack and Robinson, *J.*, 1922, **121**, 427) required the assumption that the reactive carbon atoms in phenols and amines and their derivatives acquire a negative charge in the course of polarisation, the postulated precedent of all reactions. In the case of a phenol ether the mechanism of activation is represented by the annexed expressions.

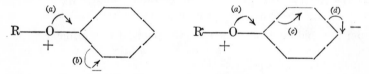

The oxygen, by means of its free electrons, increases its co-valency with the ring C_α (process *a*). C_α recovers its normal co-valency by giving up correspondingly electrons to C_β (process *b*) (*o*-substitution) or by relinquishing $C_\alpha C_\beta$ co-valency electrons to $C_\beta C_\gamma$ (process *c*). C_γ must then relinquish $C_\gamma C_\delta$ co-valency electrons to the sole use of C_δ (process *d*) (*p*-substitution). In the activated form the oxygen is positively charged and is exhibiting oxonium character, a *rôle* in which it far more closely resembles, in its general stability, the satisfied ions ($\overline{Cl}$, $\overset{+}{Na}$) than does the negatively charged carbon atom. The latter is intensely reactive and easily forms new co-valencies (compare *J. Soc. Chem. Ind.*, *loc. cit.*, for the details of

---

* As usual, a group derived from acetylene is exceptional.

the mechanism of diazo-coupling on this hypothesis). This type of activation involves the displacement of electrons in a particular direction, *e.g.*, from left to right in the figures. Furthermore, since the oxygen acquires a smaller negative charge or an actual positive charge, the process must be the more facile the more highly negatively charged is the oxygen atom before the activation. This explains the descending order of reactivity in the series :

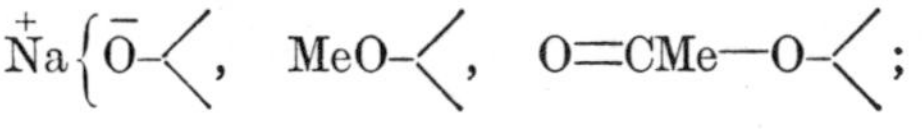

$$\overset{+}{Na}\left\{\overset{-}{O}-\diagdown , \quad MeO-\diagdown , \quad O{=}CMe{-}O-\diagdown \right. ;$$

and in the series :

$$Me_2N-\diagdown , \quad O{=}CMe{-}NH-\diagdown , \quad \overset{-}{Br}\left\{Me_3\overset{+}{N}-\diagdown \right. .$$

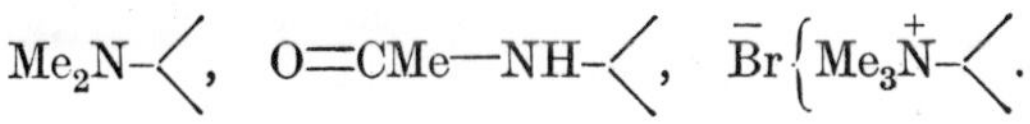

In the acetoxy- and acetylamino-groups, conjugation gives the atom attached to the nucleus a positive charge (compare Rây and Robinson, J., 1925, **127**, 1618). It remains to add that the aromatic nucleus has a special stability of its own which Armit and Robinson (J., 1925, **127**, 1604) consider to be due to the possession of a stable electronic structure, the aromatic sextet. Electronic displacements are resisted by the sextet and it is a fact that the activation of a benzenoid centre in conjunction with any external group is feeble compared with that of an ethenoid complex in similar circumstances. Thus nuclear alkylation by the action of an alkyl halide on a crotenoid base occurs only with the more active aromatic systems. In the course of this investigation our views on the part played by the phenomenon of conjugation in organic chemistry have been more clearly focussed and it now appears possible to classify conjugated systems without arbitrary assumptions. Among the unit reactive groupings from which more complex structures may be derived, especial interest attaches to the highly unsaturated centres * typified by C=C, C=O (C≡N, N=O, etc.), and −O− (−NR−). Of these, C=O alone is kationoid. Certain groupings, C−R, to which definite conditions are attached, must be included. Combining the unsaturated groups two at a time in every possible way, we get :

(1) C=C−C=C; *butadienoid*; polarisation— $+|C{=}C{-}C{=}C|-$; reactivity—anionoid.

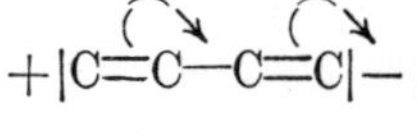

Examples are isoprene, aromatic hydrocarbons.

---

* Certain special structures (ketens, acetylenes) are not considered and it is not suggested that the classification is a complete one.

(2) $C\!=\!C\!-\!C\!=\!O$; *crotonoid*; polarisation— $+|C\!=\!C\!-\!C\!=\!O|-$; reactivity—kationoid.

Examples are methylenemalonic ester, mesityl oxide.

(3) $C\!=\!C\!-\!O\!-$; *crotenoid*; polarisation— $-|C\!=\!C\!-\!O\!-|+$; reactivity—anionoid.

Examples are ethyl β-aminocrotonate, dimethylaniline, resorcinol.

(4) $-O\!-\!C\!=\!O$; neutralised system; polarisation—

$$+|\!-\!O\!-\!C\!=\!O|-;$$

reactivity—feebly kationoid at C and special characters (see below).

Examples are esters, amides, dianisylideneacetone.

(5) $O\!=\!C\!-\!C\!=\!O$, *quinonoid*, and (6) $-O\!-\!O\!-$, *peroxidic*, are heterogeneous systems which we do not propose to discuss.

Many more complex combinations of the unsaturated units are possible and especially it will be recognised that all the systems may be expanded by the inclusion of further $C\!=\!C$ groups. In addition there are derived forms of which the following are the most important.

(7) $O\!=\!C\!-\!C\!-\!X$, where X is an atom or group independently capable of separating with a positive charge; *semi-crotonoid*; polarisation— $-|O\!=\!C\!-\!C\!-\!X|+$; reactivity—dissociation; often followed by rearrangement of the negative ion and anionoid character exhibited by the carbon atom previously joined to X. The process is analogous to the dissociation of a carboxylic acid.

Examples are acetone, 2 : 4-dinitrotoluene, ethyl α-bromoacetoacetate.

(8) $C\!=\!C\!-\!C\!-\!Y$, where Y is an atom or group independently capable of separating with a negative charge; *allyloid*; polarisation—

$+|C\!=\!C\!-\!C\!-\!Y|-$; reactivity—kationoid.

Examples are phenyl allyl ether (Claisen and Tietze, *Ber.*, 1925, **58**, 275), geraniol.

(9) $O\!-\!C\!-\!Y$ occurs in $MeO\!\cdot\!CH_2Cl$, etc.

The General Polar Effect.—Conjugation occurs by virtue of electronic displacements which produce an alternating polar effect* as

---

* An alternating polar effect in a chain $\overset{-+-+-}{ABCDE}$ does not mean and never has meant either to Lapworth or to Robinson that the atoms are alternately positively and negatively charged. The phrase is taken to imply that evidence exists that in certain reactions, due to separate polarisations, an inevitable consequence of the laws of valency operating in relation to changes in co-valency. Electronic displacements which do not involve co-valency changes require no alternation and may be continuous but diminishing in degree along a chain (compare Lapworth and Robinson, *Nature*, 1923, **112**, 722). Such displacements should occur in almost all types of molecules and will be propagated by electrostatic induction (Lewis, *J. Amer. Chem. Soc.*, 1916, **38**, 762; " Valence and Structure of Atoms and Molecules," pp. 84, 143; Thomson, *Phil. Mag.*, 1923, **46**, 497; Lowry, *Trans. Faraday Soc.*, 1923, **18**, 293; Lucas and Jameson, *J. Amer. Chem. Soc.*, 1924, **46**, 2475). We concur * with Lucas and Moyse (*ibid.*, 1925, **47**, 1459), for instance, in their application of the theory to the case of the addition of hydrogen bromide to Δ^2-pentene. The general effect of charged centres is obvious and Thomson (*loc. cit.*) has suggested both practical and theoretical methods of estimating the disposition of electrostatic doublets in various types of atomic combinations. In addition, the general effect of a group R can often be estimated by a consideration of the strength of the acid $R \cdot CO_2H$. All the evidence goes to show that hydrogen has a greater attraction for electrons than has the methyl group; we shall find it more convenient to express this statement in the converse form. This effect is represented, as in former cases (Malkin and Robinson, J., 1925, **127**, 370), by a straight arrow showing the direction in which the electrons are displaced. As an example of the interaction of the two types of electron displacement, we consider the carboxylic

acids $R \cdot CO_2H$. The polarisation $O \!=\! C \!-\! OH$ proceeds until the positive charge † on the hydroxyl oxygen increases to such an extent

---

A, C, or E may exhibit anionoid character and, on the other hand, one of the centres B or D may exhibit kationoid character. The alternation of stable and less stable octets was suggested by Kermack and Robinson (*loc. cit.*) as a possible, admittedly speculative, explanation of the tendency underlying the exhibition of this property. This suggestion was never intended to be regarded as a *mechanism* of activation, for which Kermack and Robinson retained an electronic translation of the theory of partial dissociation of conjugated complexes as developed by Robinson and Robinson (*loc. cit.*).

* Except, naturally, in considering that clear cases of the operation of continuous electron displacement dispose of the necessity for recognising the other type of displacement which occurs in conjugated systems.

† Positive and negative are taken to mean also less negative and less positive respectively. Similarly, a smaller attraction is relatively a repulsion, and *vice versa*.

that the proton is weakly held and can be removed by solvent molecules. The two oxygen atoms then divide the negative charge and assume identical functions. The displacement (*a*) is clearly the more fundamental process, but (*b*) is, however, a necessary accessory in providing a means of adjustment of the disturbed co-valency of the carbon atom.

Contrasting $R \longrightarrow C{<}^{O}_{OH}$ and $R' \longleftarrow C{<}^{O}_{OH}$ it is apparent that the group R in repelling electrons *competes* with OH and to some extent inhibits the process (*a*), whilst the opposite is true of a group R′ which attracts electrons. Thus $R' \cdot CO_2H$ is a stronger acid than $R \cdot CO_2H$. The case of the phenols is simpler and again $R' \cdot OH$ should be a stronger acid than $R \cdot OH$. Conjugation $\overset{R \underline{\quad\quad} C=O}{(\swarrow \ \ \overset{|}{OH})}$ is also a factor, weakening an acid. This system does not exclude the consideration of the effect of a steric factor * (Flürscheim, J., 1909, **95**, 718) and is in excellent agreement with the available data.

The whole of the foregoing can be independently justified and we proceed to consider how these principles apply to the results recorded in the preceding communications.

In the ethyl ether of guaiacol we have the condition

because the methyl group exercises a greater repulsion on electrons than hydrogen does. Therefore the polarisation of the crotenoid system, including the oxygen of the ethoxyl group, is facilitated as compared with the other system, not represented, which includes the oxygen of the methoxyl group. It follows that ethoxyl should have a higher directive power than methoxyl † (Found : EtO, 135; MeO, 100). The substitution of methyl for a second hydrogen atom should still further increase the directive power (Found : $Pr^\beta O$,

---

* Possibly also an electrical effect exercised across the intervening space rather than through the chain.

† The case of OH itself as against OMe cannot be considered on similar lines on account of the possibility of ionisation or removal of the proton from OH by the reagent.

150). It is very interesting, however, that in the catechol series EtO, among n-alkyloxy-groups, appears to reach a maximum directive power (Found : EtO, 135; Pr^{a}O, 128; n-C$_4$H$_9$·O, 123). This phenomenon we regard as due to the fact that as the chain lengthens a greater proportion of the general effect is distributed over the molecule and a smaller proportion, therefore, is effective through the attached atoms of the chain. Thus the ratio Directive power RO/Directive power MeO can be expressed as $y + a/x + a$,* where R is a higher alkyl group, y is its directive power apart from a; x is the directive power of methoxyl apart from a, a is a quantity depending on the general polar effect of the excess methylene groups in R — Me and is that portion of the effect which, owing to its distribution over the molecule, goes to assist the polarisation of the crotenoid system, including the oxygen of the methoxyl groups. As a increases, the ratio will approach some minimum value greater than 1. Our results can be interpreted on the assumption that the terminal methyl group of a n-propyl group exercises a general effect which is largely distributed over the molecule and only to a small extent transmitted through the attached chain. In the series of catechol experiments it is important to observe that the general effect must assist both conjugations, and the interest of parallel experiments in the quinol series is that this is no longer true. Thus in p-ethoxyanisole,

$$H\!-\!\!-CH_2\!-\!\!-O\!-\!\!\langle\quad\rangle\!-\!\!-O \leftarrow CH_2 \leftarrow CH_3,$$

it is clear that the conjugations of the crotenoid systems themselves involve electronic displacements in opposing directions. The argument used in the catechol series still holds; ethoxyl should have a greater directive power than methoxyl, but if a portion of the general effect of the additional CH$_2$ of the ethoxyl is distributed, we can write : Directive power of EtO/Directive power of MeO $= y' + a'/x' - a'$. It might accordingly be anticipated that ethoxyl would have a higher relative directive power in the quinol than in the catechol series (Found : EtO in catechol series, 135; EtO in quinol series, 163). Furthermore, as a' increases, the value of the ratio $(y' + a')/(x' - a')$ must also increase, and the theory, which predicts

---

* The form of this expression is justified if x, y, a are taken as representing the number of occasions in unit time on which the different factors concerned lead to effectual polarisations.

a lower value for Pr^{a}O as compared with EtO in the catechol series, also requires in the quinol series that Pr^{a}O should be greater than EtO (Found : Pr^{a}O in quinol series, 180). In the benzyl ether of guaiacol we encounter one of the postulated conjugated systems (allyloid) :

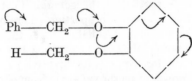

In such a case the whole chain is not to be regarded as *one* conjugated system. The allyloid system * tends to assist the oxygen atom to acquire a negative charge, and this assists the related crotenoid system to function † (Found : CH$_2$Ph·O, 113 ; MeO, 100).

In the *m*-methoxybenzyl group (directive power, 92), the methoxyl group has the general effect anticipated on the basis of Thomson's deductions concerning the situation of electrostatic doublets, and the whole group exercises less repulsion on electrons than the methyl group does. This is far more pronounced with *m*- and *p*-nitrobenzyloxy-groups (directive powers, 67). The identity of the directive powers of these two groups was unexpected and led us to adjust our views on conjugation in the direction now indicated. It must not, however, be hastily concluded that the nitro-group produces no alternating effect, even in these experiments, since the fact that *p*-nitrobenzoic acid is slightly stronger than the *m*-isomeride indicates a weak alternate effect. In the *m*-nitrobenzyloxy-group, we might have a slightly stronger general effect and a weaker alternating effect (crotonoid-type) than in the *p*-nitrobenzyloxy-group, and these small variations may balance. However this may be, the results show that if the nitro-group does produce an alternating effect it must be a very small one and this is normal because the

* It should be noted that the distribution of affinity in the butadienoid, crotenoid and allyloid systems on our electronic basis coincides with the requirements of Flürscheim's theory, but this is not the case in the crotonoid and semi-crotonoid types.

† The occurrence in some substances of quite complex combinations of general and alternate effects can be foreseen. Thus *p-iso*propoxybenzoic acid should be weaker than anisic acid or even than *p-n*-propoxybenzoic acid :

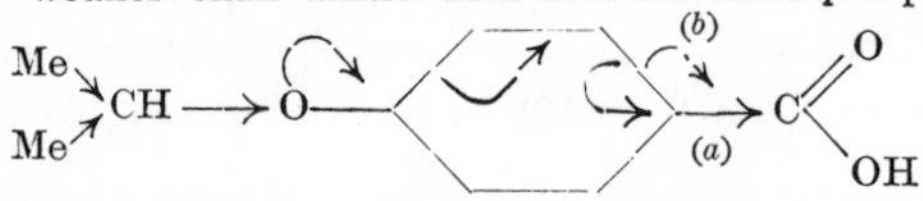

Here we have a general effect reinforcing a crotenoid system the polarisation of which produces a general effect (*a*), *or* a conjugation effect (*b*), or both; thereupon influencing the carboxyl as explained above.

reaction examined is one in which the substance exhibits anionoid character and conjugation of nitroxyl with the aromatic nucleus leads to the exhibition of kationoid properties. In the catechol series, for a group like the p-nitrobenzyloxy-group we have : Directive power of group/Directive power of MeO $= (z - b)/(x - b)$ and in the quinol series the ratio becomes $(z' - b')/(x' + b')$. Thus in the quinol series such a group should have a smaller relative directive power than in the catechol series (Found for the p-nitrobenzyloxy-group : in the catechol series, 67 ; in the quinol series, 38). In connexion with these deductions, it is important to notice that there are no side reactions to complicate the issue and that in all cases we have measured the whole effective directive power of the groups concerned. Consequently the small differences between x and x', y and y', and z and z' are not likely to affect the validity of our conclusions. We do not claim that the interpretation is more than an approximation to the truth.

The point of view now adopted is one from which the general problem of orientation in aromatic substitution can be surveyed and we regard it as necessary to approach the subject in the following stages, which are of diminishing importance.

(1) Consideration of the circumstances of the reaction and especially whether the reagent is anionoid or kationoid.

(2) Consideration of the conjugated systems.

(3) Consideration of the general effect of attached groups on the conjugated systems.

We will confine ourselves to the cases such that there is no attached group conjugated with the nucleus and the reagent is kationoid (Br_2, HNO_3, etc.). In other words, we contemplate a normal benzenoid (butadienoid) system exhibiting anionoid character and wish to deduce from fundamental principles the nature of the effect of attached groups. In the case of a group, A, which repels electrons more than hydrogen does we have the arrangement (I). Here the crowding of electrons

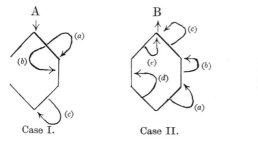

Case I.　　　　Case II.　　　　Case III.

round C_α will facilitate, by repelling $C_\alpha C_\beta$ co-valency electrons, the polarisation of that particular butadienoid system which starts with C_α. The electron will be captured by C_β (process a; o-substitution) or, if not, a $C_\alpha C_\beta$ co-valency electron will become a $C_\beta C_\gamma$ co-valency electron (process b). C_γ, to recover its normal co-valency, must then correspondingly relinquish an electron to C_δ (process c; p-substitution). An alternative statement is that the ring carbon atom around which the density of electrons is greatest most easily becomes the positive end of a conjugated polarised complex. The applications will be obvious—toluene and *tert.*-butylbenzene are in the same category. In the case of a group B, which has a *strong* attraction for electrons (II), it is easy to see in a general way that the circumstances are reversed, but in order to make the argument clear we take an extreme instance such that B has a definite positive charge. The electrical field emanating from B then produces positive electrification in diminishing degree over the portion of the molecule represented. One consequence is that all displacements of electrons in activation will tend to be towards B, and this inhibits para-substitution. Of all the remaining possible displacements (a, b, c, d, e), that indicated by (a) is the most likely to lead to reaction, because reaction depends on the acquirement of a negative charge and of all the carbon atoms which can be activated C_γ has the smallest positive charge. A less degree of electron displacement, therefore, will activate C_γ than will suffice for C_β. In order of preference we find in this case m-substitution, o-substitution, p-substitution, whilst displacement of the group B is also possible. An alternative statement is that the carbon atom (C_δ) furthest removed from the positive charge is least positive or most negative and most easily acquires a more positive charge and therefore most readily functions as the positively charged end of a polarised ethenoid or butadienoid complex. We cannot lay down any rules in regard to the required strength of the positive charge on B. The nitrogen of the nitro-group is positively charged if we accept the formulation $=\overset{|}{O}-\overset{|}{N}=\overset{|}{O}-$ in which each line represents an electron pair and it would appear that this group is effective even when separated from the nucleus by one carbon atom (Holleman, *Rec. trav. chim.*, 1895, **14**, 121).

Substitution in the m-position might also occur in a benzyl-ammonium ion.

The carbon atoms of the carboxyl, carbonyl and trichloromethyl groups can also be regarded as positively charged on the basis of independent evidence. This theory seems to harmonise better than any other which has been advanced with the facts of substitution in polycyclic aromatic groups, but a separate discussion of this subject is necessary. In the case of a group C (III) which in some phases attracts and in others repels electrons we anticipate predominating o-p-substitution because the phase in which electrons are repelled provides a favourable opportunity for activation leading to anionoid character, whereas the other phase in no way contributes to activation and in fact inhibits it.

In the case (I) a negative charge is distributed over the nucleus and anionoid character is intensified, leading to ready reaction, whilst in case (JI) the distributed positive charge inhibits the exhibition of anionoid character. We can in fact estimate the approximation of a group X to the types A or B by observing the ease of substitution of X–Ph as compared with that of benzene.

THE UNIVERSITY, MANCHESTER.　　　　　[*Received, June 18th, 1925.*]

I sent a copy of this paper to Professor C.K. Ingold in later 1925 and before it was published in the Journal of the Chemical Society. Annexed is the letter which I received in reply and there can be no reasonable doubt that this was the turning point of the theoretical views of Ingold.

The University, Leeds　　　　　　　　　　　　　　　　　*17.2.26.*

Dear Robinson,

I return your papers. Thank you for letting me see them. They represent in my opinion a very fine effort, especially on the theoretical side, and the theory is certainly one of *Organic Chemistry* and not of *Aromatic Substitution only*. Crystallisation in terms of electrons, as you have . . . . . * brought together, I find it easier to follow and I can now see in retrospect that its germination goes a long way back and is especially clear in your paper with Mrs. Robinson of 1917. I should add that I personally find it less confusing to think of it independently of any connexion it has with the principle of alternate polarities.

The scheme of 9 categories is remarkably representative, although you say it is incomplete; and I imagine you would mentally include (or at least not exclude) the type $\overset{\frown}{C}= C - \overset{\frown}{C} - X$, as a tendency existing for example in toluene (X = H). I enclose a MS in which it is argued

* Illegible in the original.

that it must be possible to extract H as ion from the CH_2 of the benzyl group and that this is still possible with methyl but more difficult. This, of course, does not preclude $\overset{\frown}{C}=C\leftarrow C\leftarrow X$, and I hardly know which view to prefer. The analogy between ordinary triad and ring — chain tautomerism, and the change in skeleton in the camphor series suggest that a weak $\curvearrowright\curvearrowright$ mechanism may operate in "saturated" chains — the "conjugation of partial valencies" again.

I did not realise before how neatly the carboxyl group fits in with the general scheme, but regarding your Part V, Flürscheim will of course utilise Smedley's idea of connecting the 2 O atoms, and, from his point of view, would, I suppose, be justified in translating it (the original formulation being absurd in 1926) as a residual non-polar link (i.e. an approach towards a peroxide 3-ring), just as my wife and I translated it as a residual electrovalence (approach towards a betain) thereby producing a special case of your general theory. I agree with the overlapping series of oxy and amino groups and although I did not discuss it fully, the examples chosen for nitration were selected with the idea of treating the N and the O as equitably as possible.

Regarding your distributed effect in long chains, — I take it you are convinced that any o-substitution which might occur is of a smaller order of magnitude than the differences between the Et, Pr and But examples. Actually I should think there would not be much

ortho in any case of the type $\Big]\begin{smallmatrix} OAlk \\ OAlk \end{smallmatrix}$, but we find in [benzene ring with NHAc and OAc],

[benzene ring with OMe and F], [benzene ring with SMe and OMe]

upwards of 20%, 60% and 80% respectively of substitution (nitration) *ortho* to the dominant groups

As you see the mode of dissociation of Cl_2 etc. is very doubtful, but I would suggest the septet definitely in cases of chlorination by reagents in which there is reason to assume an actual or potential one-electron bond, as PCl_5. If this structure is right the only alternative to a septet seems to be the ion.

I am glad to hear your benzylamine paper is shortly to be published. I shall also publish again on the subject but am not ready just yet. When I do I shall turn right round. I do not care two straws what the public in general .... (Unfortunately the penultimate page of this letter has been mislaid. R.R.)

.... Preliminary determinations have been made in the other cases but I do not quote them as they await confirmation.

I enclose the fluoroanisol case* — a mere note. The thiocatechol case is not yet written.

Yours sincerely,
(signed) C.K. Ingold

* This and the other one were sent in to Chem. Soc. about 10 days ago with the one I sent you before. Thank you for your comments and criticisms of which I will take note. C.K.I.

When the promised paper by Ingold and Ingold appeared there was nothing in it which could justify a claim to novelty of outlook. The monograph which Ingold eventually wrote was based essentially on the theories which I had advanced a short time earlier and which had been contested in the controversy which took place largely in the correspondence columns of Chemistry and Industry. I regret very much the necessity to point out that every device was used to give the readers of this book (*Structure and Mechanism in Organic Chemistry*, Cornell University Press, 1953) the impression that the electronic theories advocated were original and had relatively small beginnings in the earlier work of Lapworth and myself. Lapworth described reagents as anionoid or kationoid resembling those of chemically active anions or kations respectively. Ingold changed these terms to nucleophilic and electrophilic, but without the slightest alteration in the physical meaning. He adopted my method of representing a polarised system but as far as I know without adequate acknowledgment. I am touching this question of acknowledgment as he was apt to include a necessary reference to Lapworth or myself in a large number of references so that any idea that our contributions were original or specially applicable to the matter in hand was well and truly buried. That these and other devices were succesful has been proved to me on numerous occasions, for example when I have lectured in the United States and had been told that the idea I had mentioned in the course of my talk had already been advanced in the monograph of Ingold.

In 1932 I delivered two lectures to the Institute of Chemistry in London and several thousand copies of these were distributed. Furthermore, Dr. M. Wreschner made a German translation of my contribution to the Solvay Conference at Brussels in April 1931 (Ferdinand Enke Verlag in Stuttgart, 1932).

In addition to the study of nitration of quinol dialkyl ethers, a comparison of orienting power of the acylamino group in N-acylphenetidines was made. The orienting power of the acylamino group was found to be considerably greater than that of the ethoxy group. In full accordance with the theory the nitrobenzoylamino group had a lower orienting power than the benzoylamino group. The position was in fact noted in that this weakening was greater when the nitro group was in the o- and p-positions. The explanation was in terms of the greater electric field over the nucleus of the o-nitro-derivative [142]. We were content to carry this investigation forward to the point at which the main principles were clearly illustrated both in the matter of increase and decrease of the positive and negative fields from groups external to the actual conjugated systems. It is, however, clear that a method of investigation is indicated which can be used to study many details in the effect of structure on the distribution of the fields. The theory is evidently sound and if apparent exceptions were uncovered their study would inevitably lead to contributions to our knowledge, probably of stereochemical factors.

A theory of alternate polarities in a chain of atoms starting with a so-called key atom at the end of a chain was developed for certain special cases by Vorländer and also by Fry, but the idea was extended and generalised by Lapworth. It is still a useful mnemonic and covers the majority of cases, but exceptions were found and Lapworth himself came to regard it as a useful first guide but not a master principle. When W.O. Kermack and I defined the way in which we wished to use the theory of conjugation on an electronic basis [52], Lapworth wrote a paper, published along with that of Kermack and R.R., in which he showed how the conjugation theory could be applied over a wide range of reaction types. Unfortunately, Lapworth's paper, which was meant to be so clear and all-embracing, was actually rather obscure on account of the mode of presentation adopted and it received scant attention.

From about 1920 to 1926, B. Flürscheim and C.K. Ingold wrote a series of letters, chiefly in "Chemistry and Industry", strongly criticising the theoretical views put forward by Lapworth and myself. The controversy became focused on the theory of substitution in the aromatic nucleus and I instituted experiments designed to illustrate the application of my views. The theory developed demanded that the actual reaction system in a process such as nitration should be the enoid or poly-enoid groups in the aromatic nucleus itself or such groups included in a hetero-enoid system as in aromatic phenols or amines or their simple derivatives. Other attached groups were regarded as having a general electrical effect modifying the reactivity of the enoid or hetero-enoid groups. Two types of benzene derivatives were selected, namely, benzylamine derivatives and the alkyl ethers of catechol and quinol (see above). It was already known that the nitration of benzyldiethylamine yields a substantial proportion of the *m*-nitro-derivative. The *p*-nitro-compound was the main product of the reaction. We found that the nitration of N-benzylpiperidine afforded at least 50% of the *m*-nitro-derivative, but on the addition of rubidium nitrate to the nitration mixture the amount of *m*-nitro-derivative formed could be almost halved [146]. Recourse to theory and consideration of the experimental results strongly suggested that the amine salt was nitrated in the *m*-position. Electrostriction of the benzyl-ammonium cation was thought to have been responsible for reducing its effective charge and hence for lowering the proportion of *m*-derivative obtained. For these and other reasons we were satisfied that the benzylamine salt was nitrated in the *m*-position. However, Ingold interpreted his own results (with Holmes) in the contrary sense, as shown by the following exerpt from "Chemistry and Industry":

Substitution

Sir, At the last Chemical Society meeting the discussion was somewhat compressed, and I did not gather from Professor Robinson's statement that it contained definite predictions regarding the particular substances on which Mr. Holmes and I had worked. In the printed report (this vol., p. 564), however, I read: "The relation to the case of the benzylamines is that a sufficiently positively charged ammonium group might so strongly attract electrons as to produce the effect of 'B' (*meta*-substitution) even when separated from the nucleus by a methylene group. A relatively greater proportion of the *meta*-isomeride is therefore expected in the case of a benzylamine salt, the more powerful the base. In $CH_2Ph \cdot NH \cdot COMe$ and $CH_2Ph \cdot NEtPh$

the nitrogen will acquire a positive charge owing to its conjugation with CO and Ph respectively, and should therefore produce the 'B' effect (*meta*-substitution); this had been overlooked in a previous statement." Here, then, are three definite predictions: the facts relating to two of them can immediately be given.

(i) Benzylamine salts substitute almost exclusively *ortho-para*, and not *meta* as predicted; so far as concerns the small amounts of *meta* byproducts there is less of them the stronger the base, not more.

(ii) The compound $CH_2Ph \cdot NH \cdot COMe$ is exclusively *ortho-para* directing; no *meta*-substitution could be detected.

(iii) The compound $CH_2Ph \cdot NEtPh$ was not examined by us, because Professor Robinson had stated his intension of doing so.

That the facts (i) and (ii), though agreeing with Dr. Flürscheim's theory, are opposed to Professor Robinson's predictions, is perhaps an appropriate answer to Professor Lapworth's contention (this vol., pp. 511, 564) that it is impossible by experiments on aromatic substitutions, to distinguish between polar and non-polar theories of directive action. I am, Sir, etc.,

The University of Leeds,   C.K. Ingold.
May 29, 1925.

In order to settle this matter, once and for all, and corroborate my prediction that the benzylamine salts should be nitrated in the *m*-position, H.R. Ing and I nitrated benzyltrimethylammonium nitrate and found the only isolable product to be the *m*-nitro-derivative [107]. Ingold later repeated this result and carried out a great deal of experimental work illustrating the theory that a cationic field over the nucleus promotes *m*-substitution. Our views of the actual electronic mechanism of such *m*-substitutions were not identical. Ingold retained the notion, suggested by H.E. Armstrong, that *m*-substitution with respect to an appropriate group B was due to inhibition of reactivity in the *o,p*-positions with respect to B. I, on the other hand, proposed a new theory of penultimate substitution which takes note of the distribution of electrons as modified by the cationoid character of B. The highest concentration of electrons in the nucleus will be associated with the *p*-position and when polarisation occurs it will give reactive electrons in the *m*-position or by conjugation lead to expulsion of the group B. This latter result is a frequent occurrence. It should be understood, however, that the distribution of a positive field over the nucleus must imply a greatly reduced reactivity of the molecule as a whole.

In addition to the ammonium cation other sources of the nuclear field were studied — for example, a definite effect favouring a degree of m-substitution was found in the case of nitration of benzyl m-nitrophenyl sulphone; about 30% of the m-nitrobenzyl derivative was produced. Another example was the course of the nitration of benzylsulphonic acid and chloride [148]. The effect of sulphone and similar groups is naturally much smaller than that of the true onium cations and it was sensitive to the opposing "push" effect of attached alkyl groups.

The field of aromatic substitutions is one which has been well cultivated with a view to determining the course of chemical changes therein. E. Hückel expressed the view, which he derived from wave mechanical considerations, that the first stage of a substitution in the aromatic nucleus should be the expulsion of a proton. Lapworth and I disagreed with the pronouncement and wrote the following:

DISTRIBUTION OF ELECTRONS IN THE AROMATIC NUCLEUS AND THE EARLY STAGES OF AROMATIC SUBSTITUTIONS [205]

In a recent memoir E. Hückel has made an interesting attempt to apply modern mathematical and physical conceptions of the electron in valency bonds to an *a priori* deduction of the distribution of negative electricity in the benzene ring and ultimately to the development of a theory of orientation in aromatic substitutions. The paper has been very favourably received by physicists and also by many physical chemists, who have no doubt assumed that the dénouement in its main outlines is in harmony with the view of organic chemists. This is, however, not the case; so far as we are concerned, we expected conclusions to be reached which are the opposite of those arrived at by Hückel. Where this author postulates an excess of electrons we consider there is a defect, and *vice versa*.

It should be stated that we are confining our attention to the reactive positions, and the remarks made in this note are not intended to apply to the circumstances of any of the other carbon atoms in the nucleus. Thus there is little chemical evidence for the alternation proposed by Hückel, even if all the signs are inverted. The theory of

Hückel requires that, of two carbon atoms, the one which is the more deficient in electrons will be the more prone to undergo substitution (for example, nitration, sulphonation, or halogenation). The mechanism propounded is initially extrusion of a proton by the relatively positive centre, followed by attack of the vacant position by the reagent. On the other hand, we say that the reagent (of the electron-seeking kind, as in the processes specified) attacks the centres of electron excess, and that this is followed by the expulsion of the proton.

Our theoretical systems, though not identical in every respect, have been found successful in correlating certain important generalisations in organic chemistry with the changes observed in the properties of inorganic compounds as the charge on the nucleus of the central element alters: $B \to C \to N; P \to S \to Cl$. They have also proved useful in the interpretation of organic chemical phenomena of the most varied types.

The arguments that could be brought to bear on the present subject are accordingly very numerous, and it will suffice to mention the following three points:

(1) Any theory of aromatic substitution is inadequate if it fails to take account of the fact that the influence of groups on the course taken by substitution in the aromatic series can be perfectly correlated with the effects of the same groups on the orientation of additive reactions of non-aromatic unsaturated substances. Such reactions obviously obey the same fundamental laws as those that govern aromatic substitution and yet the expulsion of a proton does not occur at any stage of the process. We claim that in both cases the reagent seeks the centres of greater electronic density.

(2) From a study of the relative strengths of acids and bases, it is known that certain substituents have the effect of loosening the grip of a molecule on a proton; others tighten it. Clearly, in Hückel's theory the groups that make an acid stronger and a base weaker should, when introduced into the benzene molecule, facilitate the process of further substitution. Thus nitrobenzene should be more reactive than benzene, whereas toluene should be less reactive. Actually the reverse is the case, and circumstances, which from all analogies must assist in the process of extrusion of protons, do not render aromatic substitutions more facile, but, on the contrary, they make them much more difficult.

(3) Even in aromatic substitutions, the proton which is expelled

may be detached from a part of the molecule remote from the point of attack of the reagent and of attachment of the new substituent. An example is the perhalogenation of certain phenols and in general all that numerous class of reactions leading to blocked hydroaromatic types. In these cases it is not the atom suffering loss of a proton that receives the substituent, and therefore Hückel's theory could not be applied without such modifications as would amount to a reversal of the principle.

Without, therefore, going into the minutiae of the special organic reactions concerned, we venture to think that the above considerations render the view of Hückel untenable.

Unfortunately, the postulated distribution of electrons in the nucleus must stand or fall with the theory of substitutions, and we therefore assume that some error has crept into the discussion, the mathematical physics of which we are not competent to criticise.

The above remarks apply only to the course of ordinary aromatic substitution, which most organic chemists agree in attributing to the active intervention of unsaturated systems of two or more carbon atoms; substitution in saturated carbon compounds is quite a different phenomenon and may well be preceded by the loosening of the proton replaced. In this connexion the suggestion is not at all novel. Furthermore, cases in which aromatic substitution occur with great difficulty may perhaps be correctly described as of saturated hydrocarbon substitution type, a possible example being the conversion of m-dinitrobenzene into trinitrobenzene.

Nevertheless, the theory of substitutions in saturated compounds has not yet been satisfactorily treated, and we do not claim that the idea of incipient proton dissociation is proved in any one example; there are too few reliable data and the evidence is conflicting.

The object if this note is to direct attention to our opinion that the conclusions reached by E. Hückel regarding the distribution of electrons in benzene derivatives and the mechanism of substitution are quite unacceptable.

The University, Manchester   A. Lapworth

The Dyson Perrins Laboratory, Oxford   R. Robinson

The 1922 paper [52] contained a statement of a theory of alternating stabilities of octets in a chain of atoms. This idea was related to the theory of alternate polarities and could afford some explanation of the tendencies made apparent in the early stages of reactions. This conception was never developed in detailed explanations of the course of reactions. It was a contribution which Kermack made to the joint paper and I thought it likely to contain a germ of truth since it explained many facts which were otherwise hard to understand. In a case A—B—C a transfer of electrons from B to C may give the latter stable anionic character. The elctron configuration of B is accordingly weakened and A can take electrons from it. An example can be found in the stability of the silicate ion $Si^{3+} O^{4-}$. It appears that intermediate stages of oxidation are less stable than the final product. We did, however, not consider that the alternating octet stability would involve actual electron transfer, but rather produce a condition of strain which might be sufficient to affect the orientation of the reaction. This conception was undoubtedly less precise than that of conjugation and it was misunderstood to such an extent that I specifically set it aside for consideration at a much later time, and I never used the idea myself. Several authors accepted the idea of alternating stability of octets, but assumed actual appropriation of electrons by the more stable configurations. I was much interested to receive a small Chinese text book which was based on this theory.

I propose to supplement this account of my theoretical views in Volume II of these memoirs.

Chapter XII

University College, London (1928–1930)

After the customary examination work in the Honour School of Chemistry at Manchester, we spent about five weeks in the Alps and returned to London to make preparations for my new appointment as Professor of Organic Chemistry at University College, University of London. I accepted the invitation to occupy this Chair with some hesitation since I was so happy in my activities at Manchester, but it was a kind of usual sequence which had been followed by others, for example by A.V. Hill, the physiologist.

I found some very good friends at University College, especially F.G. Donnan who had come there from Liverpool, and J.N. Collie, my immediate predecessor in the Chair. He was a pioneer of mountaineering in several of its aspects but was especially fond of rock climbing. He cut a step to facilitate a difficult pitch in Moss Ghyll; this became known as Collie's step and though most climbers were glad to make use of it, some of them pretended to be shocked. At the time when I knew him, he spent the long vacation at Sligachan in The Isle of Skye. On one occasion at Sligachan, my wife and I returned to the hotel after a climb on one of the Coolin Ridges and a walk down a valley which I had never seen before. I told him about the climb and the subsequent walk in the valley. He said "Well, you have had a very good day, but do you realise that valley is the deer sanctuary?" He went on an expedition with two friends, one of whom was a poet and the other an engineer, and he said "Wouldn't it be wonderful if we could put Schiehallion on top of Ben Nevis". The poet agreed enthusiastically but the engineer walked along in moody silence, and after fifteen minutes said "But man, ye couldn'a do that". Collie also told me that walking on one of the Cairngorms, he heard steps shuffling along behind him. He turned quickly but saw nothing. A little later the sound was repeated, and Collie said that he ran down the mountain all the way to his hotel. In later life he thought up a possible explanation but said it was not very con-

230

vincing. He was, of course, one of the most active and respected Presidents of the Alpine Club. When I met him in London he was engaged in testing all kinds of rare gases of the atmosphere, alone and in mixtures in vacuum tubes, for the purpose of making illuminants.

I have already mentioned that we had a house in Hendon, namely Bramtoco, and in those days it was easy to drive a car down Hendon Way and Finchley Road to Gower Street, where the quadrangle of U.C.L. afforded a convenient parking place. This was my routine but I would be sorry to have to do the same thing under present circumstances.

A friendship formed at U.C.L. was with the Professor of Physics, E.N. da C. Andrade (1887—1971). We often lunched together at the restaurant in the rear of the headquarters of Maple & Co., and later met frequently during the Second World War in Government Committees. He was Honorary Librarian of the Royal Society and also took a great interest in the history of the Royal Society Club. Andrade had an extremely complex personality — he was an enemy of every type of humbug and a good example of this follows.

An exercise in lingua administrativa

" 'There are three necessary steps in useful research — the first to begin it, the second to end it and the third to publish it.' — Faraday.

"I have, as an exercise in what is today a branch of linguistics necessary to all who take any part in public life, turned the above sentence of Faraday's into *lingua administrativa*. The translation which does not, it is hoped, contain anything not adequately expressed in the original, runs as follows:

Having considered the ultimate and immediately attainable objectives which are the focus of rationally directed and effectively integrated scientific effort in the field of original research, it appears philosophically and economically, for the purpose of effective classification, possible to allocate the position under three main divisions, so far as oversimplification is not involved. The first necessity is that of a logically directed inception or coordinated progress from a state of preliminary consideration to that which may be regarded as an initiation of planned and active effort along lines previously recognised as possessing potential possibilities of progressive advance. So long as the attack on the problems, visualised as a coordinated whole, yields results which seem commensurate with the expenditure of available resources and effort, without any undue dispersion of effort or ineffective divagation, due consideration being paid to all relevant factors, it may be judged advisable to avoid abrupt discontinuity of purpose and to steadily pursue the enquiry towards the goal envisaged. Ultimately, however, a stage will be attained when it may appear expedient to collocate the findings of the enquire, incomplete as it may still be in some aspects, and to terminate, for the time being in any case, the particular organisation of directed scrutiny and investigation which was contemplated in the inception, account being taken of any subsidiary findings incidental to the implementation of the project as originally planned. At the stage now under review there will be definite, possibly provisional but nevertheless temporarily useful if not indefinitely permanent, findings, to implement which some method of wider communication than to those immediately concerned will be necessary. This third stage will involve necessarily a preliminary ordering of the results and a consideration of allied problems in contiguous fields, which should be followed by an incorporation of the discoveries, measurements and conclusions in an ordered descriptive sequence, arranged with a view to some form of duplication, which in many cases will, no doubt, be printing. The printing, or manifolding by other expedient methods, and the dissemination through appropriate channels of the facts, considerations and conclusions as coordinated for communication to a wider audience constitutes the third or final stage in the ordered process of research."

Andrade's emotional range was wide. At one end of the scale he wrote a book of poems, and at the other his highly irascible temperament got him into serious trouble as, for example, in the circumstances of his resignation of the directorship of the Davy-Faraday Laboratory in the Royal Institution. I found his personality highly stimulating and was always pleased to be in his company.

Harold Raistrick (1890—1971)

After graduation in 1912 Harold Raistrick, in 1914, began to work under the direction of Professor F. Gowland Hopkins. He also carried out confidential research for the Government, one of his collaborators being Dr. Dorothy Jordon Lloyd. He first became interested in the chemistry of micro-organisms in the course of an investigation, in collaboration with Anne Barbara Clark, on the production of oxalic acid by *Aspergillus niger*. This gave direction to his whole subsequent career and, incidentally, threw light on an aspect of the citric acid cycle, later developed by Krebs. An opportunity for extensive work on the micro-fungi and the metabolic products occured when, in January 1921, he became Director of the newly founded Laboratory of Applied Biochemistry at the Explosives Division of I.C.I. in Ardeer. Here, he worked in close collaboration with the Director of the whole research section of the Nobel Division, William Rintoul. The sympathetic understanding of the scientific importance of Raistrick's work and its potentialities in many directions, displayed by Rintoul, had an influence which it would be hard to overestimate. The work had already ramified in many directions when Raistrick was appointed as Professor in the London School of Hygiene and Tropical Medicine in 1929. He became Professor of Biochemistry in the University of London, the Chair being tenable at the London School, aforesaid. Here, with a succession of notable collaborators, he became the chief pioneer in the study of metabolic products of moulds. Some remarkable papers, published in the Transactions of the Royal Society, and his Bakerian Lecture, are monuments to the industry of his school of research.

I was associated with Raistrick in several projects, one of which, also in collaboration with A.R. Todd, had to do with helminthosporin, cynodontin, and a few congeners. These are produced by a *Helminthosporium* which is a rust growing on barley, and they are all anthraquinone derivatives. I had the privilege to discuss the chemistry and ranges of metabolic products without being directly concerned in investigations. This was especially the case during the period when I held the Chair of Organic Chemistry at University College, as our two laboratories were near neighbours. I acquired a great respect for Raistrick's qualities as an investigator. He was rather more of an organic chemist than a pure biochemist, but his instinctive feeling for the likely course of a biosynthesis seldom led him astray. I have just one small grievance, but it is extremely trivial; Raistrick had a collaborator named Charles, and in the particular researches on which they were jointly engaged, they produced a number of new acids, one of which was called Carlesic acid, and the names of several others were based on the same root. However, I thought that Raistrickic acid was going rather far, but the limit was surely reached by naming a new acid Clutterbuckic acid! Having had my little joke, I must add that Clutterbuck was one of Raistrick's most effective co-workers and like so many others, he had caught his senior colleague's enthusiasm. After the discovery of penicillin, Fleming asked Raistrick to attempt the isolation of the material present in the solutions. Unfortunately, this came at a time when Raistrick was in the full flush of a most significant period of development, during which many new crystalline substances were obtained as metabolic products of the growth of moulds. It was soon clear that penicillin posed a much more difficult problem than the majority of them and one can sympathise with Raistrick in his decision to devote the major part of his attention to the study of new crystalline compounds, rather than to the elusive penicillin. However, he did make some observations which were later the basis of the first succesful process for the isolation of the antibiotic. He found that penicillin was a strong acid, that it could be extracted by an organic solvent from an aqueous solution and later returned to dilute aqueous alkali, albeit with considerable loss due to its pronounced instability. It may be said, therefore, that Raistrick made an essential contribution to the study of penicillin.

He was a very good friend and one example of this, in my own experience, was the trouble he took to obtain for me a culture of *Helminthosporium* in order to enable a point in the biogenesis of helminthosporin to be studied. A.J. Birch and Herchell Smith had demonstrated the biosynthesis of the pigment from seven molecules of acetate. True as this could well be, I thought the synthesis should go through mevalonic and succinic acid. Shortly after embarking on the work in my home laboratory, the formation of anthraquinone pigments from mevalonic acid was suggested and improved by Thomas. I found that helminthosporin could be produced when the mould was grown either in solutions of succinate or of an equivalent mixture of succinate and acetate, and I thought rather better in the latter. Unfortunately, the work had to be abandoned because it involved chromatography which I was unable to undertake owing to advancing glaucoma.

Holger Erdtman (b. 1902)

Holger Erdtman entered on his University career at Stockholm in 1922. His work for his first degree, Filosofie magister (1925), was a study of the polyfructoside irisin contained in the rhizomes

H. Erdtman.

of a yellow flowered *Iris pseudacorus*. He then decided to learn something of the method of the great biochemical school of Hans von Euler. The actual subject was the so-called alkaline kidney phosphatase and he milled and extracted hundreds of pig kidneys. Dialysis of the crude preparation gave products of low activity, addition of the dialysate restored the activity. Von Euler and Myrbäck worked at the same time with the co-enzyme "co-zymase". "Had I found a co-phosphatase whose structure I could work out? Urine, a natural 'kidney dialysate', turned out to be a good source of the activator. Ultimately I found that my activator was magnesium ions". This was a most important biochemical discovery, but it disappointed Erdtman who had evidently hoped for something much more complex. He decided to go abroad "to do some real organic chemistry". He seemed to have admired the simplicity of my tropinone synthesis and decided to work in the Organic Chemical Laboratory at University College, London. Despite advice to the contrary, given him by von Euler, he applied for and was awarded a Ramsey Memorial Fellowship. Actually Erdtman's choice turned out to be a good one, not so much for the original reason, as for the fact that he took to my theoretical system like a duck to water and made many useful applications of the ideas of conjugation and polar activation, especially in his work on phenolic oxidation. Here he started work on what proved to be one of two dominating research ideas. The first of these was the study of the oxidation of phenols and the reactions of quinones. One of the first cases studied was the oxidation of pyrogallol to purpurogallin. Preliminary experiments of oxidation of isoeugenol were performed, and this was followed by studies of the Thiele acetylation of benzoquinones and a theoretical explanation of the results was advanced. He went to Oxford in 1932, but spent some time with Fr. Fichter in Basel to learn the technique of electrochemical phenol couplings, and then to E. Späth in Vienna to finish the work on dehydrodiisoeugenol. The kind of way in which Erdtman regarded his problems can best be understood from the following excerpt from a letter he wrote to me in 1971:

"From my literature studies during my early Stockholm years I had become very much intrigued by the structure of guaiaretic acid. How could such a compound be formed *in vivo*? The acid dimerization of isoeugenol was known to give a completely different compound. I felt the understanding of the biosynthesis of guaiaretic acid would give the key to the structure and biosynthesis of lignin. Guaiaretic acid could possibly be formed by dehydrogenation of isoeugenol. It is impossible to describe how difficult it was for me in those days to convince myself that the odd electron of a primary isoeugenol radical could creep out into the side-chain. Your bent arrows could explain it, but was it really true? In all other known cases the electron went to the *ortho* or the *para*-position. I had nobody with whom I could discuss this matter. However, I became absolutely convinced that the radical electron could trespass into the conjugated double bond of isoeugenol when the structure of dehydrodiisoeugenol was cleared up. In that case a side-chain radical must have reacted with a more orthodox radical with the odd electron in the *ortho*-position to the hydroxyl group. This would give a quinone methide capable of stabilization by adding on the hydroxyl group to the quinonoid system, precisely what happens when a quinone undergoes the Thiele acetylation.

When I wrote the paper on dehydrodi-isoeugenol I added a large schematic formula for lignin, exactly the one which is now believed to be representative of lignin. The starting point was of course coniferyl alcohol, not isoeugenol. The formula contained all the possible types of structures which could be formed from the oxidation of coniferyl alcohol. I wanted to publish that paper in Liebigs Annalen, but so wild a hypothesis could not be accepted in so venerable a journal, and either Holmberg or the Editor (Wieland) asked me to delete the lignin formula. (What a pity!)

I then worked on the structure of pinoresinol to which Bamberger had given a C_{19} composition. I thought, however, that a C_{20} composition was much more probable and that the substance was an analogue of guaiaretic acid, derived from two molecules of coniferyl alcohol. I was so convinced about this that I wrote down the correct structure and relative configuration before I had even seen the compound! It took some time before it was proved! Then, in Holmberg's laboratory, I worked out the gross structure of conidendrin, another 'lignan' from spruce. Spruce and pine contain pinoresinol. This seemed to indicate a chemical relation between those conifer *genera*!!''

Erdtman then took up an entirely different subject in collaboration with von Euler. The latter had formed the erroneous view that gramine is 2-dimethylaminomethylindole and Erdtman synthesised this substance. The base was not identical with gramine and was termed isogramine. In order to find out whether it was bitter, he tasted it and found that, indeed, it was. After a few seconds he noted numbness of his tongue, indicating an anaesthetic action. He folowed this up by making a substance in which the 2-3 bond of the indole nucleus was cut by imaginary addition of the elements of water; the substance thus became 2-diethylaminoaceto-*o*-toluidide. It was a long shot but it hit the target, since this basic amide was found to be a powerful local anaesthetic. It was obviously necessary to extend the series of dialkylaminoacetanilides to find the best member of it. Erdtman enlisted the help of a young student, N. Löfgren, in order to accelerate the work in which he was engaged himself. It was found that the anaesthetic property was general in the series and it was offered to the pharmaceutical firm of Astra who, however, at that point were not interested. Erdtman then found it necessary to work for a time at the Forest Products Research Laboratory. He had intended to continue the local anaesthetic project at a later date but he found to his digust that Löfgren, working at the university, had carried on alone and made some further small modification of the molecule, one of which was merely the addition of a second methyl group in position-6 of the aromatic nucleus. This substance, now known as Xylocaine, is a powerful safe anaesthetic, much used in dentistry. Löfgren had patented it without reference to Erdtman and became extremely rich in consequence. He died in tragic circumstances. From this stage on the second dominant interest in Erdtman's life was strongly developed; he must be regarded as one of the chief pioneers of chemical taxonomy, and his studies of the constituents of the conifers also lead to the discovery of numerous novel and interesting molecular types related to the terpenes. Amongst these the various tropolones are of special interest. It is true that the idea of a survey of related botanical groups had been introduced by Henry G. Smith in his study of the constituents of the genus *Eucalyptus*, and it is indeed remarkable what progress in this field Smith and his colleague Baker made. They were, however, largely self-taught and were certainly not equipped with sufficient knowledge of the relevant sciences. At any rate, there is a definite and rather long interval between H.G. Smith and Erdtman, and I have no doubt that Erdtman must be regarded as the orginator of the modern era of chemotaxonomic research. He made a very important contribution to our knowledge of lignin and of phenolic oxidation in general, and to the organic and biochemistry of the new groups of terpenoids and sesquiterpenoids which he encountered. Erdtman was the most original person as well as scientist; he showed this in forthright comment in conversation, in his dress with the symbolic, perhaps practical, jackknife which he held at the ready to top off any unusual conifers which he encountered on his travels. The latter included excursions to unusual places, such as British Burmah and, in fact, anywhere reputed to be the home of conifers.

Synthesis of some Anthocyanidins and Anthocyanins at University College, London

Examination of cranberries (*Oxycoccus macrocarpus*) from the region of Cape Cod suggested that the pigment in the skins might be peonidin 3-glucoside [198]. This substance was synthesised [189] but not directly compared with the natural colouring matter.

The anthocyanidin hirsutidin is a trimethyl ether of delphinidin and since one of the methoxyl groups is in the 7-position of the flavylium nucleus it was possible to force a sugar residue into position-5. In this way the 5-glucoside and 5-lactoside of hirsutidin were synthesised [193].

An anthocyanin prepared on an unusually large scale was oenin, the colouring matter of the skin of black grapes (cf. p. 147); oenin chloride crystallised very well [188].

The 3-β-glucoside of fisetinidin chloride [191] was readily obtained by following the chrysanthemin synthesis, using β-resorcyl aldehyde. This monoglucoside was interesting because its colour reactions over a range of pH matched closely those characteristic of cyanin. This indicated clearly that cyanin must be a 3,5-diglucoside.

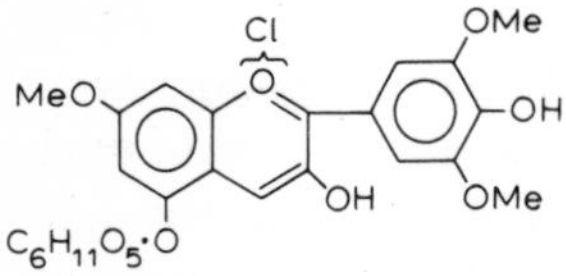

Hirsutidin 5-glucoside
(chloride)

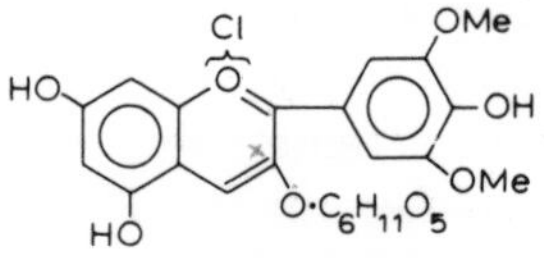

Oenin chloride

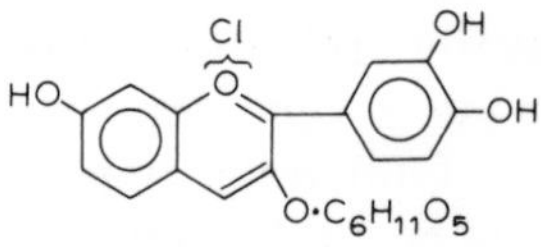

Fisetinin chloride

Willstätter was of the opinion that the nitrogenous colouring matters typified by the beet were anthocyanins. He never published anything on this to my knowledge but sent me figures for estimations of nitrogen content suggesting N_2 in a molecule of ordinary anthocyanin size. The bluish red colour appeared to be consistent with this hypothesis though all attempts to show that betanin is a phloroglucin derivative failed completely. Using the familiar methods we prepared some aminoflavylium salts and were misled by the similarity of their absorption spectra with that of betanin [216,236]. Some years later Dreiding showed that betanin and related substances are derivatives of pyridine and pyrrole and have no relation whatever with the anthocyanins.

Further developments of the chemistry and biochemistry of the anthocyanins will be described in the second volume of these memoirs.

During my short sojourn at University College, London, researches begun in earlier periods were continued. An example of this is the determination of the constitution of brazilin. My collaborator in this work was V.M. Mičovič, who later became Professor of Organic Chemistry at the University of Belgrade.

240

List of Publications

LIST OF ORIGINAL MEMOIRS, SCIENTIFIC PAPERS, SOME LETTERS AND
ADDRESSES RELEVANT TO THE CONTENT OF THIS VOLUME

Abbreviations: RR   — Robert Robinson
               GMR — Gertrude Maud Robinson
               WHP — William Henry Perkin, jun.
               J   — Journal of the Chemical Society

1. Ethyl Piperonylacetate. By WHP and RR (Proc. Chem. Soc., 1905, 287).
2. Brazilin and Haematoxylin. Part VII. Synthesis of Derivatives of Hydrindene closely allied to Brazilin and Haematoxylin. By WHP and RR (J, 1907, *91*, 1073).
3. Brazilin and Haematoxylin. Part VIII. Synthesis of Brazilinic Acid, the Lactones of Dihydrobrazilinic and Dihydrohaematoxylinic Acids, Anhydrobrazilic Acid, etc. The Constitution of Brazilin, Haematoxylin, and their Derivatives. By WHP and RR (J, 1908, *93*, 489).
4. The Synthesis and Constitution of Certain Pyranol Salts Related to Brazilein and Haematein. By WHP, RR, and (in part) Maurice Russell Turner (J, 1908, *93*, 1085).
5. Brazilin, Haematoxylin, and their Derivatives. Part IX. On Brazilein, Haematein, and their Derivatives. By Paul Engels, WHP, and RR (J, 1908, *93*, 1115).
6. Brazilin, Haematoxylin, and their Derivatives. Part X. The Constitution of Trimethylbrazilone, of α- and β-Anhydrotrimethylbrazilone, and of the corresponding Haematoxylin Derivatives. By WHP and RR (J, 1909, *95*, 381).
7. Experiments on the Constitution of the Aloins. Part I. By John Lionel Simonsen and RR (J, 1909, *95*, 1085).
8. Synthesis of Cotarnic Acid. By WHP, Frederick Thomas, and RR (J, 1909, *95*, 1977).
9. A New Synthesis of Oxazole Derivatives. By RR (J, 1909, *95*, 2167).
10. Strychnine, Berberine, and Allied Alkaloids. By WHP and RR (J, 1910, 97, 305)
11. *m*-Hemipinic and Asaronic Acids. By Bernard Dunstan Wilkinson Luff, WHP and RR (J, 1910, *97*, 1131).
12. Synthesis and Resolution of Gnoscopine (*dl*-Narcotine). By WHP and RR (J, 1910, *97*, 775).

13. Synthetical Experiments in the Group of the *iso*Quinoline Alkaloids. Part I. Anhydrocotarninephtalide. By Edward Hope and RR (J, 1910, *97*, 1153).
14. Synthetical Experiments in the Group of the *iso*Quinoline Alkaloids. Part II. The Constitution of the Condensation Products of Cotarnine and the Condensation of Cotarnine with Aliphatic and Aromatic Nitro-compounds. By Edward Hope and RR (J, 1910, *97*, 2114).
15. Anhydrohydrastininemeconin. By Edward Hope and RR (Proc. Chem. Soc., 1910, 17).
16. 1:2-Diketohydrindene. By WHP, Walter Morrell Roberts, and RR (J, 1911, *99*, 232).
17. *iso*Narcotine. By Ernest Griffiths Jones, WHP, and RR (J, 1911, *99*, 257).
18. *iso*Oxyberberine. By Norman Bland, WHP, and RR (J, 1911, *99*, 262).
19. The Exhaustive Alkylation of Tetrahydroberberine. By James Wallace McDavid, WHP, and RR (J, 1912, *101*, 1218).
20. Some Derivatives of Oxazole. By Joseph Lister and RR (J, 1912, *101*, 1297).
21. Harmine and Harmaline. Part I. By WHP and RR (J, 1912, *101*, 1775).
22. Synthetical Experiments in the Group of the *iso*Quinoline Alkaloids. Part III. The Constitution of Anhydrocotarnineacetophenone, etc., together with an Account of Some new Condensation Products of Cotarnine. By Edward Hope and RR (J, 1913, *103*, 361).
23. 2-Phenyl-5-styryloxazole. By Robinson Percy Foulds and RR (J, 1913, *103*, 1768).
24. Harmine and Harmaline. Part II. The Synthesis of *iso*Harman. By WHP and RR (J, 1913, *103*, 1973).
25. Researches on Pseudo-bases. Part I. Some Condensation Reactions of Cotarnine, Hydrastinine, and *iso*Quinoline Methyl Hydroxide. By GMR and RR (J, 1914, *105*, 1456).
26. Some Derivatives of Safrole. By Robinson Percy Foulds and RR (J, 1914, *105*, 1963).
27. Synthetical Experiments in the Group of the *iso*Quinoline Alkaloids. Part IV. The Synthesis of β-Gnoscopine. By Edward Hope and RR (J, 1914, *105*, 2086).
28. Some Derivatives of *ortho*-Vanillin. By WHP and RR (J, 1914, *105*, 2376).
29. Some Derivatives of *iso*Coumarin and *iso*Carbostyril. By David Bain, WHP and RR (J, 1914, *105*, 2392).
30. 1:2-Diketo-5:6-dimethoxyhydrindene. By WHP, Walter Morrell Roberts, and RR (J, 1914, *105*, 2405).
31. Eudesmin and its Derivatives. Part I. By RR and Henry G. Smith (J. Royal Soc. N.S.W., 1914, 449).
32. A Note on the Phenols Occurring in Some Eucalyptus Oils. By RR and Henry G. Smith (J. Royal Soc. N.S.W., 1915, 518).
33. Note on the Nitroguaiacols. By David Cardwell and RR (J, 1915, *107*, 255).
33A.A Reaction of Homopiperonyl and of Homoveratryl Alcohols. By GMR (J, 1915, *107*, 267).
34. A Decomposition of Certain *o*-Nitromandelic Acids. By GMR and RR (J, 1915, *107*, 1753).

242

35. An Extension of the Theory of Addition to Conjugated Unsaturated Systems. Part I. Note on the Constitution of the Salts of 1-Benzylidene-2-methyl-1:2:3:4-tetrahydro*iso*quinoline. By Ellice Ettie Peden Hamilton and RR (J, 1916, *109*, 1029).

36. An Extension of the Theory of Addition to Conjugated Unsaturated Systems. Part II. The C-Alkylation of Certain Derivatives of β-Aminocrotonic Acid and the Mechanism of the Alkylation of Ethyl Acetoacetate and Similar Substances. By RR (J, 1916, *109*, 1039).

36A.Experiments on the so-called Migration of Atoms and Groups. Part I. The Nitration of p-Iodophenolic Ethers. By GMR (J, 1916, *109*, 1078).

36B.Azoxycatechol Ethers and Related Substances. By GMR (J, 1917, *111*, 109).

37. A Synthesis of Tropinone. By RR (J, 1917, *111*, 762).

38. A Theory of the Mechanism of the Phytochemical Synthesis of Certain Alkaloids. By RR (J, 1917, *111*, 876).

39. Experiments on the Orientation of Substituted Catechol Ethers. By Thomas Gilbert Henry Jones and RR (J, 1917, *111*, 903).

40. The Scission of Certain Substituted Cyclic Catechol Ethers. By GMR and RR (J, 1917, *111*, 929).

41. 5-Bromoguaiacol and Some Derivatives. By Ellen Margaret Hindmarsh, Isabel Knight, and RR (J, 1917, *111*, 940).

42. The Action of Halogens on Piperonal. By Annie Mary Bleakly Orr, RR, and Margaret Mary Williams (J, 1917, *111*, 946).

43. Veratricsulphinide. By Janet Forrest McGillivray Brown and RR (J, 1917, *111*, 952).

44. Researches on Pseudo-bases. Part II. Note on some Berberine Derivatives and Remarks on the Mechanism of the Condensation Reactions of Pseudo-bases. By GMR and RR (J, 1917, *111*, 958).

45. A New Synthesis of Tetraphenylpyrrole. By GMR and RR (J, 1918, *113*, 639).

46. Nitro-derivatives of Guaiacol. By Fanny Pollecoff and RR (J, 1918, *113*, 645).

47. A Synthesis of *iso*Brazilein and Certain Related Anhydropyranol Salts. Part I. By Herbert Grace Crabtree and RR (J, 1918, *113*, 859).

48. Harmine and Harmaline. Part III. By WHP and RR (J, 1919, *115*, 933).

49. Harmine and Harmaline. Part IV. By WHP and RR (J, 1919, *115*, 967).

50. Harmine and Harmaline. Part V. The Synthesis of Norharman. By William Ogilvy Kermack, WHP, and RR (J, 1921, *119*, 1602).

51. The Conjugation of Partial Valencies. By RR (Manchester Memoirs, Vol. lxiv (1920), No. 4).

52. An Explanation of the Property of Induced Polarity of Atoms and an Interpretation of the Theory of Partial Valencies on an Electronic Basis. By William Ogilvy Kermack and RR (J, 1922, *121*, 427).

53. Polynuclear Heterocyclic Aromatic Types. Part I. Some Indenoquinoline Derivatives. By James Wilson Armit and RR (J, 1922, *121*, 827).

54. The Hydroxybenzoylphloroglucinols. By Hidejiro Nishikawa and RR (J, 1922, *121*, 839).

55. Note on 2:3- and 2:5-Dinitro-*p*-toluidines. By James Scott and RR (J, 1922, *121*, 844).
56. A Synthesis of *iso*Brazilein and Certain Related Anhydropyranol Salts. Part II. Synthesis of *iso*Haematein. By Herbert Grace Crabtree and RR (J, 1922, *121*, 1033).
57. Cevadine. Part I. By Alexander Killen Macbeth and RR (J, 1922, *121*, 1571).
58. A Synthesis of Pyrylium Salts of Anthocyanidin Type. By David Doig Pratt and RR (J, 1922, *121*, 1577).
59. Harmine and Harmaline. Part VI. The Synthesis of N-Methyltetrahydro-norharmine and the Constitution of Harmaline and of the Alkylated Harmines. By William Ogilvy Kermack, WHP, and RR (J, 1922, *121*, 1872).
60. The Mechanism of the Formation of Benzoylbenzoin by Treatment of Benzoylmandelonitrile with an Alcoholic Solution of Sodium Ethoxide. By Herbert Greene and RR (J, 1922, *121*, 2182).
61. Researches on Pseudo-bases. Part IV. A New Synthesis of Tertiary Amines of the Form $R.CH_2.NR^1R^2$. By GMR and RR (J, 1923, *123*, 532).
62. A Direct Synthesis of Certain Xanthylium Derivatives. By David Doig Pratt and RR (J, 1923, *123*, 739).
63. A Synthesis of Pyrylium Salts of Anthocyanidin Type. Part II. By David Doig Pratt and RR (J, 1923, *123*, 745).
64. The Morphine Group. Part I. A Discussion of the Constitutional Problem. By John Masson Gulland and RR (J, 1923, *123*, 980).
65. The Morphine Group. Part II. Thebainone, Thebainol and Dihydrothebainone. By John Masson Gulland and RR (J, 1923, *123*, 998).
66. A Synthesis of Pyrylium Salts of Anthocyanidin Type. Part III. A New Synthesis of Pelargonidin Chloride. By David Doig Pratt and RR (J, 1924, *125*, 188).
67. A Synthesis of Pyrylium Salts of Anthocyanidin Type. Part IV. Flavylium Salts Related to Chrysin, Apigenin and Luteolin. By David Doig Pratt, RR, and Percy Noel Williams (J, 1924, *125*, 199).
68. Some Derivatives of Benzopyrylium. By RR and (in part) Herbert Grace Crabtree, Chinyann Kumara Das, Wilfred Lawson, Robert Winstanley Lunt, Bernard Holtom Roberts, and Percy Noel Williams (J, 1924, *125*, 207).
69. Some Benzopyrylium Salts. By Leslie Randal Ridgway and RR (J, 1924, *125*, 214).
69A. Synthesis of Higher Monoalkylmalonic Acids. By GMR (J, 1924, *125*, 226).
70. Harmine and Harmaline. Part VII. A Synthesis of *apo*Harmine and of Certain Carboline and Copyrine Derivatives. By Wilfred Lawson, WHP, and RR (J, 1924, *125*, 626).
71. Harmine and Harmaline. Part VIII. The Constitution of Certain Harmaline Derivatives. By Hidejiro Nishikawa, WHP, and RR (J, 1924, *125*, 657).
72. The Mechanism of E. Fischer's Synthesis of Indoles. Application of the Method to the Preparation of a Pyrindole Derivative. By GMR and RR (J, 1924, *125*, 840).
73. Strychnine and Brucine. Part II. By George Roger Clemo, WHP, and RR (J, 1924, *125*, 1751).

244

74. A Synthesis of ψ-Pelletierine. By Robert Charles Menzies and RR (J, 1924, *125*, 2163).
75. 5-Carboline and Some Derivatives. By RR and Sidney Thornley (J, 1924, *125*, 2169).
76. An Accessible Derivative of Chromonol. By James Allan and RR (J, 1924, *125*, 2192).
77. A New Route to the 3-Hydroxybenzopyrylium Salts. By Leslie Randal Ridgway and RR (J, 1924, *125*, 2240).
78. Nitration of 2:3-Dimethoxybenzaldehyde. By WHP, RR, and Francis Wilbert Stoyle (J, 1924, *125*, 2355).
79. A Synthesis of Pyrylium Salts of Anthocyanidin Type. Part V. The Synthesis of Cyanidin Chloride and of Delphinidin Chloride. By David Doig Pratt and RR (J, 1925, *127*, 166).
80. Synthesis of Certain Higher Aliphatic Compounds. Part I. A Synthesis of Lactarinic Acid and of Oleic Acid. By GMR and RR (J, 1925, *127*, 175).
81. A Synthesis of Myricotin and of a Galangin Monomethyl Ether Occurring in Galanga Root. By Jan Kalff and RR (J, 1925, *127*, 181).
82. Phenyl Benzyl Diketone and Some Derivatives. By Thomas Malkin and RR (J, 1925, *127*, 369).
83. A Synthesis of Oxyberberine. Part I. By WHP, Jnanendra Nath Râv, and RR (J, 1925, *127*, 740).
84. 3-Chlorobenzopyrylium Derivatives. By Leslie Randal Ridgway and RR (J, 1925, *127*, 767).
85. A Qualitative Test for Weak Bases. By RR (J, 1925, *127*, 768).
86. A Synthesis of Pyrylium Salts of Anthocyanidin Type. Part VI. Polyhydroxyflavylium Salts Related to Chrysin, Apigenin, Lotoflavin, Luteolin, Galangin, Fisetin and Morin. By David Doig Pratt and RR (J, 1925, *127*, 1129).
87. A Synthesis of Pyrylium Salts of Anthocyanidin Type. Part VII. The Preparation of the Anthocyanidin with the Aid of 2:4:6-Triacetoxybenzaldehyde. By David Doig Pratt and RR (J, 1925, *127*, 1183).
88. A Synthesis of Pyrylium Salts of Anthocyanidin Type. Part VIII. A New Synthesis of Pelargonidin Chloride and of Galanginidin Chloride. By Thomas Malkin and RR (J, 1925, *127*, 1190).
89. Strychnine and Brucine. Part III. The Position of the Methoxyl Groups in Brucine. By Francis Lions, WHP, and RR (J, 1925, *127*, 1158).
90. The Constitution of Codeine and Thebaine. By John Masson Gulland and RR (Manchester Memoirs, Vol. lxix (1924-25), No. 10).
91. Synthetical Experiments in the Naphthyridine Groups. By John Masson Gulland and RR (J, 1925, *127*, 1493).
92. Polynuclear Heterocyclic Aromatic Types. Part II. Some Anhydronium Bases. By James Wilson Armit and RR (J, 1925, *127*, 1604).
93. The Nitration of *m*-Meconin. By Jnanendra Nath Ray and RR (J, 1925, *127*, 1618).
94. β-Piperonylpropionitrile and Some Derived Substances. By Wilson Baker and RR (J, 1925, *127*, 1424).
95. A Synthesis of Datiscetin. By Jan Kalff and RR (J, 1925, *127*, 1968).

96. Polarisation of Nitrosobenzene. By RR (J. Soc. Chem. Ind., 1925, *44*, 456).

97. The Synthesis of Certain 2-Stryrylchromonol Derivatives. By RR and Junzo Shinoda (J, 1925, *127*, 1974).

98. Synthetical Experiments in the *iso*Flavone Group. Part I. By Wilson Baker and RR (J, 1925, *127*, 1981).

99. The Relative Directive Powers of Groups of the Forms RO and RR'N in Aromatic Substitution. Part I. By James Allan and RR (J, 1926, 376).

100. The Relative Directive Powers of Groups of the Forms RO and RR'N in Aromatic Substitution. Part II. The Nitration of some 2-Benzyloxyanisoles substituted in the Benzyl Group. By Albert Edward Oxford and RR (J, 1926, 383).

101. The Relative Directive Powers of Groups of the Forms RO and RR'N in Aromatic Substitution. Part III. The Nitration of some *p*-Alkyloxyanisoles. By RR and John Charles Smith (J, 1926, 392).

102. The Relative Directive Powers of Groups of the Forms RO and RR'N in Aromatic Substitution. Part IV. A Discussion of the Observations Recorded in Parts I, II, and III. By James Allan, Albert Edward Oxford, RR, and John Charles Smith (J, 1926, 401).

103. The Relative Directive Powers of Groups of the Forms RO and RR'N in Aromatic Substitution. Part V. The Nitration of *p*-Methoxydiphenyl Ether. By Thomas Russell Lea and RR (J, 1926, 411).

104. The Morphine Group. Part III. The Constitution of Neopine. By Constant Frederik van Duin, RR, and John Charles Smith (J, 1926, 903).

105. The Morphine Group. Part IV. A New Oxidation Product of Codeine. By Robert Sidney Cahn and RR (J, 1926, 908).

106. Experiments on the Synthesis of Brazilin and Haematoxylin and their Derivatives. Part I. Veratrylidene-7-methoxychromanone and an Account of a New Synthesis of some Benzopyrylium Salts. By WHP, Jnanendra Nath Râv, and RR (J, 1926, 941).

107. The Orienting Influence of Free and Bound Ionic Charges on Attached Simple or Conjugated Unsaturated Systems. Part I. The Nitration of Some Derivatives of Benzylamine. By Harry Raymond Ing and RR (J, 1926, 1655).

108. Experiments on the Synthesis of Anthocyanins. Part I. By Alexander Robertson and RR (J, 1926, 1713).

109. A Synthesis of Pyrylium Salts of Anthocyanidin Type. Part IX. Some Hydroxyflavylium Salts. By Alexander Robertson and RR (J, 1926, 1951).

110. A Synthesis of Pyrylium Salts of Anthocyanidin Type. Part X. Delphinidin Chloride 3-Methyl Ether. By Elizabeth Stewart Gatewood and RR (J, 1926, 1959).

111. A Synthesis of Pyrylium Salts of Anthocyanidin Type. Part XI. A Synthesis of Peonidin Chloride. By Thomas Joseph Nolan, David Doig Pratt, and RR (J, 1926, 1968).

112. Derivatives of Homocatechol. Part I. By Franz Robert Graesser-Thomas, John Masson Gulland, and RR (J, 1926, 1971).

246

113. Derivatives of Homocatechol. Part II. By John Masson Gulland and RR (J, 1926, 1976).

114. 2:3:4-Trinitrotoluene. By Frank Howorth Gornall and RR (J, 1926, 1981).

115. Derivatives of 1-Benzyltetrahydro*iso*quinoline. By RR and Helen West (J, 1926, 1985).

116. Synthetical Experiments in the Phenanthrene Group of the Alkaloids. Part I. By RR and Junzo Shinoda (J, 1926, 1987).

117. Synthesis of Certain Higher Aliphatic Compounds. Part II. The Hydration of Stearolic Acid. By GMR and RR (J, 1926, 2204).

118. A New Synthesis of Fisetin and of Quercetin. By James Allan and RR (J, 1926, 2334).

119. A Synthesis of Kaempferide and of *iso*Rhamnetin. By Tom Heap and RR (J, 1926, 2336).

120. A Synthesis of Acacetin and Certain Other Derivatives of Flavone. By RR and Krishnasami Venkataraman (J, 1926, 2344).

121. The Fission of Some Methoxylated Benzophenones. By Thomas Russell Lea and RR (J, 1926, 2351).

122. The Hydrolytic Fission of Some Substituted Dibenzoylmethanes. By William Bradley and RR (J, 1926, 2356).

123. Synthetical Experiments in the *iso*Flavone Group. Part II. A Synthesis of Methylgenistein (Methylprunetol) Dimethyl Ether and the Constitution of Prunetol (Genistein). By Wilson Baker and RR (J, 1926, 2713).

124. The Alleged Nitration of S-Methylthioguaiacol. A Criticism. By Alfred Pollard and RR (J, 1926, 3090).

125. 3-Methoxy-2-phenylindole and 3-Benzoylamino-2-phenylindole. By RR and Sidney Thornley (J, 1926, 3144).

126. Harmine and Harmaline. Part IX. A Synthesis of Harmaline. By Richard Helmuth Fred Manske, WHP, and RR (J, 1927, 1).

127. The Decomposition of β-3-Indolylpropionic Azide. By Richard Helmuth Fred Manske and RR (J, 1927, 240). .

128. Experiments on the Synthesis of Anthocyanins. Part II. The Synthesis of 3- and 7-Glucosidoxyflavylium Salts. By Alexander Robertson and RR (J, 1927, 242).

129. A Synthesis of Rutaecarpine. By Yasuhiko Asahina, Richard Helmuth Fred Manske, and RR (J, 1927, 1708).

130. Experiments on the Synthesis of Anthocyanins. Part III. By Alexander Robertson and RR (J, 1927, 1710).

131. A Synthesis of Pyrylium Salts of Anthocyanidin Type. Part XII. By David Doig Pratt, Alexander Robertson and RR (J, 1927, 1975).

132. Strychnine and Brucine. Part IV. By George Roger Clemo, WHP, and RR (J, 1927, 1589).

133. Strychnine and Brucine. Part V. By John Masson Gulland, WHP, and RR (J, 1927, 1627).

134. The Displacement of Bromine accompanying the Nitration of 6-Bromo-homoveratrole. By Tom Heap, Thomas G.H. Jones, and RR (J, 1927, 2021).

135. A Synthesis of Pyrylium Salts of Anthocyanidin Type. Part XIII. Some Monohydroxyflavylium Salts. By Frank Mouat Irvine and RR (J, 1927, 2086).

136. A Synthesis of Pyrylium Salts of Anthocyanidin Type. Part XIV. By Alexander Robertson and RR (J, 1927, 2196).
137. Polynuclear Heterocyclic Aromatic Types. Part III. Pyrroloquinoline Derivatives. By Reginald Clifford Fawcett and RR (J, 1927, 2255).
138. Experiments on the Synthesis of Brazilin and Haematoxylin and their Derivatives. Part II. A Synthesis of Deoxytrimethylbrazilone and of iso-Brazilein Ferrichloride Trimethyl Ether. By WHP, Jnanendra Nath Rây, and RR (J, 1927, 2094).
139. The Relative Directive Powers of Groups of the Forms RO and RR'N in Aromatic Substitution. Part VI. The Nitration of m- and p-Chlorobenzyl Ethers of Guaiacol. By Albert Edward Oxford and RR (J, 1927, 2239).
140. Strychnine and Brucine. Part VI. The Catalytic Hydrogenation of Strychnine and Some Derivatives. By Albert Edward Oxford, WHP, and RR (J, 1927, 2389).
141. 3-Hydroxycyclohexylacetolactone. By RR and Ahmad Zaki (J, 1927, 2411).
142. The Relative Directive Powers of Groups of the Forms RO and RR'N in Aromatic Substitution. Part VII. The Nitration of Benzphenetidide and of o-, m- and p-Nitrobenzphenetidides. By Reginald C. Fawcett and RR (J, 1927, 2414).
143. Examples of Feeble Activation of Certain Extended Conjugated Systems by Doubly Bound Oxygen. By RR and Ahmad Zaki (J, 1927, 2485).
144. The Relative Directive Powers of the Groups of the Forms RO and RR'N in Aromatic Substitution. Part VIII. The Nitration of 4-n-Butoxyanisole. By John Clarke, RR, and John Charles Smith (J, 1927, 2647).
145. Facile Ring-closure to a Derivative of Dihydroisoquinoline contrasted with the Difficulty of Analogous Formation of a Derivative of isoIndole. By Jacques Malan and RR (J, 1927, 2653).
146. The Orienting Influence of Free and Bound Ionic Charges on Attached Simple or Conjugated Unsaturated Systems. Part II. The Nitration of 1-Benzylpiperidine and of Some Related Substances. By Alfred Pollard and RR (J, 1927, 2770).
147. The Orienting Influence of Free and Bound Ionic Charges on Attached Simple or Conjugated Unsaturated Systems. Part III. The Nitration of m-Nitrophenylbenzylsulphone. By Bibhucharan Chatterjee and RR (J, 1927, 2780).
148. The Orienting Influence of Free and Bound Ionic Charges on Attached Simple or Conjugated Unsaturated Systems. Part IV. The Nitration of of Toluene-ω-sulphonic Acid and of Toluene-ω-sulphonyl Chloride. By Arthur C. Bottomley and RR (J, 1927, 2785).
149. The Colouring Matters of Carajura. By Ernest Chapman, Arthur George Perkin, and RR (J, 1927, 3015).
150. Note on the Characterisation of the Anthocyanins and Anthocyanidins by Means of their Colour Reactions in Alkaline Solutions. By Alexander Robertson and RR (Biochem. J., 1929, 23, 35).
151. A Synthesis of Pyrylium Salts of Anthocyanidin Type. Part XV. The Synthesis of Cyanidin Chloride by Means of O-Benzoylphloroglucinaldehyde. By Alexander Robertson and RR (J, 1928, 1526).

152. A Synthesis of Pyrylium Salts of Anthocyanidin Type. Part XVI. The Synthesis of Pelargonidin Chloride by Means of O-Benzoylphloroglucinaldehyde. By Alexander Robertson, RR, and Jiro Sugiura (J, 1928, 1533).

153. A Synthesis of Pyrylium Salts of Anthocyanidin Type. Part XVII. The Synthesis of Peonidin Chloride by Means of O-Benzoylphloroglucinaldehyde. By Shinzo Murakami and RR (J, 1928, 1537).

154. A Synthesis of Pyrylium Salts of Anthocyanidin Type. Part XVIII. A Synthesis of Malvidin Chloride. By William Bradley and RR (J, 1928, 1541).

155. Strychnine and Brucine. Part VII. The Constitution of the Alkaloids discussed in Relation to the Hypothesis that Dinitrostrychol is an isoQuinoline Derivative. By Reginald Clifford Fawcett, WHP, and RR (J, 1928, 3082).

156. The ortho-para Ratio in Aromatic Substitutions. By A. Lapworth and RR (Manchester Memoirs, Vol. lxxii (1927-28), No. 4).

157. The Interaction of Benzoyl Chloride and Diazomethane together with a Discussion of the Reactions of the Diazenes. By William Bradley and RR (J, 1928, 1310).

158. Experiments on the Synthesis of Anthocyanins. Part IV. By Alexander Robertson, RR, and A.M. Struthers (J, 1928, 1455).

159. Experiments on the Synthesis of Anthocyanins. Part V. A Synthesis of 3-β-Glucosidylpelargonidin Chloride, which is believed to be identical with Callistephin Chloride. By Alexander Robertson and RR (J, 1928, 1460).

160. 3:4:5:6-Tetrahydro-4-carboline. By Julius Nicholson Ashley and RR (J, 1928, 1376).

161. Experiments on the Synthesis of Brazilin and Haematoxylin and their Derivatives. Part III. By WHP, Jnanendra Nath Rây, and RR (J, 1928, 1504).

162. Anthoxanthins. Part VIII. A Synthesis of Morin and of 5:7:2':4'-Tetrahydroxyflavone. By RR and Krishnasami Venkataraman (J, 1929, 61).

163. Anthoxanthins. Part IX. Syringetin. By Tom Heap and RR (J, 1929, 67).

164. Anthoxanthins. Part X. The Synthesis of Gossypetin and of Quercetagetin. By Wilson Baker, Ryuzaburo Nodzu, and RR (J, 1929, 74).

165. Synthetical Experiments in the isoFlavone Group. Part III. A Synthesis of Genistein. By Wilson Baker and RR (J, 1928, 3115).

166. Synthetical Experiments in the isoFlavone Group. Part IV. A Synthesis of 2-Methylirigenol. By Wilson Baker and RR (J, 1929, 152).

167. Synthetic Experiments in the isoFlavone Group. Part V. By RR, Wilson Baker, and Alfred Pollard (J, 1929, 1468).

168. Strychnine and Brucine. Part VIII. The Action of Hydriodic Acid on Strychnidine. Dihydrostrychnidine (B) and Substances derived therefrom. By WHP and RR (J, 1929, 964).

169. Bemerkungen zur Abhandlung von T. Malkin und M. Nierenstein, "Zur Kenntnis des Cyanidins, I". By RR and Richard Willstätter (Ber., 1928, 2504).

170. Notiz über Chrysanthemin und Asterin. By RR and Richard Willstätter (Ber., 1928, 2503).

171. 6:7-Dimethoxyisatin, 5:6-Methylenedioxyisatin and the Nuclear Degradation of 3:4-Methylenedioxyquindoline. By John Masson Gulland, RR, James Scott, and Sidney Thornley (J, 1929, 2924).

172. Harmine and Harmaline. Part X. The Synthesis of 7- and 8-Methoxyketo-

tetrahydro-β-carbolines and the Constitution of Acetylharmaline. By Herbert S. Boyd Barrett, (the late) WHP, and RR (J, 1929, 2942).

173. Attempts to find New Anti-malarials. Introduction by George Barger and RR. Part I. Some Pyrroloquinoline Derivatives. By GMR (J, 1929, 2947). Part II. Aminoalkylquinolinium Salts and Some Related Substances. By Tiruventaka Rajendra Seshadri (J, 1929, 2952). Part III. Some Substituted Aminoalkylaminoquinolines. By Alfred William Baldwin (J, 1929, 2959). Part IV. β-Benziminazolylethylamine and β-5 (or 6)-Ethoxybenziminazolylethylamine. By Bibhucharan Chatterjee (J, 1929, 2965).

174. Strychnine and Brucine. Part IX. Preparation of Some Isomerides of Dinitrostrychol and Trinitrostrychol. By Julius Nicholson Ashley, (the late) WHP, and RR (J, 1930, 382).

175. The Action of Diazomethane on Benzoic and Succinic Anhydrides and a Reply to Malkin and Nierenstein. By W. Bradley and RR (J. Amer. Chem. Soc., 1930, 52, 1558).

176. A Synthesis of Certain Higher Aliphatic Compounds. Part III. A Variation of the Keto-acid Synthesis, constituting an Improved Method for the Extension of Normal Carbon Chains. By GMR (J, 1930, 745).

177. A Synthesis of Pyrylium Salts of Anthocyanidin Type. Part XIX. A Synthesis of Delphinidin Chloride not involving a Demethylation Process and Synthesis of Hirsutidin Chloride, and of Delphinidin Chloride 3'-Methyl Ether, possibly identical with Petunidin Chloride. By William Bradley, RR, and Gerold Schwarzenbach (J, 1930, 793).

178. Anthoxanthins. Part XI. A Synthesis of Diosmetin and of Luteolin 3'-Methyl Ether. By Albert Lovecy, RR, and Shigehiko Sugasawa (J, 1930, 817).

179. Anthoxanthins. Part XII. Transition from a Flavylium Salt to a Flavone, illustrated by a New Synthesis of Scutellarein Tetramethyl Ether. By RR and Gerold Schwarzenbach (J, 1930, 822).

180. Strychnine and Brucine. Part X. The Degradation of Dinitrostrycholcarboxylic Acid: its Recognition as a Derivative of Quinoline and the Consequent Modifications of the Constitutional Formulae for the Strychnos Bases Proposed in Part VII. By Kottiazath Narayana Menon, (the late) WHP, and RR (J, 1930, 830).

181. The Orienting Influence of Free and Bound Ionic Charges on Attached Simple or Conjugated Unsaturated Systems. Part V. Nitration of Benzyldiethylsulphonium Picrate. By Alfred Pollard and RR (J, 1930, 1765).

182. Strychnine and Brucine. Part XI. Note on Dihydrobrucine and Some Derivatives. By Osman Achmatowicz, Reginald Clifford Fawcett, (the late) WHP, and RR (J, 1930, 1769).

183. Strychnine and Brucine. Part XII. The Constitution of Dinitrostrycholcarboxylic Acid. By Kottiazath Narayana Menon and RR (J, 1931, 773).

184. The Nitration of Benzylpiperidine. By RR and John Stephen Watt (J, 1931, 236).

185. A Synthesis of Hydrastine. Part I. By Edward Hope, Frank Lee Pyman, Frederik George Remfry, and RR (J, 1931, 236).

186. Experiments on the Synthesis of Anthocyanins. Part VI. A Synthesis of

Chrysanthemin Chloride. By Shinzo Murakami, Alexander Robertson, and RR (J, 1931, 2665).

187. Experiments on the Synthesis of Anthocyanins. Part VII. The Four Isomeric β-Glucosides of Pelargonidin Chloride. By Andrés Léon, Alexander Robertson, RR, and Tiruvenkara R. Seshadri (J, 1931, 2672).

188. Experiments on the Synthesis of Anthocyanins. Part VIII. A Synthesis of Oenin Chloride. By Leopold Ferdinand Levy, Theodore Posternack, and RR (J, 1931, 2701).

189. Experiments on the Synthesis of Anthocyanins. Part IX. Synthesis of Oxycoccicyanin Chloride. Observations on the Distribution Numbers of the Anthocyanins. By Leopold Ferdinand Levy and RR (J, 1931, 2715).

190. Experiments on the Synthesis of Anthocyanins. Part X. Synthesis of 3-β-Galactosidylcyanidin Chloride, which is believed to be identical with Idaein Chloride, and of 3-β-Galactosidylpeonidin Chloride. By Miss Kathryn E. Grove and RR (J, 1931, 2722).

191. Experiments on the Synthesis of Anthocyanins. Part XI. Fisetinin Chloride. By Eric Lawrence Fonseka and RR (J, 1931, 2730).

192. Experiments on the Synthesis of Anthocyanins. Part XII. Fisetinidin and Luteolinidin Chlorides. By Andrés Léon and RR (J, 1931, 2732).

193. Experiments on the Synthesis of Anthocyanins. Part XIII. 5-β-Glucosidyl- and 5-Lactosidyl-hirsutidin Chlorides. By Leopold Ferdinand Levy and RR (J, 1931, 2738).

198. An Anthocyanin of *Oxycoccus Macrocarpus Pers.* By Miss Kathryn E. Grove and RR (Biochem. J., 1931, 25, 1706).

199. A Survey of Anthocyanins. Part I. By GMR and RR (Biochem. J., 1931, 25, 1687).

205. Distribution of Electrons in the Aromatic Nucleus and the Early Stages of Aromatic Substitution. By A. Lapworth and RR (Nature, Feb. 20, 1932).

215. Kationic Reactivity of Aromatic Compounds. Part I. By William Bradley and RR (J, 1932, 1254).

216. Synthetical Experiments on the Nature of Betanin and Related Nitrogenous Anthocyanins. Part I. By Mrs. Alice Mary Robinson and RR (J, 1932, 1439).

217. The Orienting Influence of Free and Bound Ionic Charges on Attached Simple or Conjugated Unsaturated Systems. Part VI. Nitration of Phenylalkylsulphones. By William Alfred Baldwin and RR (J, 1932, 1445).

219. A Ring Homologue of Tropacocaine. By Bertie Kennedy Blount and RR (J, 1932, 1429).

220. β-Pseudognoscopine. By Morrison Greenwood and RR (J, 1932, 1370).

223. Orientation in the Substitution Reactions of Alkylnaphthalenes. Part I. Side-chain Nitration of 1:4-Dimethylnaphthalene. By RR and Henry W. Thompson (J, 1932, 2015).

226. Theory of Induced Polarities in Benzene. By A. Lapworth and RR (Nature, August 20, 1932).

230. Some Analogues of Pseudopelletierine, namely, Thiotropinone, Selenotropinone, and *N*-Methylaztropinone. By B.K. Blount and RR (J, 1932, 2485).

251

233. Outline of an Electrochemical (Electronic) Theory of the Course of Organic Reactions. By RR (Institute of Chemistry Pamphlet, 1932).

236. Synthetical Experiments on the Nature of Betanin and Related Nitrogenous Anthocyanins. Part II. By Mrs. Alice M. Robinson and RR (J, 1933, 25).

239. Synthetical Experiments in the isoFlavone Group. Part VII. Synthesis of Daidzein. By Wilson Baker, RR, and N.M. Simpson (J, 1933, 274).

242. Attempts to prepare Derivatives of 1:2-Dihydroisoquinoline. New Interpretation of J.S. Buck's Experiments on the Synthesis of so-called 1:2-Dihydropapaverine. By P.C. Young and RR (J, 1933, 275).

252. The Relation of Electromeric Effects and Relative Polarisabilities of the the Halogens. By RR (J, 1933, 1115).

253. Derivatives of 1-Methyltropane. By B.K. Blount and RR (J, 1933, 1511).

258. Attempts to find New Anti-malarials. Part VI. Preparation of β-6:7-Dimethoxyquinaldyl(4)-ethylamine Dihydrochloride. By K. Miki and RR (J, 1933, 1467).

273. Formation of an Intermediate Product in the Nitration and Simultaneous Demethylation of 6:7-Dimethoxy-1:2:3:4-tetrahydronaphthalene. By H.J. Lewis and RR (J, 1934, 1253).

276. Substitution in the Benzene Nucleus. By RR (J. Soc. Dyers and Colourists, 1934, 65).

277. Stereoisomerides of Narcotine and Hydrastine. By Miss M.A. Marshall, F.L. Pyman, and RR (J, 1934, 1315).

279. The Nitration of 2-Methylindole. By F.C. Mathur and RR (J, 1934, 1415).

283. Kationoid Reactivity of Aromatic Compounds. Part II. The Action of Potassium Cyanide on 1-Nitroso-2-naphtol and 1-Benzeneazo-2-naphtol. By W. Bradley and RR (J, 1934, 1484).

283A.A Synthesis of Certain Higher Aliphatic Compounds. Part IV. Synthesis of n-Triacontanoic Acid from Stearic Acid. By GMR (J, 1934, 1543).

308. The Transformation of d-Catechin into Cyanidin Chloride. By Herbert Appel and RR (J, 1935, 426).

327. Synthesis of Bicuculline. Part I. By P.G. Groenewoud and RR (J, 1936, 199).

341. The Constitution of Brazilein. By V.M. Mičovič and RR (J, 1937, 43).

342. Experiments on the Synthesis of Brazilin and Haematoxylin. Part IV. Synthesis of O-Diethylenehaematoxylone. By (the late) WHP, A. Pollard, and RR (J, 1937, 49).

351. Synthetical Experiments relating to Carpaine. Part I. Synthesis of a Basic Long-chain Lactone. By G. Barger, RR, and Y. Urushibara (J, 1937, 714).

352. Synthetical Experiments relating to Carpaine. Part II. By G. Barger, RR, and W.F. Short (J, 1937, 715).

356. Experiments on the Synthesis of Brazilin and Haematoxylin. Part V. By H. Appel, W. Baker, H. Hagenbach, and RR (J, 1937, 738).

362. Synthetic Cyperones and their Comparison with α- and β-Cyperones. By P.S. Adamson, F.J. McQuillin, RR, and J.L. Simonsen (J, 1937, 1576).

378. Arthur George Perkin, 1861—1937. By F.M. Rowe and RR (J, 1938, 1738).

252

398. The Yellow Pigment of *Papaver Nudicaule*. Part I. By J.R. Price, RR, and (in part) R. Scott-Moncrieff (Mrs. Meares) (J, 1939, 1465).

404. Mechanism of the Benzidine Transformation and some Allied Topics. Presidential Address delivered to the Chemical Society on April 3, 1941. By RR (J, 1941, 220).

464. Arthur Lapworth, 1872—1941. By RR (Royal Society, Obit., 1947, 5, 555).

467. Presidential Address at the Anniversary Meeting of the Royal Society, December 1, 1947. By RR (Proc. Roy. Soc. B, 1947, 135, v).

469. Development of Electrochemical Theories of the Course of Reactions of Carbon Compounds. The Eighteenth Faraday Lecture, delivered before the Chemical Society, July 16, 1947. By RR (J, 1947, 1288).

493. A Synthesis of β-Anhydrotrimethylbrazilone. By K.W. Bentley and RR (J, 1950, 1353).

500. Conversion of Hydrastine into Berberine, and an Instance of the Asymmetrical Quaternization of a Tertiary Base. By R. Mirza and RR (Nature, 1950, 166, 271).

515. The Structure of Phenyldihydrothebaine. By K.W. Bentley and RR (J, 1952, 947).

516. The Reduction of Thebaine and Dihydrothebaine by Sodium and Ammonia. By K.W. Bentley, RR, and A.E. Wain (J, 1952, 958).

528. Richard Willstätter — Willstätter Memorial Lecture, delivered to the Chemical Society, November 6, 1972. By RR (J, 1953, 999).

565. Mechanism of Some Reactions of Organo-Metallic Compounds. By RR (Chemical Age, May 5, 1956).

574. Chemistry of Brazilin and Haematoxylin. By RR (Bull. Soc. Chim. France, 1958, 1, 125).

586. John Lionel Simonsen, 1884—1957. By RR (Biographical Memoirs of the Fellows of the Royal Society, 1960, 5, 237).

594. The Nitration of Some Catechol and Quinol Derivatives. By RR (J. Indian Chem. Soc., 1961, 38, 445).

619. The Concept of the Aromatic Sextett. By RR (Special Publication No. 21 of the Chemical Society, 1967. Aromaticity, an International Symposium held at Sheffield on July 6—8, 1966).

623. The Synthesis of Brazilin and Haematoxylin. By F. Morsingh and RR (Tetrahedron, 1970, 26, 281).

625. Foreword to a Communication submitted by H.-D. Scharf, J. Fleischhauer, and F. Korte. By RR (Tetrahedron, 1970, 26, 2067).

630. Syntheses in the Brazilin Group by Way of Indeno-Coumarins. By J.N. Chatterjee, RR, and M.L. Tomlinson (Tetrahedron, 1974, 30, 507).

631. Reduction of Brazilein. Occurrence of Reductive Coupling. By R.H. Jaeger, P.M.E. Lewis, and RR (Tetrahedron, 1974, 30, 1295).